ESSENTIAL JAZZ PIANO EXERCISES

EVERY PIANO PLAYER SHOULD KNOW

Learn jazz basics, including blues scales, ii - V - I chord progressions, modal jazz improv, right hand licks and riffs, and more.

MUSIC MENTOR

JERALD SIMON

Music Motivation®
musicmotivation.com

Cool music that excites, entertains, and educates!

Music Motivation® books are designed to provide students with music instruction that will enable them to improve and increase their successes in the field of music. It is also intended to enhance appreciation and understanding of various styles of music from classical to jazz, blues, rock, popular, new age, hymns, and more. The author and publisher disclaim any liability or accountability for the misuse of this material as it was intended by the author.

I hope you enjoy **"Essential Jazz Piano Exercises."** With this book, I hope piano teachers and piano students learn what I feel are the essential jazz piano exercises that everyone who plays jazz should know and be able to do well. I don't want teachers and students to simply read the notes on the page. I would like everyone who plays these exercises to know them inside and out. There are quite a few additional books in this series - and more to come. If you like this book, please look at my other books: **"Essential Piano Exercises Every Piano Player Should Know," "Essential New Age Piano Exercises Every Piano Player Should Know," "100 Left Hand Patterns Every Piano Player Should Know," and "100 Chord Progressions Every Piano Player Should Know."** I hope you enjoy these various books! You can learn more at **http://essentialpianoexercises.com**. Join the course today!

Your Music Mentor, Jerald Simon

This book is dedicated to my many piano students, young and old, who have asked me over the years to put together a book with all of the jazz piano exercises I feel are essential to help pianists play better in all keys and in all inversions. This book is also dedicated to the many piano students enrolled in my Essential Piano Exercises Course **(http://essentialpianoexercises.com).** I am amazed by how many members we have in over 23 countries around the world, and more joining every day! I create these books from this series for all of you!

Also, for my wife, Suzanne (Zanny), my daughter, Summer, and my sons, Preston and Matthew.

CONNECT with Jerald

http://musicmotivation.com/jeraldsimon
https://facebook.com/jeraldsimon
http://youtube.com/jeraldsimon
http://linkedin.com/in/jeraldsimon
http://pinterest.com/jeraldsimon
https://twitter.com/jeraldsimon
http://cdbaby.com/artist/jeraldsimon
http://instagram.com/jeraldsimon
jeraldsimon@musicmotivation.com

CONTACT Music Motivation®

Music Motivation®
Cool music that excites, entertains, and educates!

Music Motivation®
P.O. Box 1000
Kaysville, UT 84037-1000
http://musicmotivation.com
https://facebook.com/musicmotivation
https://twitter.com/musicmotivation
info@musicmotivation.com

First Printing 2021 - Originally created from 2006-2021 - Printed in the United States of America - 10 9 8 7 6 5 4 3 2 - Simon, Jerald - Music Motivation® Essential Piano Exercises - $25.95 US/ $27.95 Canada - Paperback book - ISBN-13: 978-1-948274-03-6 ; Music Motivation Cataloging: MM00001064

Welcome to "ESSENTIAL JAZZ PIANO EXERCISES" by JERALD SIMON

In order to better help piano teachers, piano students, and parents of piano students effectively learn music theory and what to do with that knowledge, thus bridging the gap between learning the scales and chords and using them to enhance music and make music of your own, I have created a course featuring step-by-step piano lesson videos to accompany this book: "Essential Jazz Piano Exercises." You can visit **ESSENTIALPIANOEXERCISES.COM** to learn more about this course and gain access to hundreds of videos where I demonstrate how to play these exercises and many others, and then teach what you can do with them. Learning the theory is good, but knowing what to do with it is the practical application where I demonstrate how to use music theory to arrange, to improvise, to compose, and to create music of your own. More important than simply learning the theory is the practical application of *why* we are learning these scales and chords, and *what* we can do with them once we have learned them. It is the hands on approach to teaching music theory. In addition, I explain the theory in practical and simple terms so everyone can easily understand and know music theory for what it can do to help them in three primary ways: (1) sight-read piano music better and faster as a result of knowing the scales and chords, (2) take their music playing and music creating to the next level so they can improvise, arrange, and compose music of their own, and (3) ultimately feel comfortable and excited to learn music theory - the "FUN way!"

"My purpose and mission in life is to motivate myself and others through my music and writing, to help others find their purpose and mission in life, and to teach values that encourage everyone everywhere to do and be their best." - Jerald Simon

A message from Jerald to piano students and parents:

If you come to piano lessons each week and walk away only having learned about music notation, rhythm, and dots on a page, then I have failed as a Music Mentor. Life lessons are just as important, if not more important than music lessons. I would rather have you learn more about goal setting and achieving, character, dedication, and personal improvement. To have you learn to love music, appreciate it, and play it, is a wonderful byproduct you will have for the rest of your life - a talent that will enrich your life and the lives of others. To become a better musician is wonderful and important, but to become a better person is more important.

As a Music Mentor I want to mentor students to be the very best they can be. If you choose not to practice, you essentially choose not to improve. This is true in any area of life. Everyone has the same amount of time allotted to them. What you choose to do with your time, and where you spend your time, has little to do with the activities being done and more to do with the value attached to each activity.

I believe it's important to be well-rounded and have many diverse interests. I want students to enjoy music, to learn to be creative and understand how to express themselves musically - either by creating music of their own, or interpreting the music of others - by arranging and improvising well known music. In addition, I encourage students to play sports, dance, sing, draw, read, and develop all of their talents. I want them to be more than musicians, I want them to learn to become well-rounded individuals.

Above all, I want everyone to continually improve and do their best. I encourage everyone to set goals, dream big, and be the best they can be in whatever they choose to do. Life is full of wonderful choices. Choose the best out of life and learn as much as you can from everyone everywhere. I prefer being called a Music Mentor because I want to mentor others and help them to live their dreams.

Your life is your musical symphony. Make it a masterpiece!

The first book in this series is called **Essential Piano Exercises Every Piano Player Should Know.** This is the second book in the series. Other books in this series will soon be available as well (i.e. **Essential New Age Piano Exercises Every Piano Player Should Know, Essential Pop Piano Exercises Every Piano Player Should Know, Essential Rock Piano Exercises Every Piano Player Should Know, 100 Chord Progressions Every Piano Player Should Know, 100 Improvised Licks Every Piano Player Should Know,** and so forth).

Some of the exercises in this book are written out in every key signature, as are the blues pentascales. Other exercises are only written in the key of C Major and the pianist is asked to then play the same exercise in every key signature. I personally think you should be able to play anything by reading it in any key signature and also transpose or play something that is only written in one key signature to every other key signature.

I have tried to combine exercises that are both written in every key signature and only in the key of C to help you learn how to do both. It's funny because when I came out with my best-selling book, "**100 Left Hand Patterns Every Piano Player Should Know,**" I primarily wrote all of the left hand patterns and additional Fakebook songs contained within the FUN fake book section of the book (100 songs in Fakebook format) in the key of C Major. I did this intentionally because I wanted everyone to then transpose the left hand patterns and fake book songs into every other key signature. One of the main comments I received as feedback about the book was how so many piano players were having a difficult time transposing everything into every other key signature without having the music written out for them in every key.

When I came out with my next book, "**Essential Piano Exercises Every Piano Player Should Know,**" I decided to intentionally write out the exercises in every key signature. I wrote out and notated all intervals, scales, chords, chord progressions, etc., in every key signature so everything would be notated. I also did this because I added the fingering in every key signature which changes according to various key signatures. One of the main comments I received as feedback about that book was how so many piano players/piano teachers asked why I wrote everything out in every key signature and did not just write out the exercises in the key of C and ask them to transpose to other keys.

Therefore, I decided with this book I would do a little of both to try and please everyone. Most of this book, however, will be in the key of C Major and I will ask you to transpose and take every note up in half steps through every key signature. You can also transpose by following the circle of 5ths. We go over how to do this in the course which you can sign up for at **https://www.essentialpianoexercises.com/**.

I believe piano players need to know how to read everything in every key signature, how to play from a lead sheet or fake book, how to play anything by ear, and transpose what they play from reading music to playing by ear in every key signature.

On pages 13 - 21, you will find a brief review of basic music theory concepts you should know as you start working on jazz exercises. This is a good review even if you are more familiar with everything. Pages 22 - 29 contain the basic and most common chords everyone should know. After that, the book introduces and teaches you the essential jazz basics every jazz piano player should learn.

The *Music Motivation*® Mentorship Map (for piano students)

by Music Mentor™ Jerald Simon

Music Motivation® ™
musicmotivation.com

MOTIVATION ™

	Apprentice for 1st & 2nd year students	Maestro for 2nd - 4th year students	Virtuoso for 3rd year students and above
Repertoire In addition to the books listed to the right, students can sign up to receive the weekly "Cool Song" and "Cool Exercise" composed by Jerald Simon every week. Visit musicmotivation.com/annualsubscription to learn more and sign up!	**Music Motivation® Book(s)** What Every Pianist Should Know (Free PDF) Essential Piano Exercises (section 1) Cool Songs for Cool Kids (pre-primer level) Cool Songs for Cool Kids (primer level) Cool Songs for Cool Kids (book 1) The Pentascale Pop Star (books 1 and 2) Songs in Pentascale position: Classical, Jazz, Blues, Popular, Students Choice, Personal Composition (in pentascale position - 5 note piano solo) etc.	**Music Motivation® Book(s)** Essential Piano Exercises (section 2) An Introduction to Scales and Modes Cool Songs for Cool Kids (book 2) Cool Songs for Cool Kids (book 3) Variations on Mary Had a Little Lamb Twinkle Those Stars, Jazzed about Christmas, Jazzed about 4th of July Baroque, Romantic, Classical, Jazz, Blues, Popular, New Age, Student's Choice, Personal Composition.	**Music Motivation® Book(s)** Essential Piano Exercises (section 3) Cool Songs that ROCK! (books 1 & 2) Triumphant, Sea Fever, Sweet Melancholy, The Dawn of a New Age, Sweet Modality, Jazzed about Jazz, Jazzed about Classical Music, Jingle Those Bells, Cinematic Solos, Hymn Arranging Baroque, Romantic, Classical, Jazz, Blues, Popular, New Age, Contemporary, Broadway Show Tunes, Standards, Student's Choice, Personal Composition
Music Terminology	Piano (*p*), Forte (*f*) Mezzo Piano (*mp*) Mezzo Forte (*mf*) Pianissimo (*pp*) Fortissimo (*ff*) ***Music Motivation® 1st Year Terminology***	Tempo Markings Dynamic Markings Parts of the Piano Styles and Genres of Music ***Music Motivation® 2nd Year Terminology***	Pocket Music Dictionary (2 - 3 years) Harvard Dictionary of Music (4 + years) Parts/History of the Piano Music Composers (Weekly Biographies) ***Music Motivation® 3rd Year Terminology***
Key Signatures	C, G, D, A, F, B♭, E♭ & A♭ (Major) A, E, B, F♯, D, G, C & F (Minor) Begin learning all major key signatures	Circle of 5ths/Circle of 4ths All Major and Minor key signatures (Identify each key and name the sharps and flats)	Spiral of Fifths, Chord Progressions within Key Signatures. Modulating from one Key Signature to another.
Music Notation	Names and Positions of notes on the staff (both hands - Treble and Bass Clefs) 	Names and Positions of notes above and below the staff (both hands) 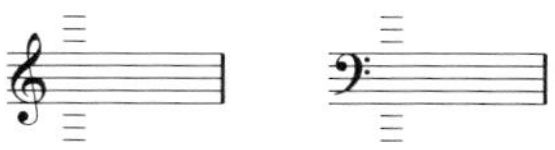	History of Music Notation (the development of notation), Monks & Music, Gregorian Chants, Music changes over the years and how music has changed. Learn **Finale** and **Logic Pro** (notate your music)
Rhythms	Whole notes/rests (say it and play it - count out loud) Half notes/rests (say it and play it - count out loud) Quarter notes/rests (say it and play it - count out loud) Eighth notes/rests (say it and play it - count out loud)	Sixteenth notes/rests (say it and play it - count out loud) Thirty-second notes/rests (say it and play it - count out loud) Sixty-fourth notes/rests (say it and play it - count out loud)	One-hundred-twenty-eighth notes/rests For more on rhythm, I recommend: "Rhythmic Training" by Robert Starer and "Logical Approach to Rhythmic Notation" (books 1 & 2) by Phil Perkins
Intervals	1st, 2nd, 3rd, 4th, 5th, 6th, 7th, 8th, and 9th intervals (key of C, G, D, F, B♭, and E♭). Harmonic and Melodic intervals (key of C, G, D, A, E, and B)	All Perfect, Major, Minor, Augmented, and Diminished intervals (in every key) All Harmonic and Melodic intervals Explain the intervals used to create major, minor, diminished, and augmented chords?	9th, 11th, and 13th intervals Analyze music (Hymns and Classical) to identify intervals used in each measure. Identify/Name intervals used in chords.
Scales	All Major Pentascales (5 finger scale) All Minor Pentascales (5 finger scale) All Diminished Pentascales (5 finger scale) C Major Scale (1 octave) A min. Scale (1 oct.) (Do, Re, Mi, Fa, Sol, La, Ti, Do) (solfege) All Major and Natural Minor Scales - 1 octave	All Major Scales (Every Key 1 - 2 octaves) All Minor Scales (Every Key 1 - 2 octaves) (natural, harmonic, and melodic minor scales) (Do, Di, Re, Ri, Mi, Fa, Fi, Sol, Si, La, Li, Ti, Do) (solfege - chromatic)	All Major Scales (Every Key 3 - 5 Octaves) All Minor Scales (Every Key 3 - 5 Octaves) All Blues Scales (major and minor) Cultural Scales (25 + scales)
Modes	Ionian/Aeolian (C/A, G/E, D/B, A/F♯)	All Modes (I, D, P, L, M, A, L) All keys	Modulating with the Modes (Dorian to Dorian)
Chords	All Major Chords, All Minor Chords, All Diminished Chords, C Sus 2, C Sus 4, C+ (Aug)., C 6th, C minor 6th, C 7th, C Maj. 7th, C minor Major 7th, A min., A Sus 2, A Sus 4,	All Major, Minor, Diminished, Augmented, Sus 2, Sus 4, Sixth, Minor Sixth, Dominant 7th and Major 7th Chords	Review All Chords from 1st and 2nd year experiences All 7th, 9th, 11th, and 13th chords inversions and voicings.
Arpeggios	Same chords as above (1 - 2 octaves)	Same chords as above (3 - 4 octaves)	Same chords as above (4 + octaves)
Inversions	Same chords as above (1 - 2 octaves)	Same chords as above (3 - 4 octaves)	Same chords as above (4 + octaves)
Technique (other)	Schmitt Preparatory Exercises, (Hanon)	Wieck, Hanon, Bach (well tempered clavier)	Bertini-Germer, Czerny, I. Philipp
Sight Reading	Key of C Major and G Major	Key of C, G, D, A, E, F, B♭, E♭, A♭, D♭	All Key Signatures, Hymns, Classical
Ear Training	Major versus Minor sounds (chords/intervals)	C, D, E, F, G, A, B, and intervals	Key Signatures and Chords, Play w/ IPod
Music History	The origins of the Piano Forte	Baroque, Classical, Jazz, Blues	Students choice - All genres, Composers
Improvisation	Mary Had a Little Lamb, Twinkle, Twinkle...	Blues Pentascale, Barrelhouse Blues	Classical, New Age, Jazz, Blues, etc. Play w/ IPod
Composition	5 note melody (both hands - key of C and G)	One - Two Page Song (include key change)	Lyrical, Classical, New Age, Jazz, etc.

This is only an outline or suggestion - add to it or subtract from it! If you are doing something different all together that works, keep doing it. This is meant to give you ideas and supplement what you're already doing.

The books from the Music Motivation® Series by Jerald Simon are not method books, and are not intentionally created to be used as such (although some piano teachers use them as such). Jerald simply creates fun, cool piano music to motivate piano students to play the piano and teach them music theory - the FUN way!

Key Signatures
Major Penta Scales, and Scales:

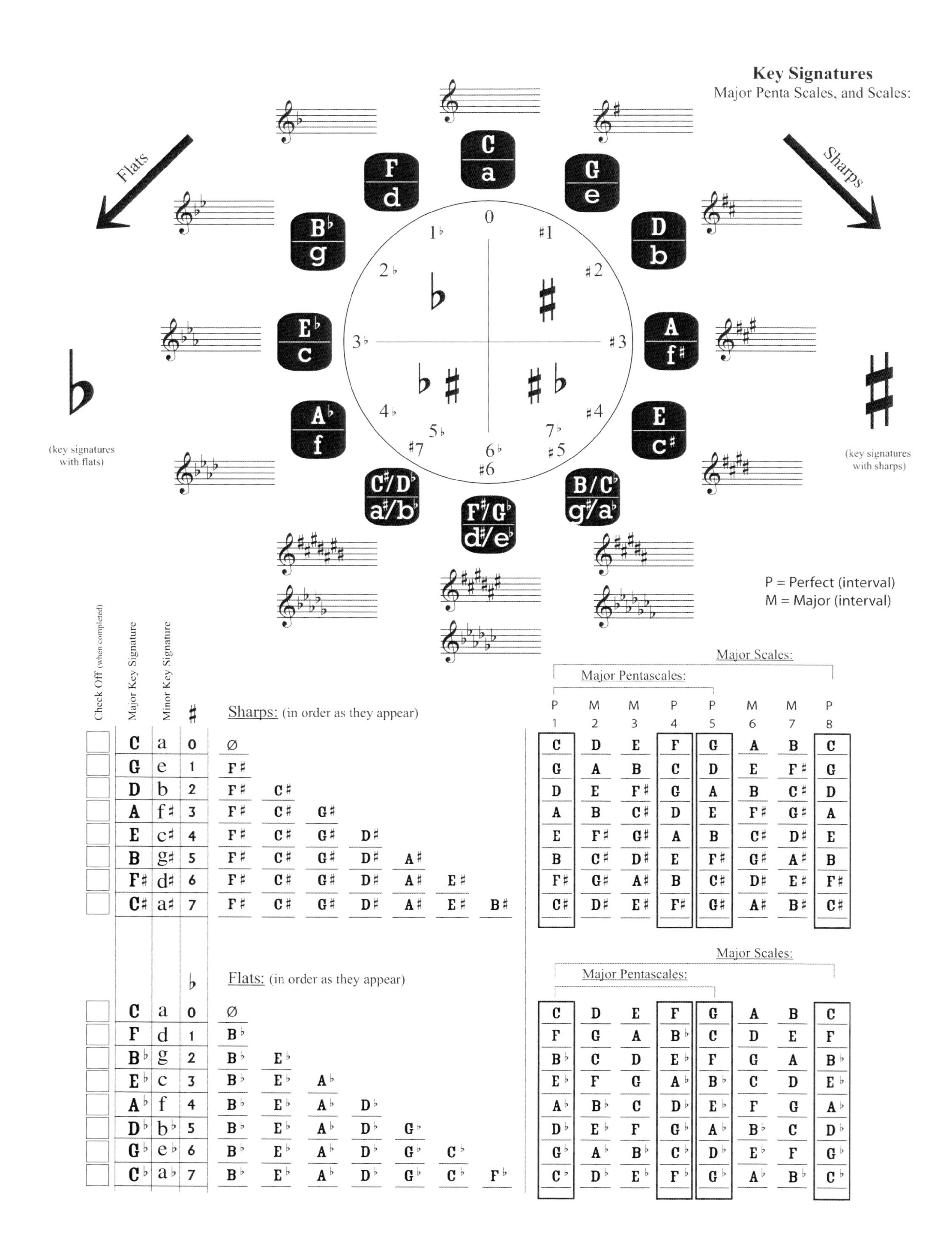

P = Perfect (interval)
M = Major (interval)

Check Off (when completed)	Major Key Signature	Minor Key Signature	♯	Sharps: (in order as they appear)						
	C	a	0	Ø						
	G	e	1	F♯						
	D	b	2	F♯	C♯					
	A	f♯	3	F♯	C♯	G♯				
	E	c♯	4	F♯	C♯	G♯	D♯			
	B	g♯	5	F♯	C♯	G♯	D♯	A♯		
	F♯	d♯	6	F♯	C♯	G♯	D♯	A♯	E♯	
	C♯	a♯	7	F♯	C♯	G♯	D♯	A♯	E♯	B♯

Major Scales:

Major Pentascales:

P 1	M 2	M 3	P 4	P 5	M 6	M 7	P 8
C	D	E	F	G	A	B	C
G	A	B	C	D	E	F♯	G
D	E	F♯	G	A	B	C♯	D
A	B	C♯	D	E	F♯	G♯	A
E	F♯	G♯	A	B	C♯	D♯	E
B	C♯	D♯	E	F♯	G♯	A♯	B
F♯	G♯	A♯	B	C♯	D♯	E♯	F♯
C♯	D♯	E♯	F♯	G♯	A♯	B♯	C♯

Check Off (when completed)	Major Key Signature	Minor Key Signature	♭	Flats: (in order as they appear)						
	C	a	0	Ø						
	F	d	1	B♭						
	B♭	g	2	B♭	E♭					
	E♭	c	3	B♭	E♭	A♭				
	A♭	f	4	B♭	E♭	A♭	D♭			
	D♭	b♭	5	B♭	E♭	A♭	D♭	G♭		
	G♭	e♭	6	B♭	E♭	A♭	D♭	G♭	C♭	
	C♭	a♭	7	B♭	E♭	A♭	D♭	G♭	C♭	F♭

Major Scales:

Major Pentascales:

P 1	M 2	M 3	P 4	P 5	M 6	M 7	P 8
C	D	E	F	G	A	B	C
F	G	A	B♭	C	D	E	F
B♭	C	D	E♭	F	G	A	B♭
E♭	F	G	A♭	B♭	C	D	E♭
A♭	B♭	C	D♭	E♭	F	G	A♭
D♭	E♭	F	G♭	A♭	B♭	C	D♭
G♭	A♭	B♭	C♭	D♭	E♭	F	G♭
C♭	D♭	E♭	F♭	G♭	A♭	B♭	C♭

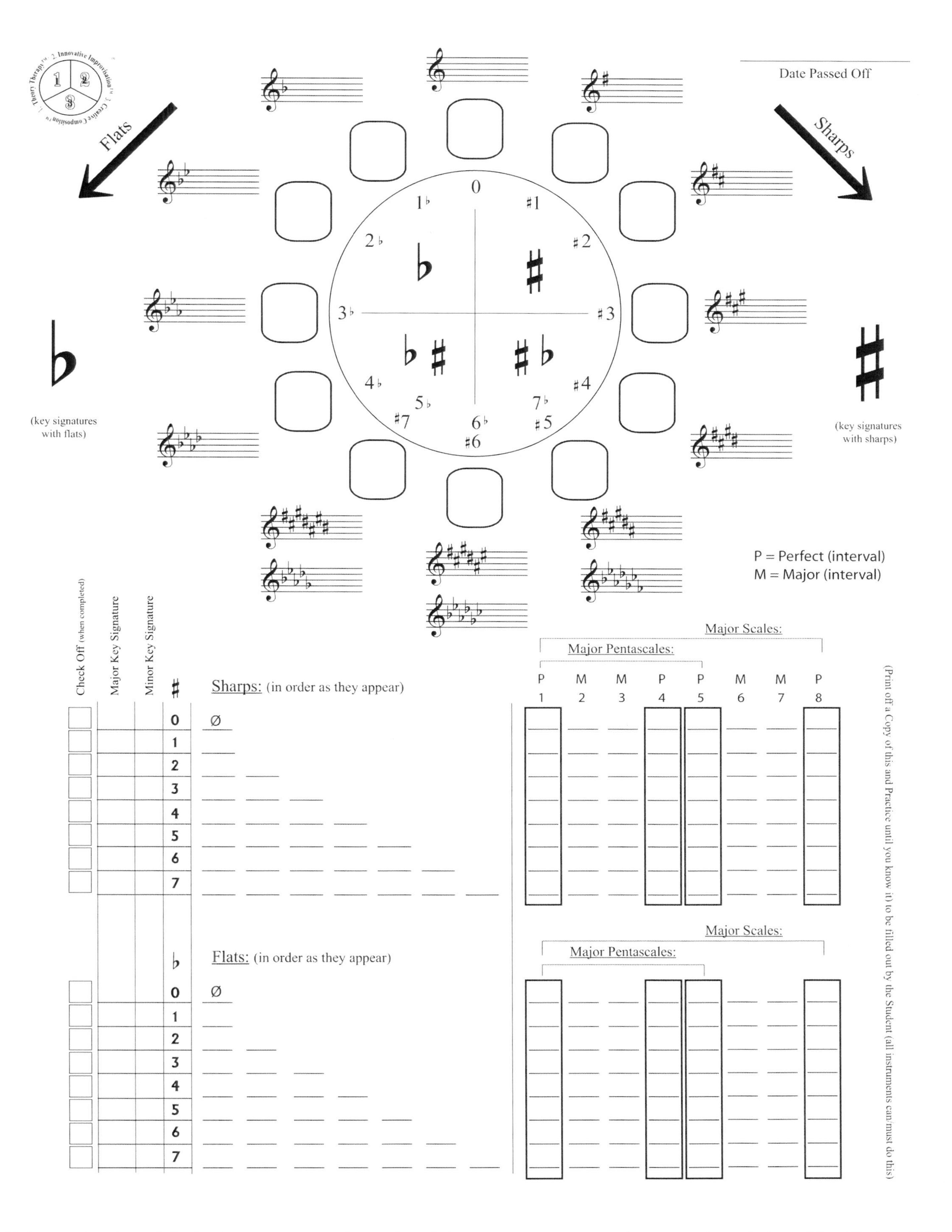

This page has been left blank so you can make copies of this page to practice and test your knowledge of the Circle of 5ths.

All Major Key Signatures

(following the circle of 5ths)

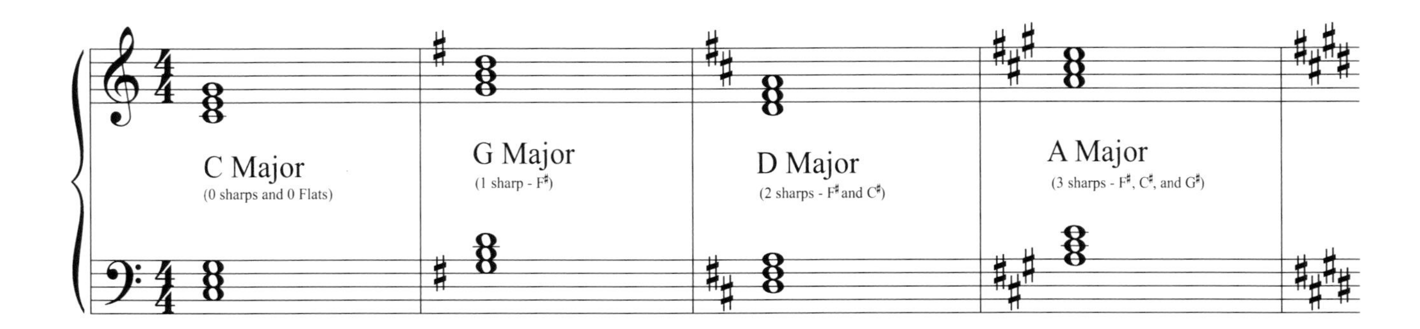

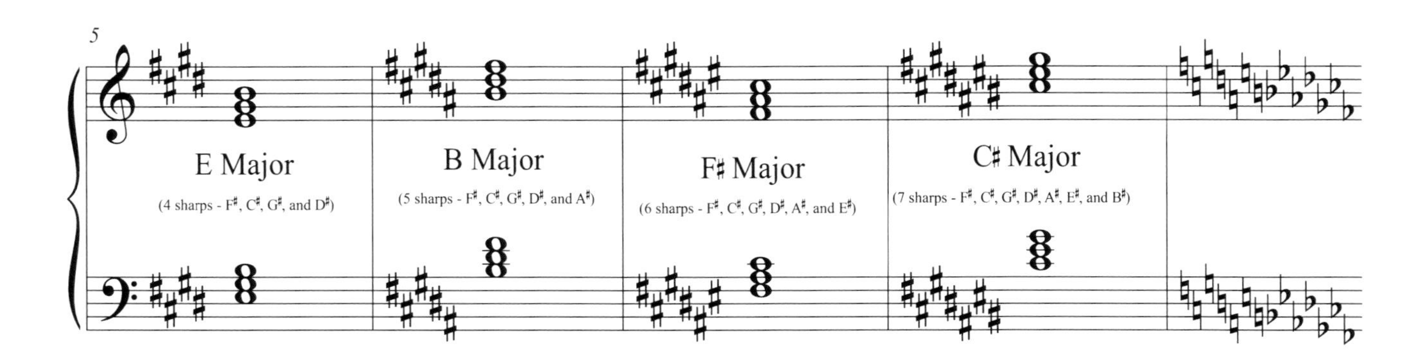

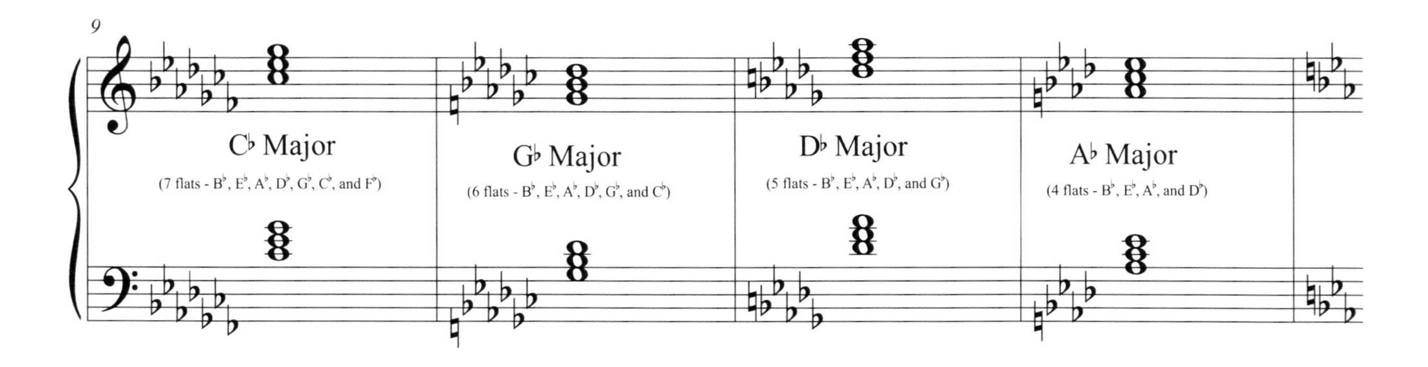

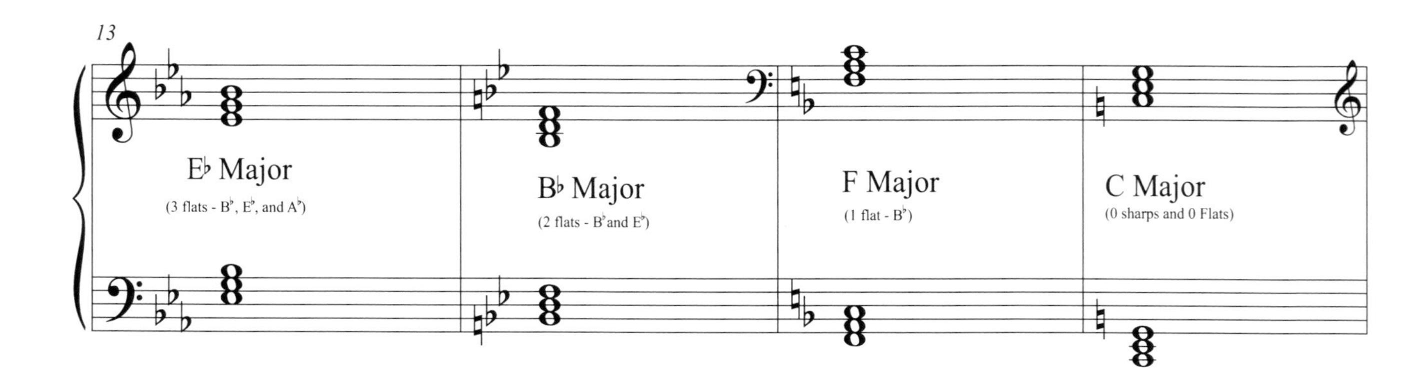

All Minor Key Signatures

(following the circle of 5ths)

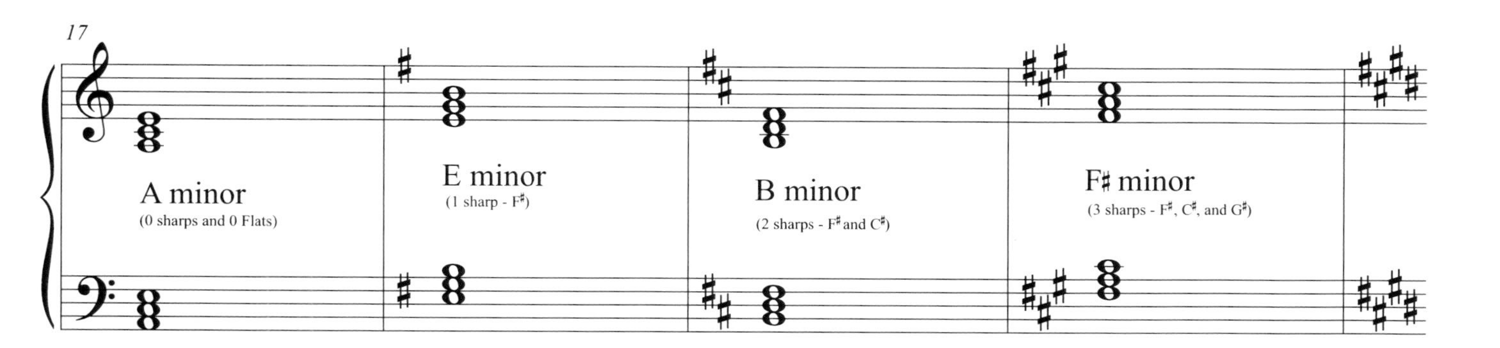

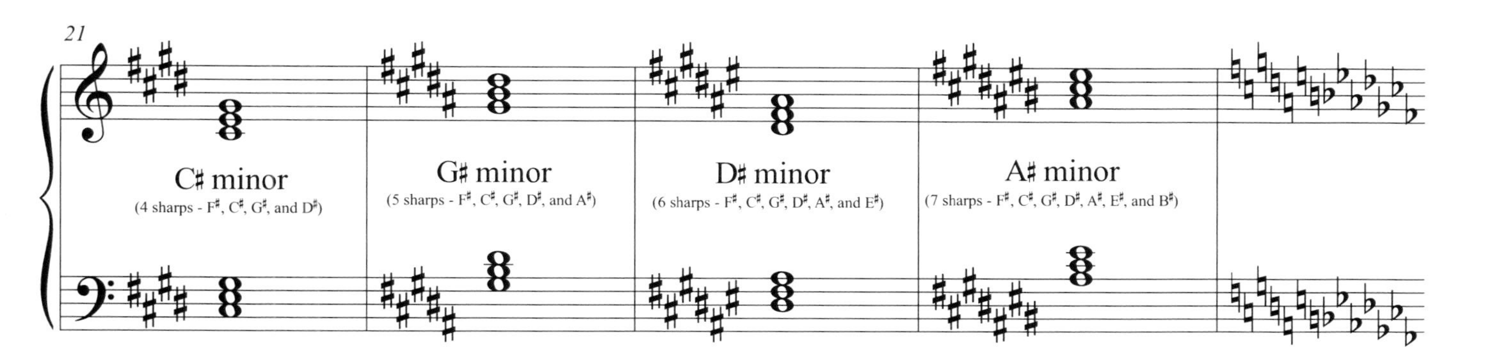

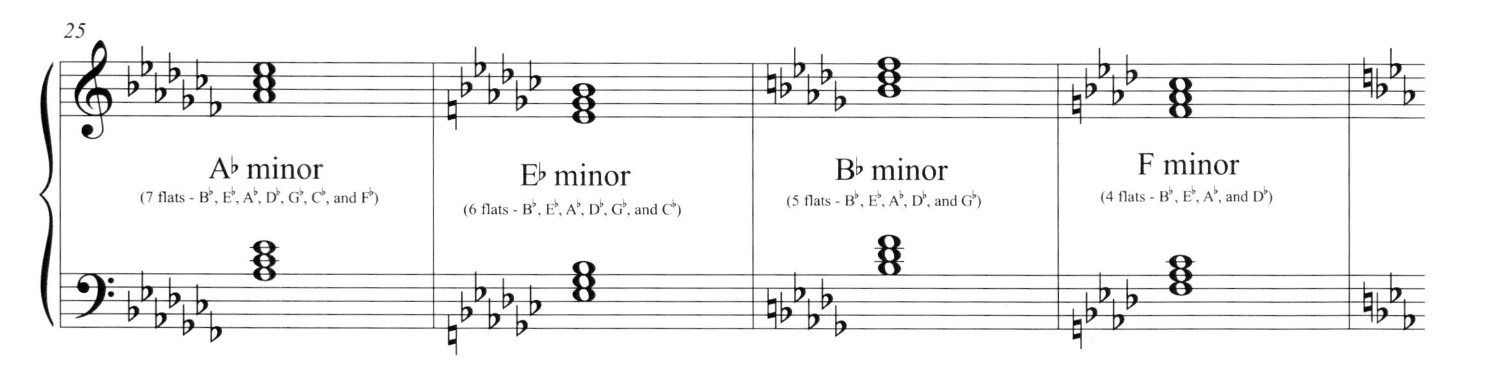

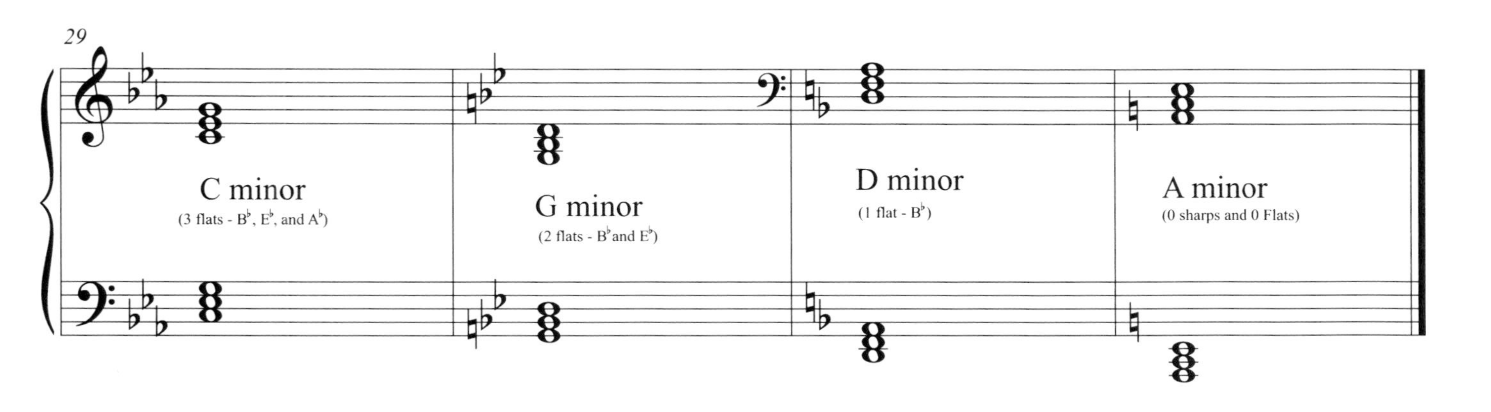

Let's talk about key signatures. You can refer to pages 8 - 11 as we talk about key signatures. When we talk about key signatures, the easiest way to explain them is by thinking about languages. Look at the chart of the circle of fifths on page 8 (a blank version is found on page 9). In the key of C major we have no sharps or flats. If we move to the right of the circle of fifths we will be in the key signature of G major. Think of this like learning to speak a second language. We have one sharp - F sharp (F ♯) in the key signature. When we are playing a piece in the key of G major we will always have an F sharp (every time you see F, play F sharp {F ♯} instead of F natural).

Any note in the musical alphabet (A, B, C, D, E, F, and G) can have a sharp sign (♯) or a flat sign (♭) placed in front of it. When this happens, the note either moves down half a step to the left for flats, or up half a step to the right for sharps. Let's look at the F note. The regular F note is the fourth above C. The F note is a white note, but when it has a sharp placed in front of it the note is taken up half a step to the right. The black note directly to the right of F is F sharp (F ♯).

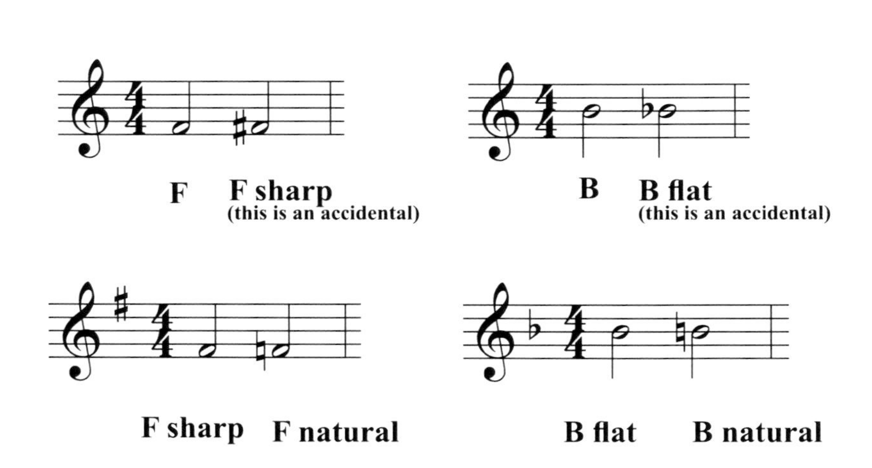

The first example to the left is in the key of C major. When the sharp symbol (♯) is added in the measure, you will play the sharp for that measure only. This is called an accidental note because it is not part of the key signature. After you finish playing the measure with the sharp, you will play the F natural again unless you see another accidental note. Below, the first example shows the key of G major (which has an F sharp in the key signature) followed by an F natural. The same examples are shown with B flat and B natural.

I like to have students memorize the order of the sharps introduced by saying this:

Five **C**ool **G**orillas **D**ance **A**nd **E**at **B**annanas. Once they have memorized this saying, I tell them the order of the sharps is F♯, C♯, G♯, D♯, A♯, E♯, and B♯. For flats, I have them say: Better Exercise And Drink Good Cold Fluids. Once they have memorized this saying, I tell them the order of the flats as B♭, E♭, A♭, D♭, G♭, C♭, and F♭.

Memorize This! for key signatures with sharps **F**ive **C**ool **G**orillas **D**ance **A**nd **E**at **B**ananas

Memorize This! for key signatures with flats **B**etter **E**xercise **A**nd **D**rink **G**ood **C**old **F**luids

I like to have students first play all major pentascales in all keys following the circle of fifths. After they can play all of the major pentascales in all keys, I then have them learn the minor and diminished pentascales in all keys. They can learn the patterns and the feel of playing the pentascales in all keys quickly. After doing so, they are then ready to play the major and minor scales 1 octave, then 2, and 3 octaves contrary motion (opposite directions starting on the same note - right hand goes up, left hand goes down), and parallel motion (both hands moving the same direction up and down the piano. I like to start with contrary motion because the fingering is the same for both hands and students learn the patterns quickly.

Rhythm Review (the basics)

Music is made up of notes (whole, half, quarter, eighth, 16th, 32nd, 64th, etc.) and rests (whole, half, quarter, eighth, 16th, 32nd, 64th, etc.). For now, we will introduce only the rhythms below. The whole note receives 4 beats (clap your hands once while counting to 4). The half note receives 2 beats (clap your hands twice while counting to 4 - clap once on 1 and once on 3). The quarter note receives 1 beat (clap your hands 4 times while counting to 4 - clap on 1, 2, 3, and 4. The eighth note receives 1/2 of a beat (clap your hands 8 times while counting 1 & 2 & 3 & 4 & - clap on everything. The 16th note receives a fourth of a beat. Think 1 e & a which equals 1 & but now you will clap four times or play four 16th notes for every one quarter note. The rests mean you don't play anything for the same duration. I recommend the books "Rhythmic Training" by Robert Starer and "Logical Approach to Rhythmic Notation" (books 1 and 2) by Phil Perkins for a more in depth training in rhythm.

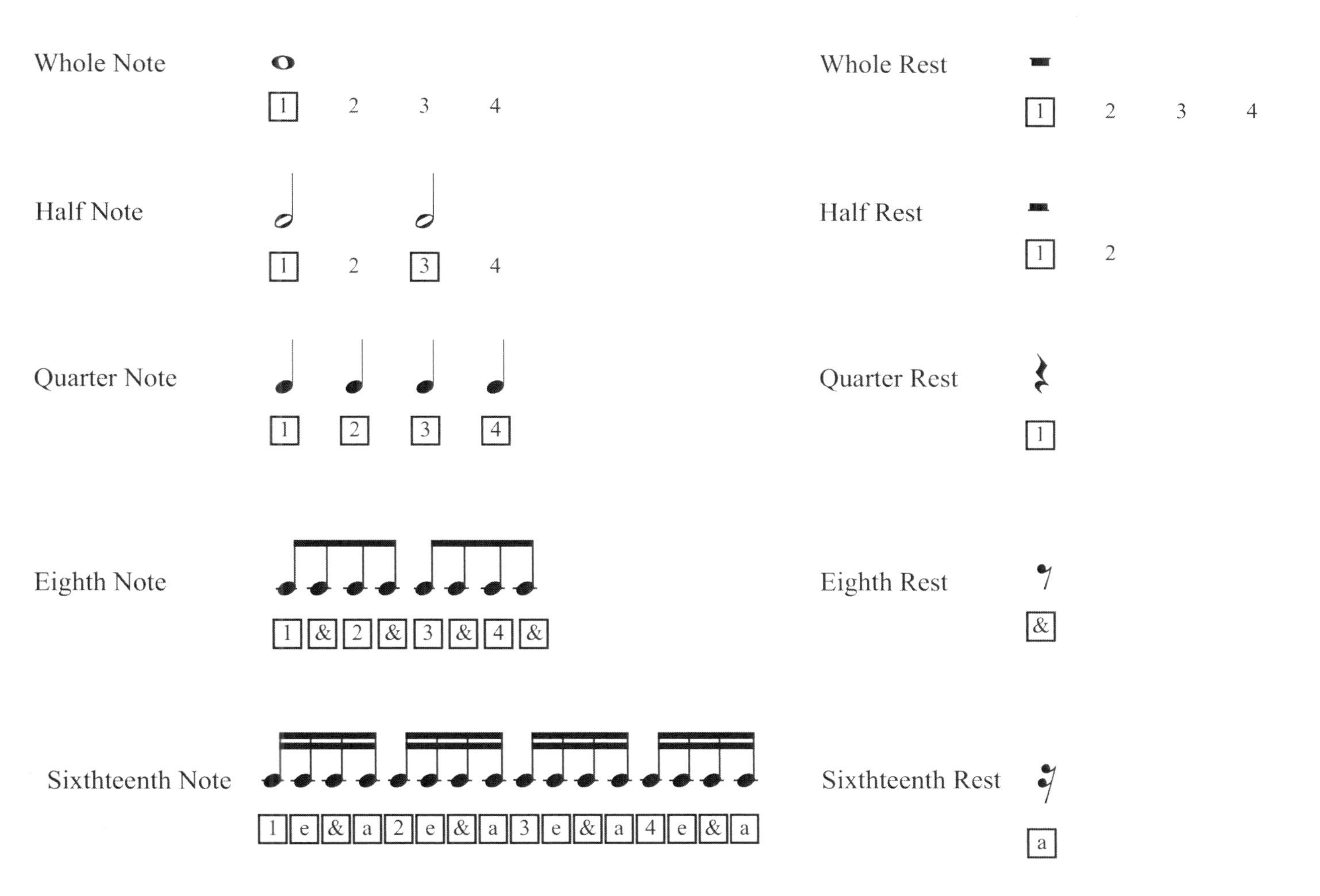

Try playing each of these rhythms on the piano. You can play these rhythms using A, B, C, D, E, F, or G. Try to play these rhythms on each of the black keys and all of the white keys. Try playing these rhythms using a simple C major chord (C E and G played together at the same time).

If you have a drum practice pad, try playing one of these notes with the left hand and a different note with the right hand. It's fun to play around with different rhythms.

The Musical Alphabet
A B C D E F and G

Learning music is similar to learning a foreign language. If you know your A B Cs, you already know the musical alphabet. The musical alphabet is A B C D E F and G. On the piano, the white note farthest to the left is A. That is the beginning of the musical alphabet. The white notes then continue as the alphabet does: A, B, C, D, E, F, and G. After G, it starts over again with A and continues up the piano (to the right).

The piano has a total of 88 keys. There are **52** white keys and **36** black keys. The note farthest to the left is A and the note farthest to the right is C. Here is what the **88** keys look like on a piano:

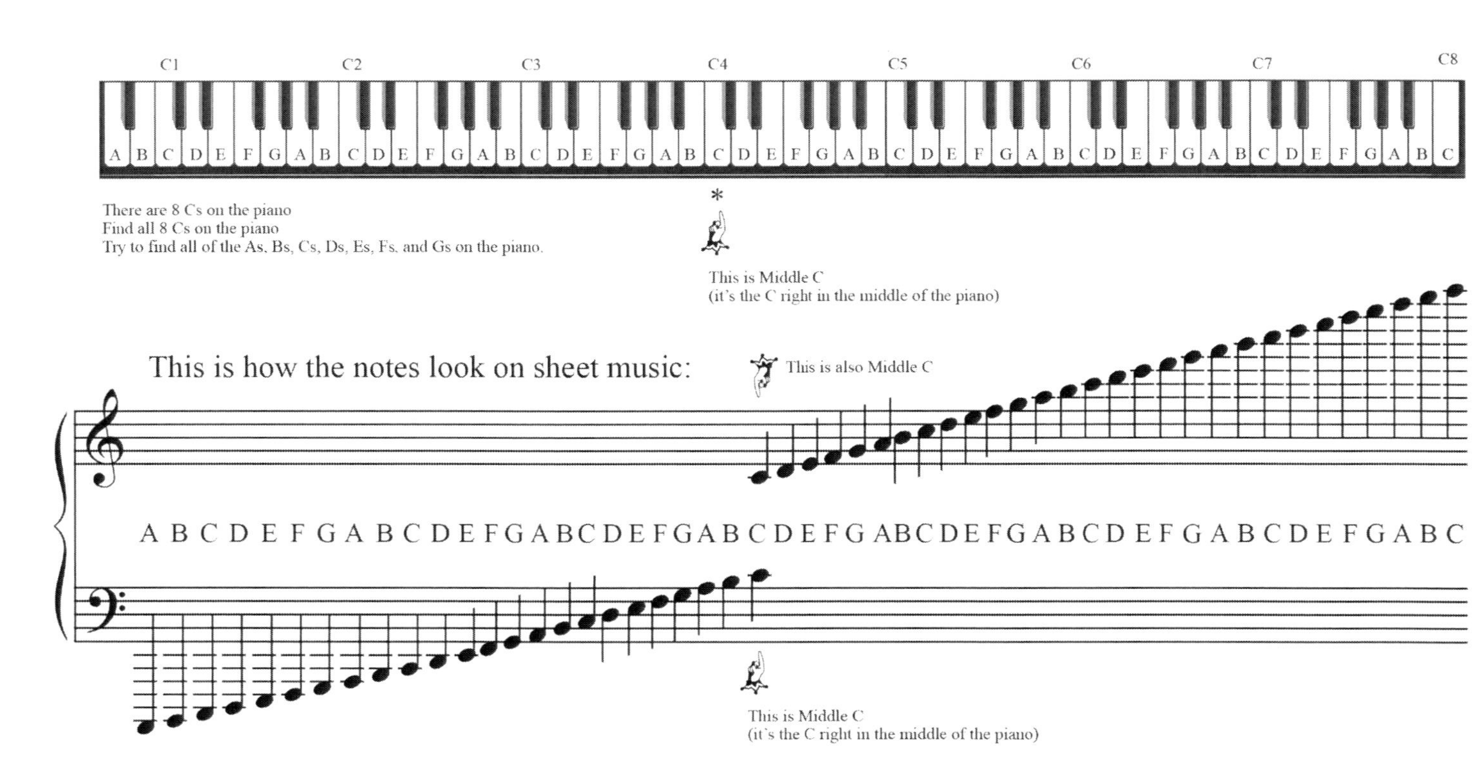

The first thing I have students do is play every note on the piano with one finger, starting with the lowest note "A" and continuing up to the highest note "C." I have students "Say it and Play it" - meaning they say the note name while they play the note (i.e. A, B, C, D, E, F, G, etc.). After they have done this, I have them find the pattern of 2 black notes together followed by 3 black notes together. I have students take two fingers with the left hand (the middle finger and the index finger) and play all of the 2 black note groups (both fingers play together at the same time) up and down the piano. Then I have students take three fingers with the right hand (the ring finger, the middle finger, and the index finger) and play all of the 3 black note groups (all three fingers play together at the same time) up and down the piano. After they have done this, students play with both hands (left hand plays the 2 black note groups and then the right hand plays the 3 black note groups) up and down the piano.

I then teach easy ways to find the musical notes according to these black note group patterns. All Cs are found to the left of the 2 black note groups (except for the last C - farthest to the right). Have the students find all of the Cs. All Fs are found to the left of the 3 black note groups. Have the students find all of the Fs. All Es are found to the right of the 2 black note groups. Have the students find all of the Es. All Bs are found to the right of the 3 black note groups. Have the students find all of the Bs. Once students have found these notes, I have them find all of the Cs on the piano and play (with either hand) C D E F G. This is the C major pentascale (5 note scale). Have students find all of the Cs on the piano and have them play C D E F G, first with the left hand and then with the right hand or vice versa. Students should be able to identify all of the notes on the piano and find all of the As, Bs, Cs, Ds, Es, Fs, and Gs on the piano. Make sure they can play the C pentascale (C D E F G) beginning on each of the Cs of the piano (except for the C farthest to the right, of course).

Now that you know the musical alphabet, let's see how the notes are written down so you can read and play music. Music is written on what is called a staff. One way to think of the staff is to compare the staff to your hand. There are five lines on the staff (this relates to the five fingers on your hand) and four spaces, one in between each line (because there is a space in between each finger). Here is what the music staff looks like - five lines with four spaces - one in between each line (hold your right hand horizontally in front of you).

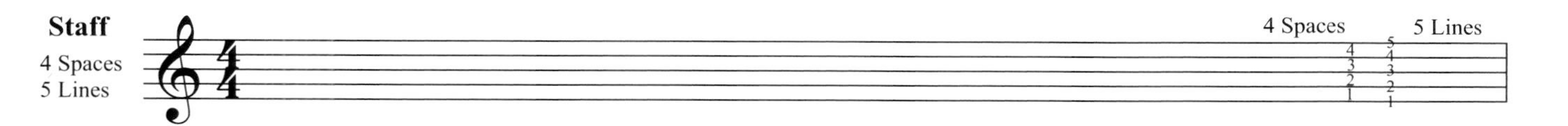

The spaces on the music staff are numbered one through four counting from the bottom space (1) to the top space (4). The lines on the music staff are numbered one through five counting from the bottom line (1) to the top line (5). There are two principle staffs used in music when playing the piano (one for the right hand and one for the left hand). Each of these staffs has its own clef sign. Clef signs are symbols that organize a staff and help musicians know the order and position of the notes.

In piano, the two most common clef signs are the Treble Clef and the Bass Clef. The treble clef is also called the G clef because the second line (counting up from the bottom) is the G note and the treble clef wraps around the line. The top of the treble clef also wraps around the top space outside of the staff (which is also a G note). The bass clef is also called the F clef because the fourth line (counting from the bottom) is the F note and the two dots after the bass clef are on both sides of the line. This is what the treble and bass clefs look like. When you combine the treble and bass clef together (treble clef on top - played by the right hand and the bass clef on the bottom - primarily played by the left hand), it is called the Grand Staff.

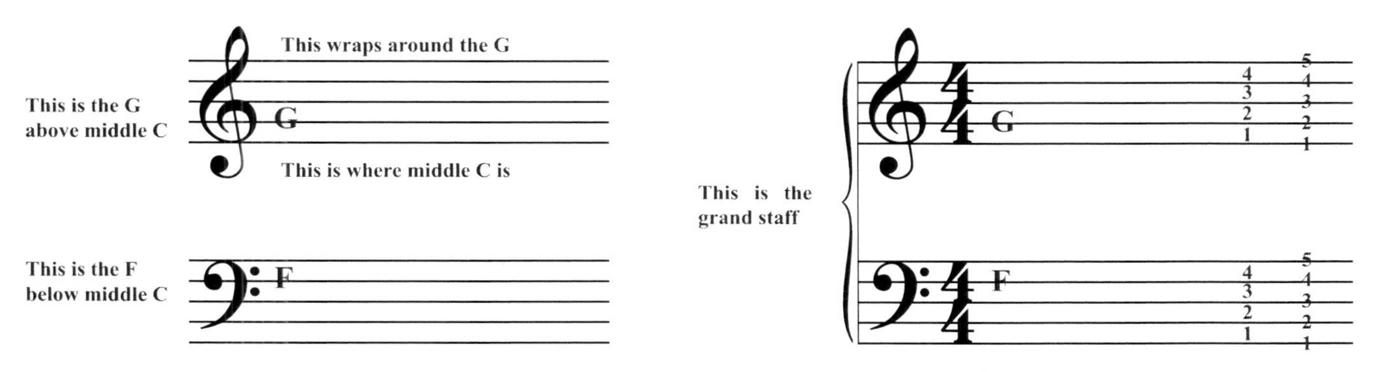

The two dots after the bass clef are on both sides of the F note.

Music is written out by having notes, which look like circles or circles with lines on the side placed in the spaces or on the lines of either the bass or treble clef staffs. There is a different note (musical alphabet: A, B, C, D, E, F, or G) assigned to each space or line. Let's look at the notes of the grand staff (treble and bass clefs). We'll start with the bottom space of the bass clef. If you know your musical alphabet, it's pretty easy. The first space (on the bass clef) is A. The second line (on the bass clef) is B. It goes up alphabetically from there.

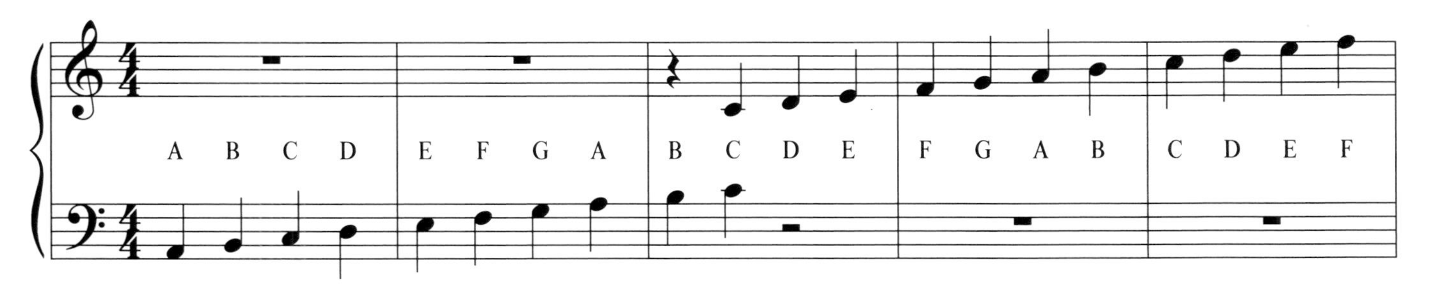

Watch your counting (M.M. ♩ = c. 120)

Have fun (Say it and Play it - count the rhythm out loud) play the right hand first, then the left hand, and then both hands together

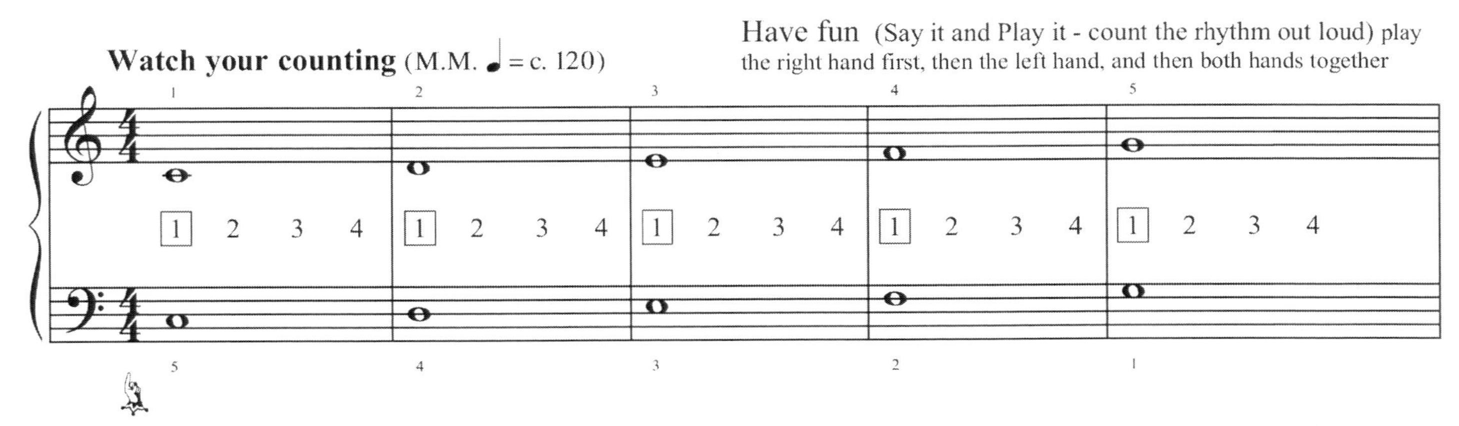

This is the time signature. This practice exercise is in 4/4 time signature. When you see this time signature at the beginning of the piece it means there are 4 beats per measure (clap and count to 4) The 4 on top means that there are 4 beats in each measure and the 4 on the bottom means that the quarter notes receive one beat. An easier way to explain this is by saying there are 4 quarter notes in every measure or something that equals 4 quarter notes.

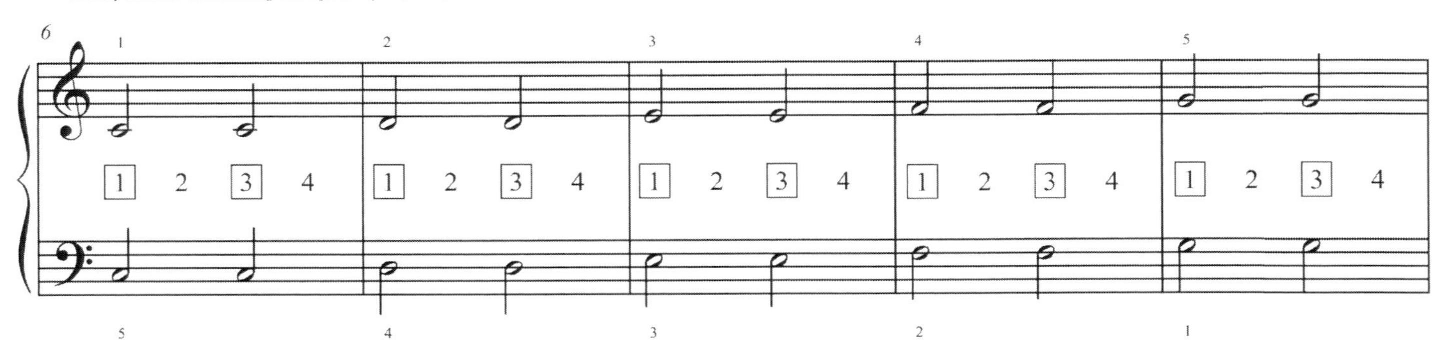

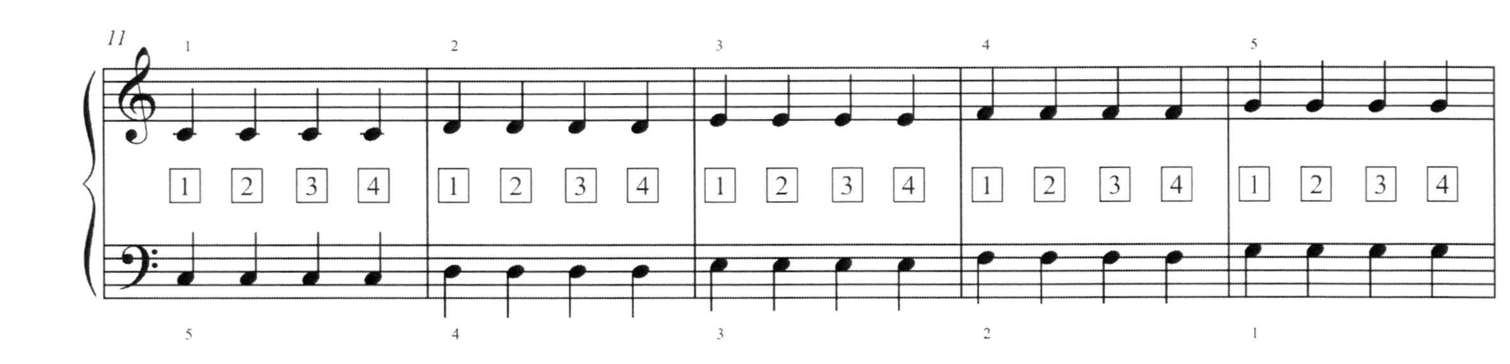

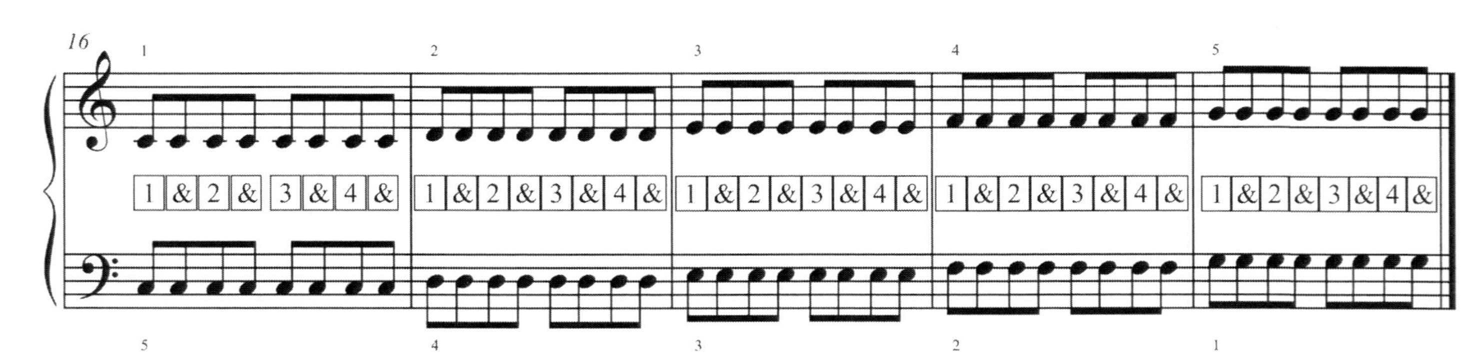

This exercise and some of the next few easy exercises are for beginning piano students and all of the exercises are taken from the Cool Songs for Cool Kids Primer level book by Jerald Simon ($14.95 - spiral bound book or $6.95 - PDF download of the book).

8va and 8vb

Not all 88 notes would fit on the bass and treble clef staffs alone. There are lines extending above and below the standard five lines of the staff. These lines are called ledger lines. The farther we go to the right, the higher the notes become and more ledger lines are needed. The farther we go to the left, the lower the notes become and once again, more ledger lines are needed. This is what all the white notes on the piano written in musical notation look like on the staff. Only the 52 notes represented by the white keys are shown here because the notes played on the black keys are the exact same notes as the ones shown below but there is either a sharp symbol (♯), or a flat symbol (♭) placed in front of them.

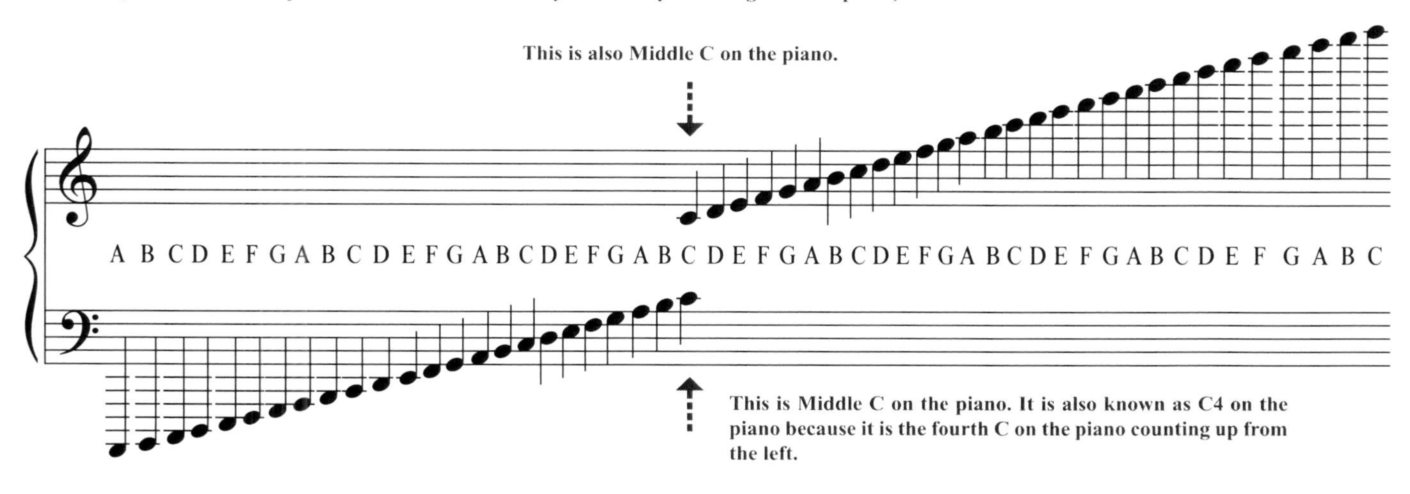

The use of octaves (the same note eight notes above or below itself) was created to help the musician avoid having to count all of the little tiny lines above and below the staffs of the treble and bass clefs. The previous example is a little difficult to read because there are so many ledger lines. The octave sign (8va) makes reading the notes much easier because it removes several ledger lines. Below is an example of the same grand staff shown above but with the octave signs above (8va) and below (8vb) some of the highest and lowest notes on the piano.

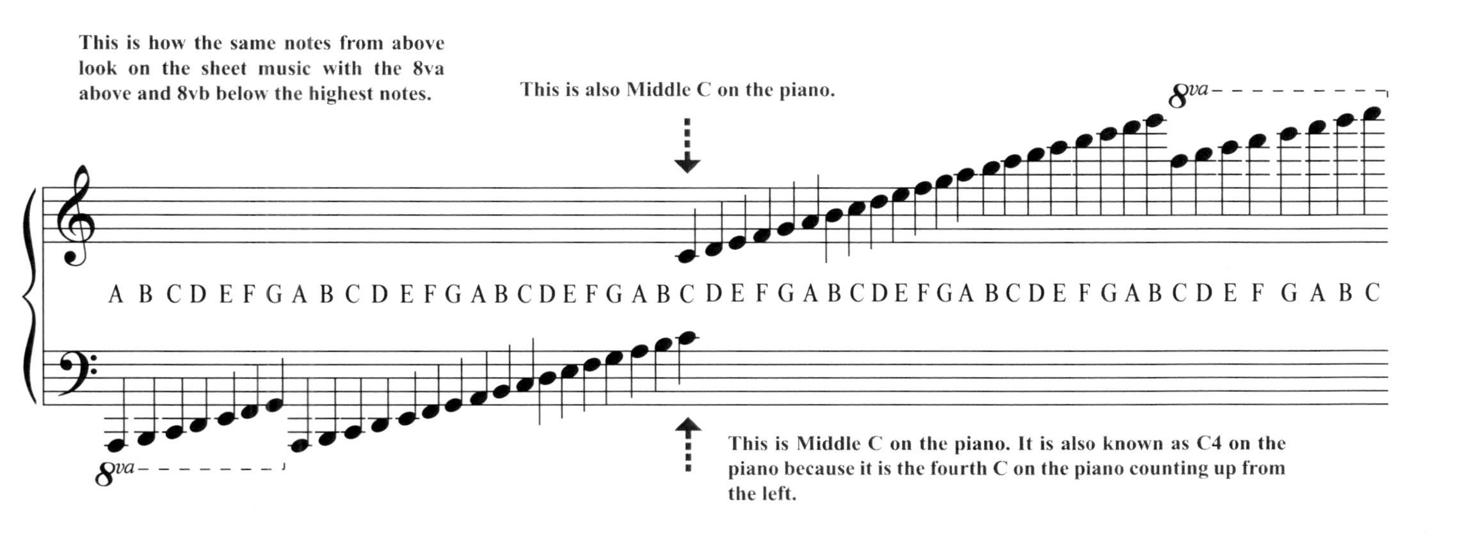

With these simple building blocks of music theory, we can understand the basics of music.

Major scales are notes in alphabetical order. Let's take a closer look at the characteristics of a scale (we will use the C major scale for this example).

The individual notes of which each major scale is comprised, can also be thought of as degrees (1 2 3 4 5 6 7 8). The first degree is the tonic, the second degree is the super tonic, the third degree is the mediant, the fourth degree is the sub-dominant, the fifth degree is the dominant, the sixth degree is the sub-mediant, the seventh degree is the leading tone, and the eighth degree (which is the same as the first degree) is also called the tonic. These are additional names that can be given to any letter in a scale (such as C D E F G A B C, etc.), depending on its position in the scale. All of the notes in the musical alphabet can be arranged in different orders (which creates the various scales and modes - we talk about modes later in this book).

The tonic is always the first and last note of the major scale. It is also known as the key note because scales begin and end on it. The super tonic is the next note or second note to the right from the tonic (i.e. D is the second note to the right from the tonic C, so D is the super tonic in the key of C major). The mediant is the third note to the right from the tonic (i.e. E is the third note to the right from the tonic C, so E is the mediant in the key of C major). The sub-dominant is the fourth note to the right from the tonic, which can also be viewed as the fifth note below the tonic (i.e. F is the fourth note to the right from the tonic C so F is the sub-dominant in the key of C major). The dominant is the fifth note to the right from the tonic C (i.e. G is the fifth note to the right from the tonic C so G is the dominant in the key of C major). The sub mediant is the sixth note to the right from the tonic C, which can also be viewed as the third note below the tonic (i.e. A is the sixth note to the right from the tonic C so A is the sub mediant in the key of C major). The leading tone is the seventh note to the right from the tonic C, which can also be viewed as the second note below the tonic, (i.e. B is the seventh note to the right from the tonic C so B is the leading tone in the key of C major). This is what the C major scale looks like on music. Each degree name has been assigned to their corresponding notes. The degrees are shown with numbers and Roman numerals (which are often used when referring to chords - upper case Roman numerals mean the chord is a major chord, lower case Roman numerals mean the chord is a minor chord). Roman numerals can also have additional symbols added after them (a plus symbol {+} for augmented chords, a minus symbol { - } for minor chords, a raised circle { o } for diminished chords, and a 6, 7, 9, 11, 13 after it identifying the chord as a sixth chord {6}, a seventh chord {7}, a ninth chord {9}, an eleventh chord {11}, or a thirteenth chord {13} - with any combination of the previous symbols).

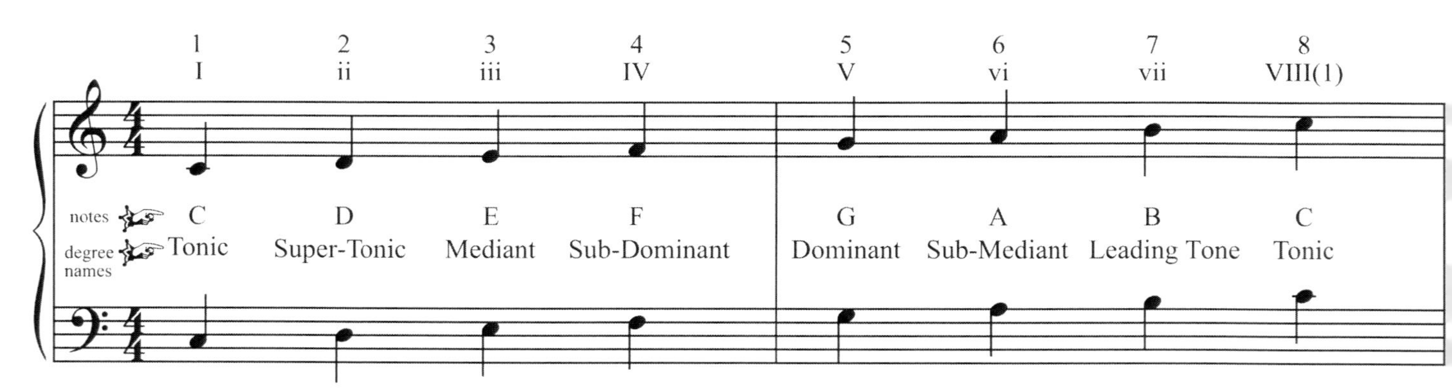

Memorize the degree names in order: (1) Tonic, (2) Super Tonic, (3) Mediant, (4) Sub-Dominant, (5) Dominant, (6) Sub-Mediant, (7) Leading Tone, and (8/1) Tonic. This is the same order of every key signature. In the key of C, the notes of the scale would be: (1) C (tonic), (2) D (super tonic), (3) E (mediant), (4) F (sub-dominant), (5) G (dominant), (6) A (sub-mediant), (7) B (leading tone), and (8/1) tonic. The key of G major has the same order but the note names of the degrees change, nothing else changes. In the key of G, the notes of the scale would be: (1) G (tonic), (2) A (super tonic), (3) B (mediant), (4) C (sub-dominant), (5) D (dominant), (6) E (sub-mediant), (7) F (leading tone), and (8/1) tonic. The degree names are the same!

Prime or Perfect First, Major Second, Major Third, Perfect Fourth, Perfect Fifth, Major Sixth, Major Seventh, Perfect Eighth (or octave)

Look at the example below - these are intervals. An interval is defined as the distance (comprised of whole and half steps) between two notes. The major scale uses "Perfect" and "Major" intervals. The perfect intervals are the primary notes (from which the primary chords are created) from the major scale (i.e. 1 or C; 4 or F: and 5 or G). The major intervals are the secondary notes (from which the secondary chords are created) from the major scale (i.e. 2 or D; 3 or E; 6 or A; and 7 or B). Look at the intervals of the C major scale below. Once you feel comfortable playing this exercise in the key of C, try playing it in every key moving up chromatically in half steps. I recommend playing every exercise and jazz piece in this book in every key!

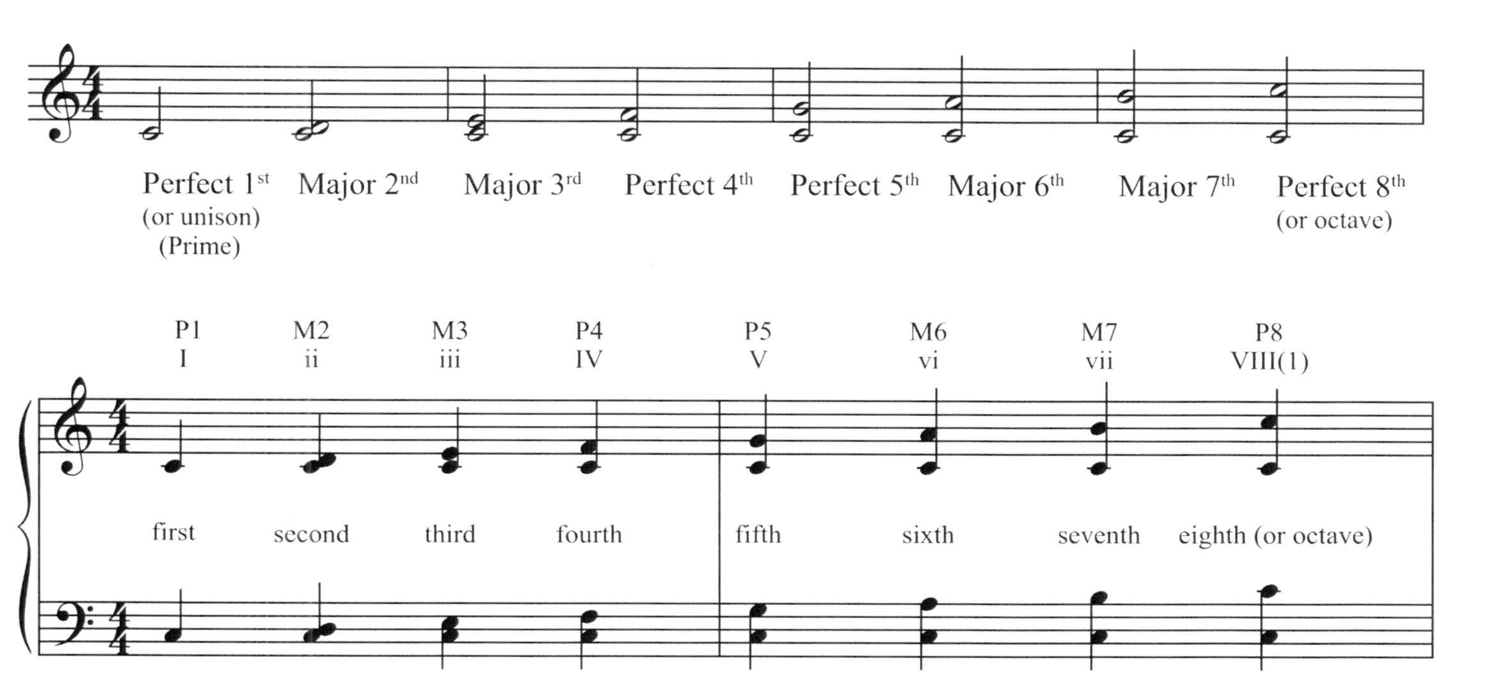

Perfect intervals can become a diminished interval by playing the flat (i.e. C and G♭ is a diminished 5th interval) and an augmented interval by playing the sharp (i.e. C and G♯ is an augmented 5th interval). Major intervals can become a diminished interval by playing the double flat (C and B𝄫 is a diminished 7th interval), a minor interval by playing the flat (i.e. C and B♭ is a minor 7th interval), and an augmented interval by playing the sharp (i.e. C and B♯ is an augmented 7th interval).

When 2 or more intervals are stacked on top of each other, they are called blocked intervals. Blocked intervals are also called harmonic intervals (i.e. a harmonic major 3rd interval is C and E played together at the same time). When they are placed next to each other (one after the other), they are called broken intervals (these are not stacked on top of each other and are not played at the same time. Broken intervals are also called melodic intervals (i.e. a melodic major 3rd interval is C and E played one after another).

Chords are created when two or more intervals (generally three) are stacked on top of each other. Some chords are major (happy sounding), some are minor (sad sounding), some are diminished (spooky and scary or deranged sounding), and there are many more. On the next page, I want you to play the triads (three note chords) created from stacking thirds on top of the notes from the C major scale. Notice the chord progression is Major - minor - minor - Major - Major - minor - diminished - Major. This is the same chord progression for all of the major scales. The corresponding Roman numerals are I - ii - iii - IV - V - vi - vii° - I.

On the next page I have included a simple and **"Quick Chord Chart"** to help you quickly begin to create the most common chords. In the chart below, I use the most common chords created from the notes of the C major scale (i.e. C Major, C minor, C diminished, etc.). Let me explain the chart on the next page.

On the left side, there is a column that says, "Most Common Chords," and has the chord name listed below (i.e. Major, Minor, Diminished, Augmented, etc.). This can be applied to all key signatures and you can do this for every key signature.

I use the key of C Major as an example. The next two columns show the chord symbols (i.e. C, Cm, C°, C⁺, etc.). I have listed the short and long variations of the chords. They mean the same thing. The next columns are listed P1, m2, M2, m3, M3, P4, d5, P5, A5, M6/d7, m7, and M7. These abbreviations mean the following:

Try playing these intervals in all keys on the piano!

P1 = Perfect 1st interval (or Prime/Unison) (i.e. C)

m2 = minor 2nd interval (i.e. C - D flat)

M2 = major 2nd interval (i.e. C - D)

m3 = minor 3rd interval (i.e. C - E flat)

M3 = major 3rd interval (i.e. C - E)

P4 = Perfect 4th interval (i.e. C - F)

Memorize all of these intervals . This example shows C.

d5 = diminished 5th interval (i.e. C - G flat)

P5 = Perfect 5th interval (i.e. C - G)

A5 = augmented 5th interval (i.e. C - G sharp)

M6 = major 6th interval (i.e. C - A), or
d7 interval (i.e. C - B double flat which is an A)

m7 = minor 7th interval (i.e. C - B flat)

M7 = major 7th interval (i.e. C - B)

An interval is the distance from one note to another note. As an example, a major 2nd interval (M2) is from C to D.

These intervals are used to create all chords in all keys!

Quick Chord Chart for reference purposes (use this to quickly identify how to create your chords) In this example we demonstrate with chords created from the C Major Scale. You can do this for all keys!															
Most Common Chords			**Qualities and attributes of individual notes within the chord**												
Chord Name (This applies to all keys)	Chord Symbols (I use C as an example)		Interval	**P1**	**m2**	**M2**	**m3**	**M3**	**P4**	**d5**	**P5**	**A5**	**M6/d7**	**m7**	**M7**
Notes from the C Major Scale	Short	Long		C	D♭	D	E♭	E	F	G♭	G	G♯	A or B♭♭	B♭	B
Major triad	C	Cmaj		P1				M3			P5				
Minor triad	Cm	Cmin		P1			m3				P5				
Diminished triad	C°	Cdim		P1			m3			d5					
Augmented triad	C⁺	Caug		P1				M3				A5			
Sus4 triad	Csus	Csus4		P1					P4		P5				
Sus2 triad	Csus2	Csus2		P1		M2					P5				
Major sixth chord (6th)	C6	Cmaj6		P1				M3			P5		M6		
Minor sixth chord (m6th)	Cm6	Cmin6		P1			m3				P5		M6		
Major seventh chord	CM7	Cmaj7		P1				M3			P5				M7
Minor-major seventh chord	CmM7	CminMaj7		P1			m3				P5				M7
Dominant seventh chord	C7	Cdom7		P1				M3			P5			m7	
Minor seventh chord	Cm7	Cmin7		P1			m3				P5			m7	
Minor seventh flat five chord	Cm7(-5)	Cmin7(-5)		P1			m3			d5				m7	
Minor seventh sharp five chord	Cm7(+5)	Cmin7(+5)		P1			m3					A5		m7	
Diminished seventh chord	C°7	Cdim7		P1			m3			d5			d7		
Augmented seventh chord	C+7	Caug7		P1				M3				A5		m7	

P = perfect interval (i.e. P4), **m** - minor interval (i.e. m2), **M** = major interval (i.e. M7), **d** = diminished interval (i.e. d5), **A** = augmented interval (i.e. A5)

Now try to create these same chords in every key signature on the piano - C, C♯, D, E♭, E, F, F♯, G, A♭, A, B♭, and B. It's a great exercise and something you should learn how to do if you don't already know. Sit down at the piano and play these in the key of C. After doing that, try to play all major scales on the piano in every key signature (I include all of the major scales and chords in my book, "Essential Piano Exercises Every Piano Player Should Know").

As a fun review, I would like you to play the most common chords in every key signature and read them printed out on the paper. These next few pages are taken from my book, "Essential Piano Exercises Every Piano Player Should Know." For those who have already purchased that book, this will be a review. For everyone else who has not yet purchased that book, I highly recommend purchasing it to learn what I personally feel are the basics every piano player should know (i.e. intervals, pentascales, major and minor scales, triad chords, 6th, 7th, chord progressions etc.). If you are a member of the Essential Piano Exercises course (essentialpianoexercises.com), you already have access to this book in PDF format.

With a good understanding of major and minor intervals, you can begin creating the basic triad chord (or three note chord). The three most common triad chords are the major chord, the minor chord, and the diminished chord. There are, of course, augmented chords, suspend the fourth chords, and suspend the second chords, but for now, we will only cover the major, minor, and diminished chords.

All major chords are created by combining the perfect 1st and 5th intervals (i.e C and G) with the major 3rd interval (i.e. E). With all three combined, the major triad chord is created (i.e. C, E, and G played together create the C major chord). All minor chords are created by combining the perfect 1st and 5th intervals (i.e. C and G) with the minor 3rd interval (i.e. E♭). With all three combined, the minor triad chord is created (i.e. C, E♭, and G played together create the C minor chord). All diminished chords are created by combining the perfect 1st interval (i.e. C) the diminished 5th interval (i.e. G♭) and the minor 3rd interval (i.e. E). With all three combined, the diminished triad chord is created (i.e. C, E♭, and G♭ played together create the C diminished chord).

Play the triads created from the C major scale below (each of the triads begin on one of the notes from the C major scale - moving up one octave - C, D, E, F, G, A, B, and ending with C).

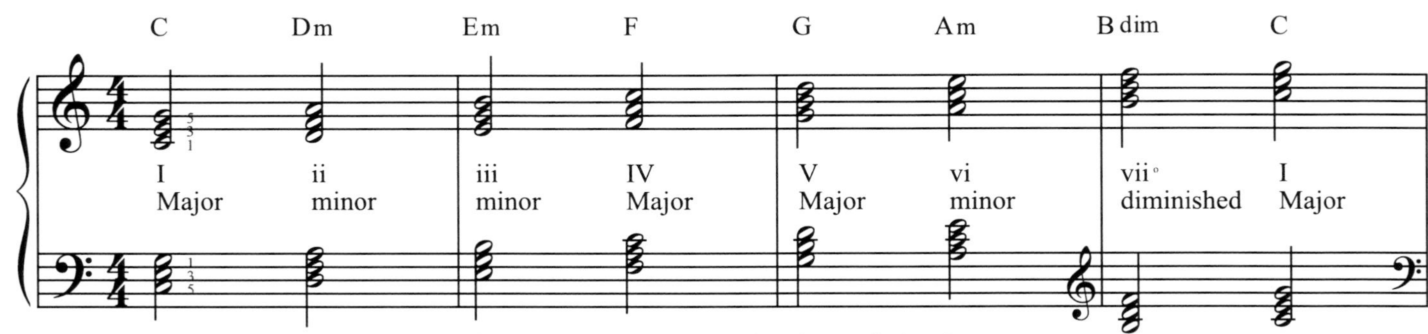

Same fingering of 5, 3, 1 (left hand) and 1, 3, 5 (right hand) on all chords

The chord progression of Major, minor, minor, Major, Major, minor, diminished, Major is the same in every key signature. Above the grand staff you will find the name of the chord(s). In the middle of the grand staff you will find the corresponding roman numeral. If the Roman numeral is upper case (i.e. I) it means the chord is major, and if the Roman numeral is lower case (i.e. i) it means the chord is minor. If the Roman numeral is lower case with the diminished symbol after it (i.e. i°) it means the chord is diminished. Since all I, IV, and V chords are always major chords (when created from the major scale) they are called the primary chords and used more frequently. The ii, iii, vi, and vii chords are called secondary chords because they are not major chords (they are minor chords and one diminished chord). Play the primary chords below for C major and A minor key signatures.

Primary chords for C Major

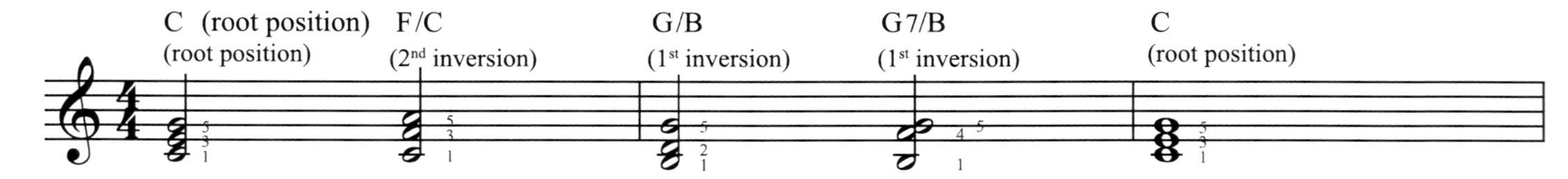

Primary chords for A minor

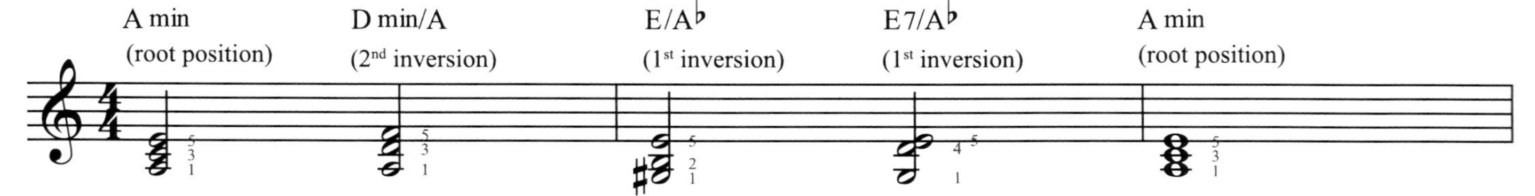

On this page, I will talk a little bit about jazz and blues. There are several jazzy piano solos in this book and it helps to understand a little about the jazz style.

To begin, I will explain about a jazz term called "swinging the 8ths". In traditional or classical music, the music is played straight - meaning that the music is played as it is written and the rhythms remain the same. In jazz music, to simplify rhythms and interesting syncopations, the music could be written out as normal, but when it was played it had a swing effect. Here is an easy way to describe it:

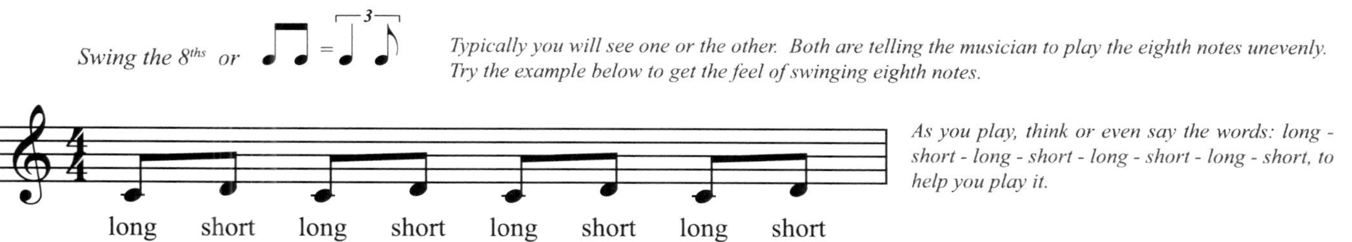

The eighth notes are played unevenly. The first eighth note is held longer than the second eighth note. They follow a pattern of long - short - long - short - long - short - long - short. It's an easier way to notate the music - otherwise the notation would be much more complicated (but you should still learn how to count and play those more challenging rhythms as well - you'll get there). I tell students to think of, what I call, the *"Drunken Sailor" effect.* Everything is slurred and blended together. To help you feel the swing rhythm, play the blues pentascale below. These are the first five notes of the C blues scale (C E♭F F♯ G).

When I teach the blues pentascale(s) to my students, I describe it like this: Play a C minor chord with your right hand, but instead of using the traditional 1 - 3 - 5 fingering (1 on C, 3 on E♭, and 5 on G), put your thumb on C, your second finger on E ♭ and your pinky on the G. Your fourth finger will play the note that is half a step below your pinky (F♯ or G♭), and your third finger will play the note that is half a step below your fourth finger (F natural). Once students can comfortably play the C and F blues pentascales, I then challenge them to play all of the blues pentascales through every key (moving up chromatically in half steps).

Below is an example of a "Barrel House blues" left hand pattern. The Barrel House blues left hand pattern is created with a perfect fifth interval (i.e. C and G - played together) then a major sixth interval (i.e. C and A played together). To vary the pattern, in the second measure is a perfect fifth interval (i.e. C and G played together) followed by the major sixth interval (i.e. C and A played together) and going to the minor seventh interval (i.e. C and B ♭- played together).

Most Common Chords (in all keys)

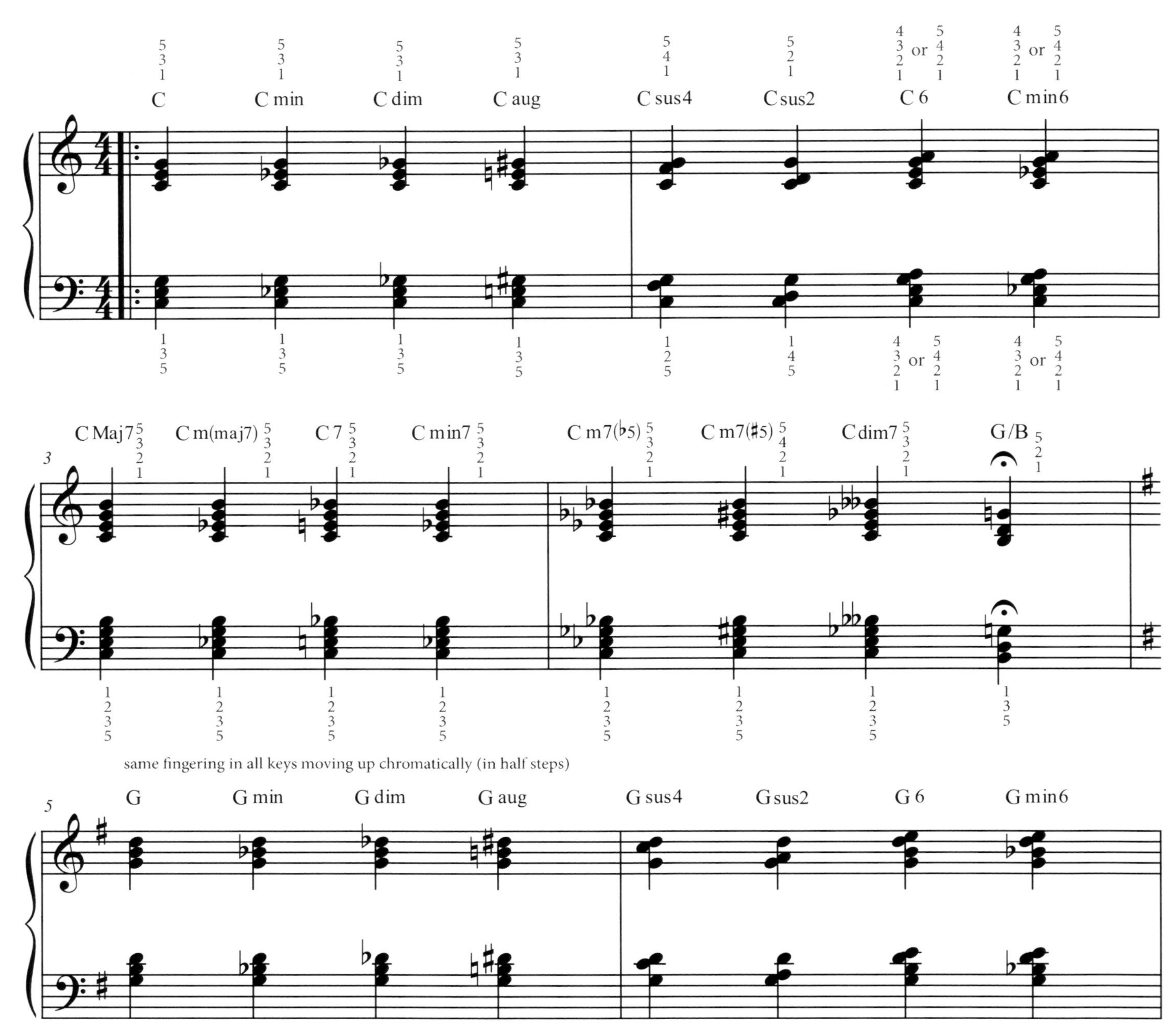

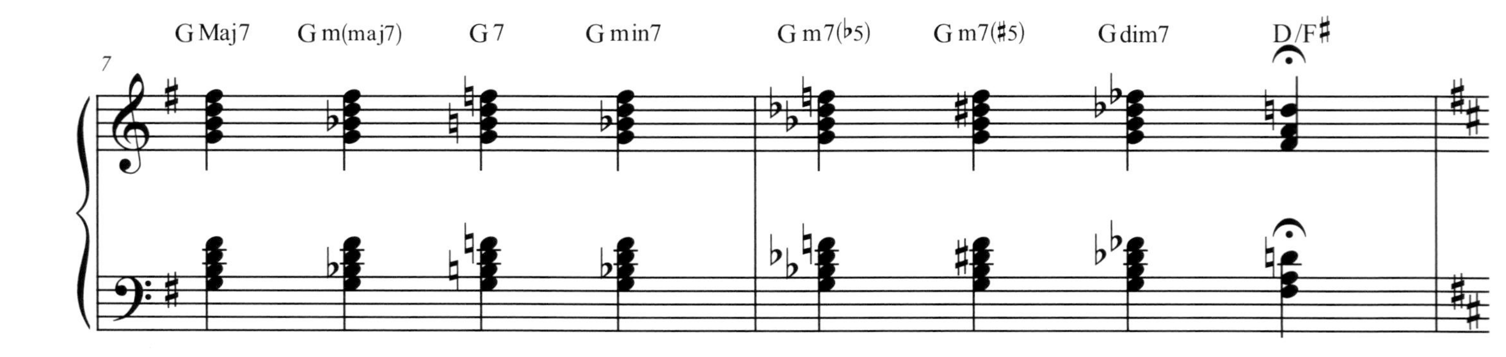

9
D
D min
D dim
D aug
D sus4
D sus2
D 6
D min6
11
D Maj7
D m(maj7)
D 7
D min7
D m7(♭5)
D m7(♯5)
D dim7
A/C♯
13
A
A min
A dim
A aug
A sus4
A sus2
A 6
A min6
15
A Maj7
A m(maj7)
A 7
A min7
A m7(♭5)
A m7(♯5)
A dim7
E/G♯
17
E
E min
E dim
E aug
E sus4
E sus2
E 6
E min6

E Maj7
E m(maj7)
E 7
E min7
E m7(♭5)
E m7(♯5)
E dim7
B/D♯
B
B min
B dim
B aug
B sus4
B sus2
B 6
B min6
B Maj7
B m(maj7)
B 7
B min7
B m7(♭5)
B m7(♯5)
B dim7
F♯/A♯
F♯
F♯min
F♯dim
F♯aug
F♯sus4
F♯sus2
F♯6
F♯min6
F♯Maj7
F♯m(maj7)
F♯7
F♯min7
F♯m7(♭5)
F♯m7(♯5)
F♯dim7
C♯/E♯

29
C♯
C♯min
C♯dim
C♯aug
C♯sus4
C♯sus2
C♯6
C♯min6
31
C♯Maj7
C♯m(maj7)
C♯7
C♯min7
C♯m7(♭5)
C♯m7(♯5)
C♯dim7
G♯/B♯
33
A♭
A♭min
A♭dim
A♭aug
A♭sus4
A♭sus2
A♭6
A♭min6
35
A♭Maj7
A♭m(maj7)
A♭7
A♭min7
A♭m7(♭5)
A♭m7(♯5)
A♭dim7
E♭/G
37
E♭
E♭min
E♭dim
E♭aug
E♭sus4
E♭sus2
E♭6
E♭min6

E♭Maj7
E♭m(maj7)
E♭7
E♭min7
E♭m7(♭5)
E♭m7(♯5)
E♭dim7
B♭/D
B♭
B♭min
B♭dim
B♭aug
B♭sus4
B♭sus2
B♭6
B♭min6
B♭Maj7
B♭m(maj7)
B♭7
B♭min7
B♭m7(♭5)
B♭m7(♯5)
B♭dim7
F/A
F
F min
F dim
F aug
F sus4
F sus2
F 6
F min6
F Maj7
F m(maj7)
F 7
F min7
F m7(♭5)
F m7(♯5)
F dim7
C/E

Now that you have played the most common and basic chords in every key signature in root position, I will ask you to play every one of the chords found on the previous six pages in every key signature and in every inversion as well. Every chord has a root position, (which is what you played on these pages), and additional positions called inversions. If a chord has three notes as is the case in a Major, Minor, Diminished, Augmented, Sus4 or Sus2 chord, then you will have three positions - root position, first inversion, and second inversion.

Let's take a C Major chord as an example. There are three notes in the C Major chord - C E G. When C is on the bottom and E and G are on top, it is called a C Major chord in root position (C E G - look at measure 49 of this page as an example of a C Major chord in root position). When the chord is inverted and the C is added to the top of the chord instead of the bottom (i.e. E G C - where E is on the bottom and C is on the top), this is called a C Major chord in first inversion. When the chord is inverted again and the E is on the top of the chord instead of the bottom (i.e. G C E - where G is on the bottom and E is on the top), this is called a C Major chord in second inversion. The same is true for the Major, Minor, Diminished, Augmented, Sus4 or Sus2 chord. Each of these chords has a root position, first inversion, and second inversion.

If a chord has four notes as is the case in the 6th, minor 6th, Major 7th, Minor Major 7th, Dominant 7th, Minor 7th, chord, then you will have four positions - root position, first inversion, second inversion, and third inversion.

In my book, "Essential Piano Exercises Every Piano Player Should Know," I wrote out all of the root positions and first, second, and third inversions in every key signature for all of the chords written above. If you have that book, you can play every chord in every key and in every inversion by reading what is written out in the sheet music. For those who don't have that book yet, simply take what I have written out above and play all of the most common chords in every key signature and in every inversion (root, first, second, and third inversions when playing the 6th or 7th chords). Before moving on in this book, play these chords in every key and in every inversion.

List of Jazz Pieces in this book with the accompanying page number:

BEAT-CHA TO IT!

JERALD SIMON

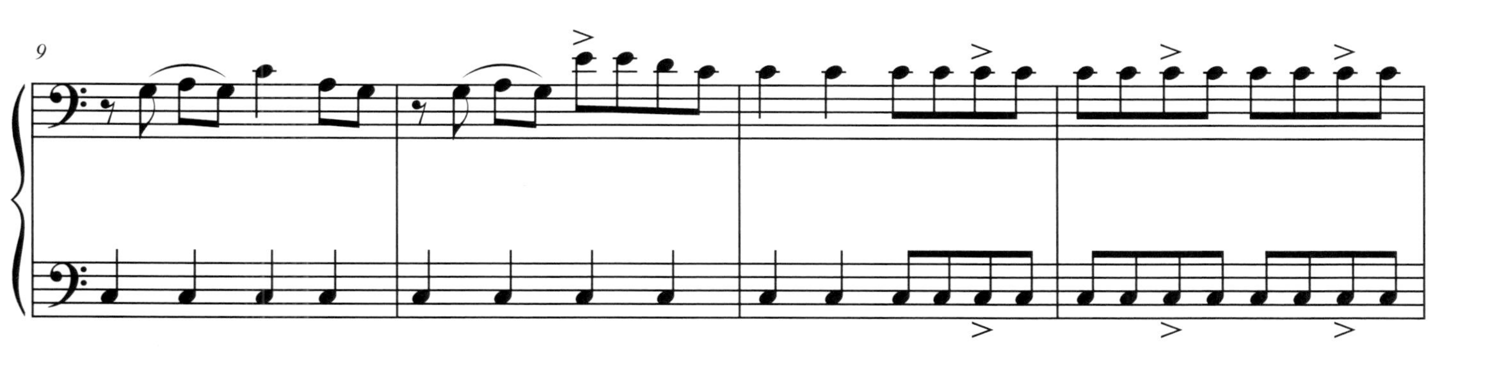

In this exercise, you will practice playing the perfect 5th interval, major 6th interval, and minor 7th interval played as quarter notes and eighth notes.

17
21
25
29
33

37
41
45
49

In this exercise, you will practice playing the perfect 5th interval and major 6th interval with the left hand while the right hand plays a broken triad (i.e. C, F, and G).

Earlier we learned about a barrel house blues left hand pattern (rotating between a perfect 5th and a major 6th interval), and we also learned how to play a blues pentascale (the first five notes of the complete blues scale) with the right hand while the left hand plays a barrel house blues left hand pattern.

In the piece below, I follow the barrel house blues left hand pattern as we have demonstrated it previously, but I also show how you can take the notes from the C blues pentascale and start improvising with it in the right hand. This is a fun piece to start putting everything together. At the end of the piece we have a fun glissando - or slide - that looks like a long squiggly line connecting two notes. Essentially you start at the top note all the way to the right of the piano (the last C), and slide down the piano playing all of the white keys on the piano. It produces a fun jazzy sound. Try it!

Water Boy Blues

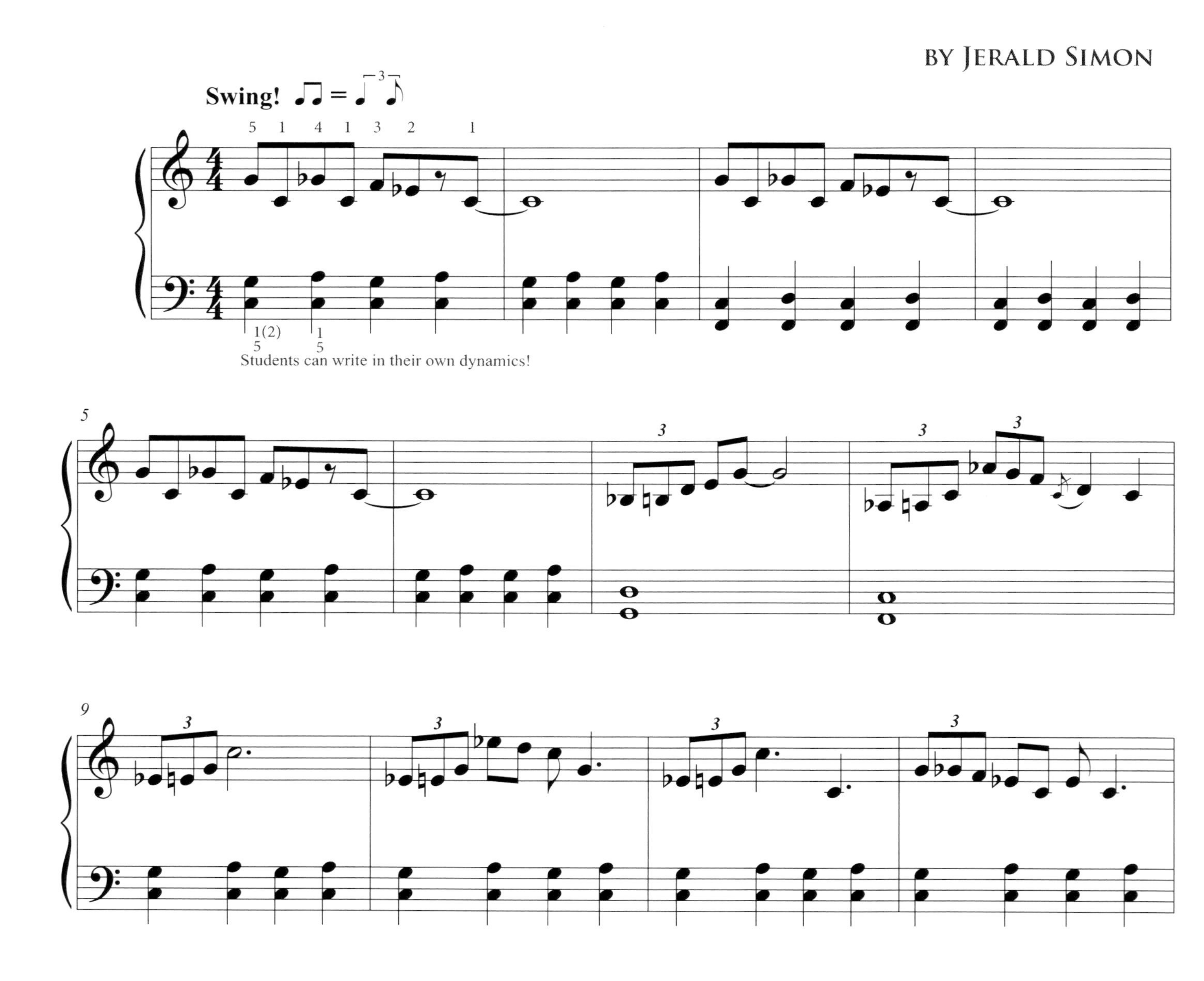

13
17
21
3
15ma

We are now going to work on various jazz pieces that use the C Blues Pentascale in either the left or right hand.

As a review from the previous two pages, the C Blues Pentascale features the first five notes from the complete C minor blues scale.

The notes from the C Blues Pentascale are C, E flat, F, F sharp, and G. You can play these notes in any order using any rhythm you'd like. It's fun to create and see what you can come up with as you play these five notes.

In this first example, I show the left hand playing these five notes moving up and down in order while the right hand plays a C (middle C).

Below I have included the C blues pentascale played with the perfect 5th and major 6th intervals.

Now try to play this example in every key signature on the piano - C, C♯, D, E♭, E, F, F♯, G, A♭, A, B♭, and B.

Bebop Blues

By Jerald Simon

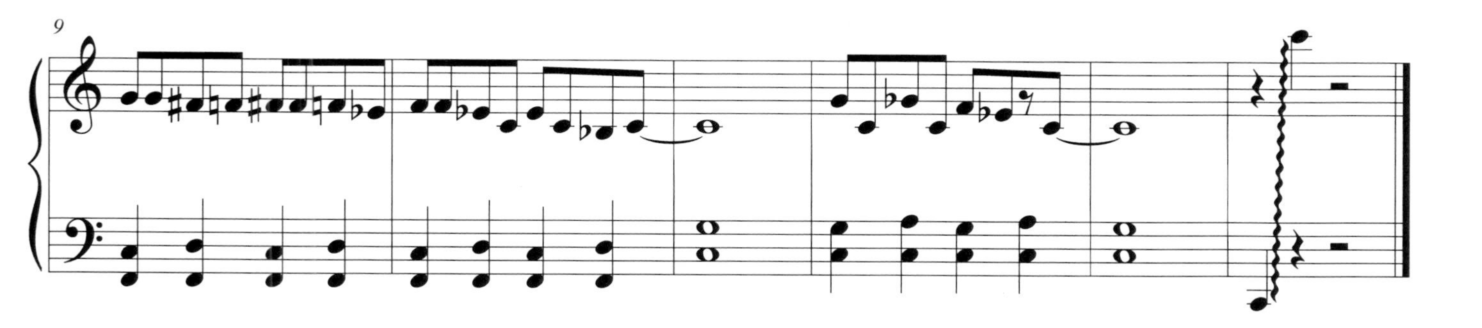

With the last measure of this piece, simply slide up the piano from C2 (the second C on the piano counting up from the left of the piano), to C6 (the sixth C on the piano counting up from the left of the piano).

For fun, try playing this jazz piece in every key signature.

You can simply move up in half steps through every key signature, or you can follow the cycle of 4ths (i.e. C - F - B flat - E flat, etc.) or Circle of 5ths (i.e. C - G - D - A, etc.).

Have fun trying to play this piece in every key!

In this exercise, you will practice playing a simple blues pentascale with both hands. After you have perfected this in the key of C Major, try playing this in every key signature. You can move up in half steps or follow the circle of fifths/cycle of 4ths through every key signature. I have included the fingering for the right hand below the notes in the treble clef and the fingering for the left hand above the notes in the bass clef.

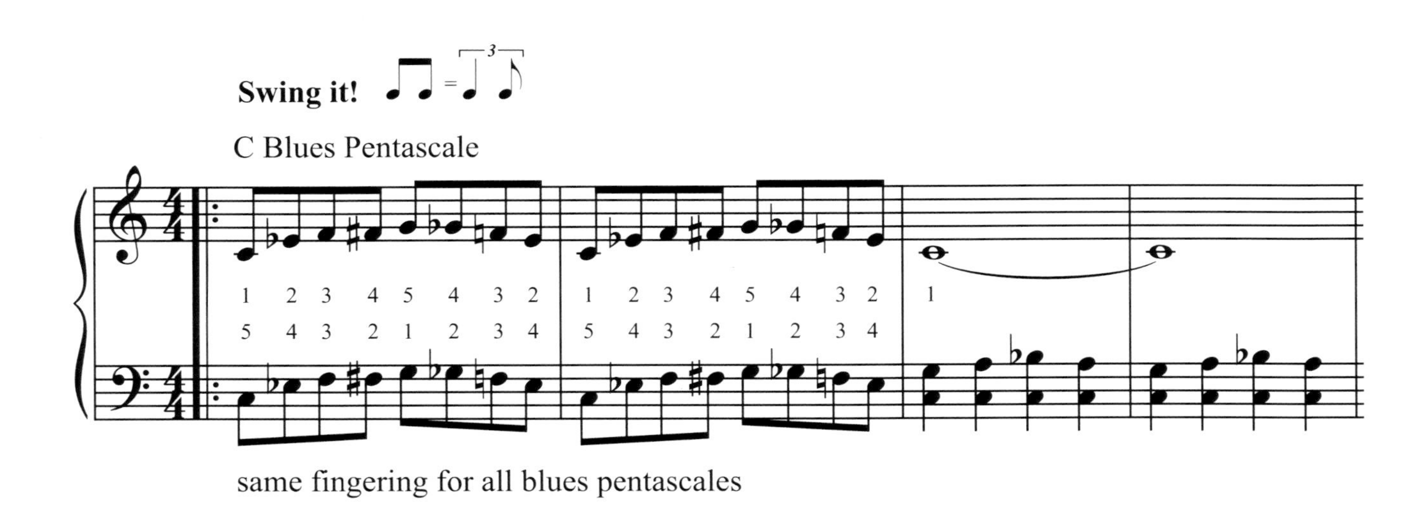

Now that you have played the C blues pentascale with both hands moving the same direction, I'd like to have you play the C blues pentascale moving in different direction where the right hand goes up while the left hand goes down.

Now try to play this example in every key signature on the piano - C, C♯, D, E♭, E, F, F♯, G, A♭, A, B♭, and B.

In this exercise you will play the blues pentascale as quarter notes with the left hand while the right hand plays the blues pentascale as 8th notes. I have intentionally written this out in every key signature so you can see how it is supposed to look. Some of the exercises in this book are only written in the key of C Major and others are written out in every key signature. I ask everyone to play every exercise or jazz piece found in this book in every key signature, either moving up in half steps or following the circle of 5ths or cycle of 4ths.

17
21

25
29

33

Right Hand Variations (numbered 1-5 according to the right hand fingering - e.g. 1 = thumb, 2 = pointer finger, and so on)

1 & 2 & 3 & 4 &	1 & 2 & 3 & 4 &	1 & 2 & 3 & 4 &
1 2 3 4 5 4 3 2	1 1 2 1 4 3 2 1	1 1 2 3 1 - 4 3
5 4 3 2 1 2 3 4	5 1 4 1 3 1 2 1	5 5 5 4 3 2 1 2
1 1 2 1 3 2 1 2	4 3 2 1 4 3 2 1	1 4 3 2 5 - - -
5 5 4 3 2 1 2 1	1 2 1 3 - - - -	4 3 2 5 3 2 1 -
4 3 2 1 - - - -	1 2 3 4 - - - -	4 3 2 1 2 - 1 -

In this exercise, the left hand is playing the blues pentascale played as quarter notes while the right hand improvises with the notes from the blues pentascale. We are only using the C, F, and G blues pentascales with this exercise. Starting in measure 11, the right hand (treble clef) is intentionally blank because I want you to practice improvising with the right hand. Take the notes from the C, F, and G blues pentascales and play around with them. See what you can create and have fun with in this simple exercise. I have also intentionally not included any dynamic markings so you can play this how you would like to play it! Once you have played this in the key of C, try playing this exercise in every key signature!

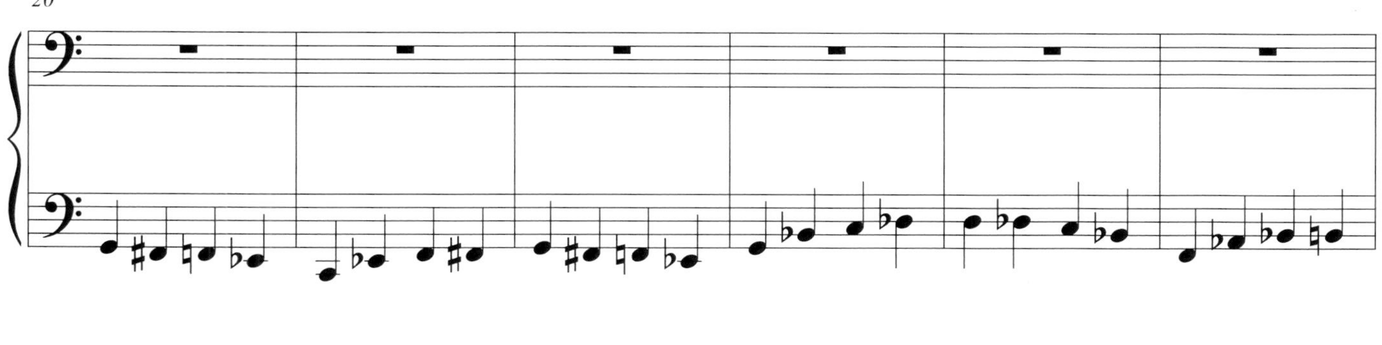

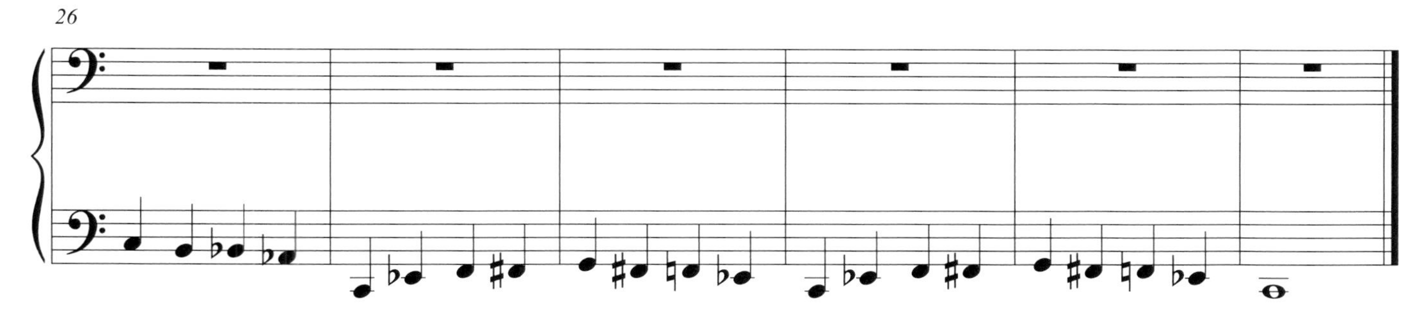

Try this fun variation. I have added some triplets with the right hand. Once you can do this on C where it is written, try playing the same pattern on F and G (the I - IV - and V chords).

The past several pages have covered simple jazz piano exercises primarily dealing with the blues pentascale. Hopefully you have practiced playing the blues pentascale in all keys moving up in half steps through every key signature. It's important to practice playing the blues pentascale where the left hand plays quarter notes while the right hand plays 8th notes. Once you master doing this in all keys, you can start playing around with the order of the notes from the blues pentascales. Try playing them up and down. Try playing the blues pentascales on every register of the piano up and down the piano.

Here is a simple jazz piece I composed to help students learn how to play the barrel house blues left hand pattern combined with the notes from the blues pentascale. In this piece, we follow a simple chord progression. We start with two measures of the C6 chord followed by two measures of the F6 chord. We then do two more measures of the C6 chord followed by one measure of the G6 chord and then one measure of the F6 chord. After playing that much, we then have two measures of the C6 chord. On the second page of this jazz piece, I have you play the notes from the C blues pentascale with the left hand while the left hand also improvises with the notes of the blues pentascale. The only difference is that the left hand is playing quarter notes while the right hand primarily plays 8th notes. I add a few triplets moving up and down the entire blues scale (i.e. C E flat F F sharp G B flat C).

Have fun playing this and try to play this jazz piece in every key signature moving up in half steps!

Jazzin' it Up!

By Jerald Simon

MM00001064

MM00001064

A Little Jazz Groove

This jazz piece is more of an exercise to get you feeling the swing rhythm. Feel free to embellish or improvise on this little jazz piece and see what you can create using the C blues pentascale.

Locker Jam!

By Jerald Simon

A 12 bar blues progression is a chord progression that has 12 measures (bars) and follows a specific pattern or progression that usually uses 7th chords in the right hand. The most basic 12 bar blues progression is shown below: C7 - C7 - C7 - C7 - F7 - F7 - C7 - C7 - G7 - F7 - C7 - C7, where each chord represents one measure (hence the 12 "bars" blues progression). Below I have shown these 7th chords in root position (i.e. C7 in root position is C E G B flat where C is on the bottom). I have intentionally left the right hand (treble clef) blank so you can improvise using the notes from the 7th chord shown in each measure. Try breaking the chord apart and play it in root position, first inversion, second inversion, and even third inversion - blocked (together) and broken (one note after another). Change the rhythm of the notes you play with the right hand. Try playing the notes from the 7th chord as whole notes, half notes, quarter notes, eighth notes, 16th notes, 32nd notes, etc.. You can also change the order of the notes. Start at the bottom and go up to the top of the chord. Start at the top and go down to the bottom note. You can start in the middle and zigzag around in any order you want. The point of this exercise is to become familiar with the 12 bar blues chord progression and try to improvise and play around with it. Throughout this book, we will have different examples where I demonstrate how you can do this on your own. Try it!

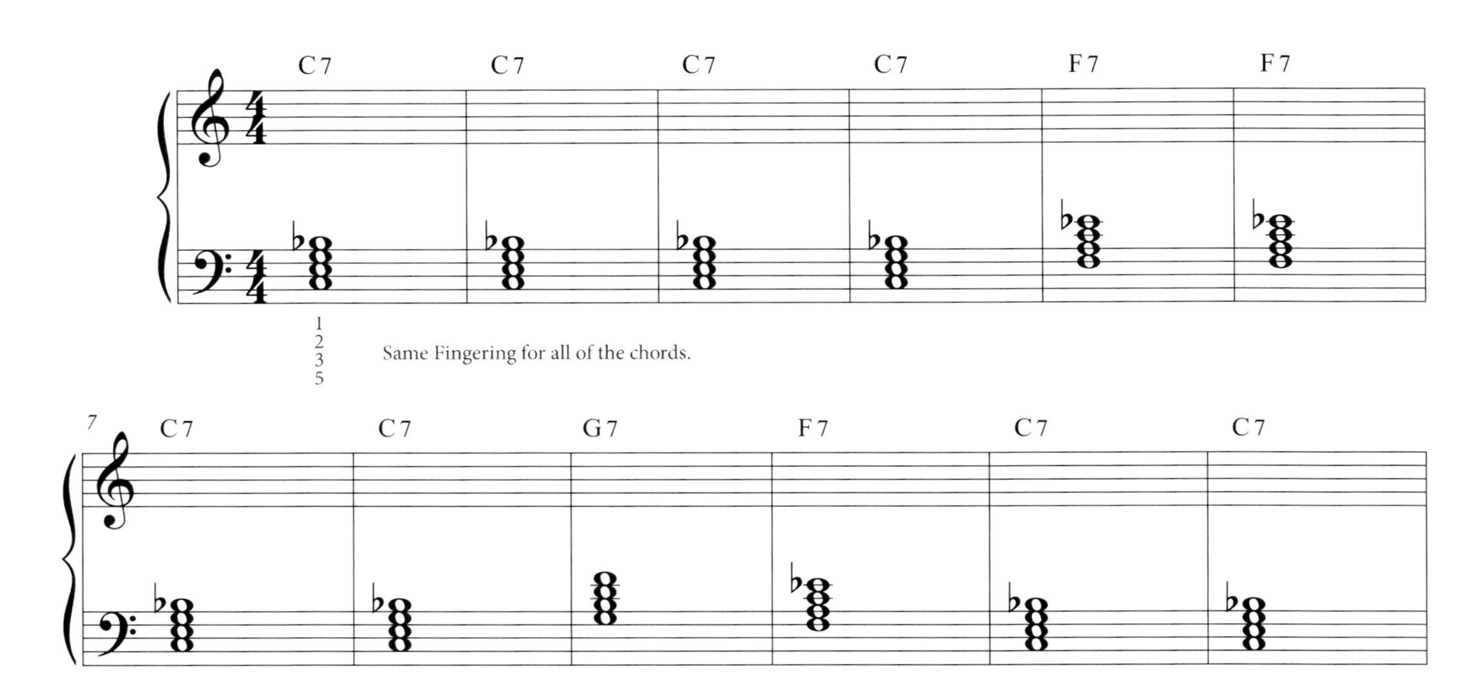

For fun, play the same 12 measures (bars) as half notes. Pretend that each chord is a half note and play two of the same chord as half notes in each measure. Follow the same progression and after you have tried this example as half notes, try it as quarter notes and then eighth notes. When playing the quarter notes you would play each chord four times in each measure, and when playing it as eighth notes, you would play each chord eight times in each measure before switching to the new chord.

There are several different 12 bar blues chord progressions. On this page I show you some of the more common variations. You can essentially create your own order and variations as well. Play around with these and see what you come up with. You will most likely see this variation. It was popular in the 1920s. Most modern blues music uses the 12 bar blues progression found on the previous page. Again, I left the right hand (treble clef) blank so you can improvise using the notes from the 7th chord shown in each measure.

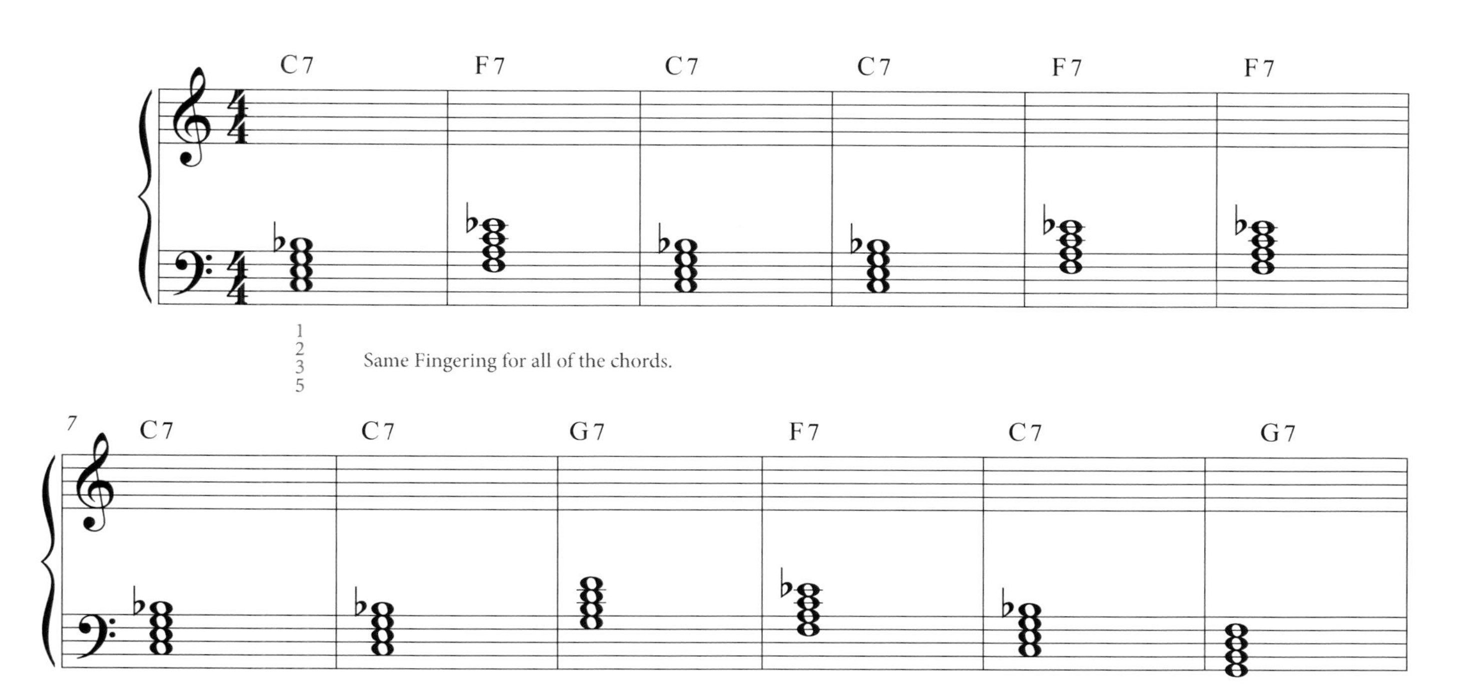

For fun, play the same 12 measures (bars) as half notes. Pretend that each chord is a half note and play two of the same chord as half notes in each measure. Follow the same progression and after you have tried this example as half notes, try it as quarter notes and then eighth notes. When playing the quarter notes you would play each chord four times in each measure, and when playing it as eighth notes, you would play each chord eight times in each measure before switching to the new chord.

Once you have tried this chord progression as half notes, quarter notes, and eighth notes, try to play the left hand as whole notes while the right hand plays the chords as half notes, then quarter notes, and finally, eighth notes.

You can switch up both hands and try different rhythms with each hand. You can even try to play one hand as blocked chords where the notes are all played together at the same time, and play the other hand as broken chords where each of the notes from the chord are played one after another.

On this page, we go over a simple 12 bar blues progression you can play in the key of C Major. In this example, the right hand is playing the 7th chord while the left hand is playing a simple walking bass pattern. The example on this page is the same as the one on the next page, but I have modified the rhythm of the right hand a little. Notice how the rhythm of the right hand completely changes the overall feeling of the piece. It is amazing how a little tweak can completely change how a piece feels and sounds. Try playing both of these pieces in all key signatures by simply moving up in half steps through every key signature. It's simple to do and it can completely revolutionize your piano playing!

The left hand is a simple broken sixth chord while the right hand plays the dominant 7th chords!

Now try to play this example in every key signature on the piano - C, C♯, D, E♭, E, F, F♯, G, A♭, A, B♭, and B.

On this page I have taken the previous exercise and changed it. I intentionally did not want to change the right hand significantly because I wanted to show you how simple it is to start improvising and arranging by only changing the right hand rhythm. Everything else stays the same. Take any music you are learning and simply do what I have done on this page and play the notes or chords with the right hand right before the left hand plays. If you notice, the right hand notes or chords are played in between the left hand notes. It is important to try and improvise your pieces like this before you start adding additional notes. Try playing both of these pieces in all key signatures by simply moving up in half steps through every key signature. It's simple to do and it can completely revolutionize your piano playing!

Now try to play this example in every key signature on the piano - C, C♯, D, E♭, E, F, F♯, G, A♭, A, B♭, and B.

12 Bar Boogie Blues

Now try to play this example in every key signature on the piano - C, C♯, D, E♭, E, F, F♯, G, A♭, A, B♭, and B.

Simple 12 Bar Jazz Riff

In this exercise, the left hand pattern uses the perfect 5th, major 6th, and minor 7th intervals. The right hand is a fun pattern created by playing the C Major Blues scale and the 6th chord. Try playing this exercise in all key signatures by simply moving up in half steps through every key signature. It's simple to do and it can completely revolutionize your piano playing!

Now try to play this example in every key signature on the piano - C, C♯, D, E♭, E, F, F♯, G, A♭, A, B♭, and B.

MM00001064

On the next page, I have composed a simple piece where we put into practical application the left hand pattern of the perfect 5th, Major 6th, and minor 7th intervals. With the right hand, I have composed a simple melody using a broken 6th interval (descending) and I also add the major blues scale. Have fun playing this simple jazz piece. After playing this in the key of C Major, try to play this jazz piece in every key signature on the piano - C, C♯, D, E♭, E, F, F♯, G, A♭, A, B♭, and B.

The right hand of this piece uses the notes from the C6 chord in first inversion. Try playing the C6, F6, and G6 chords below in root position, 1st, 2nd, and 3rd inversions.

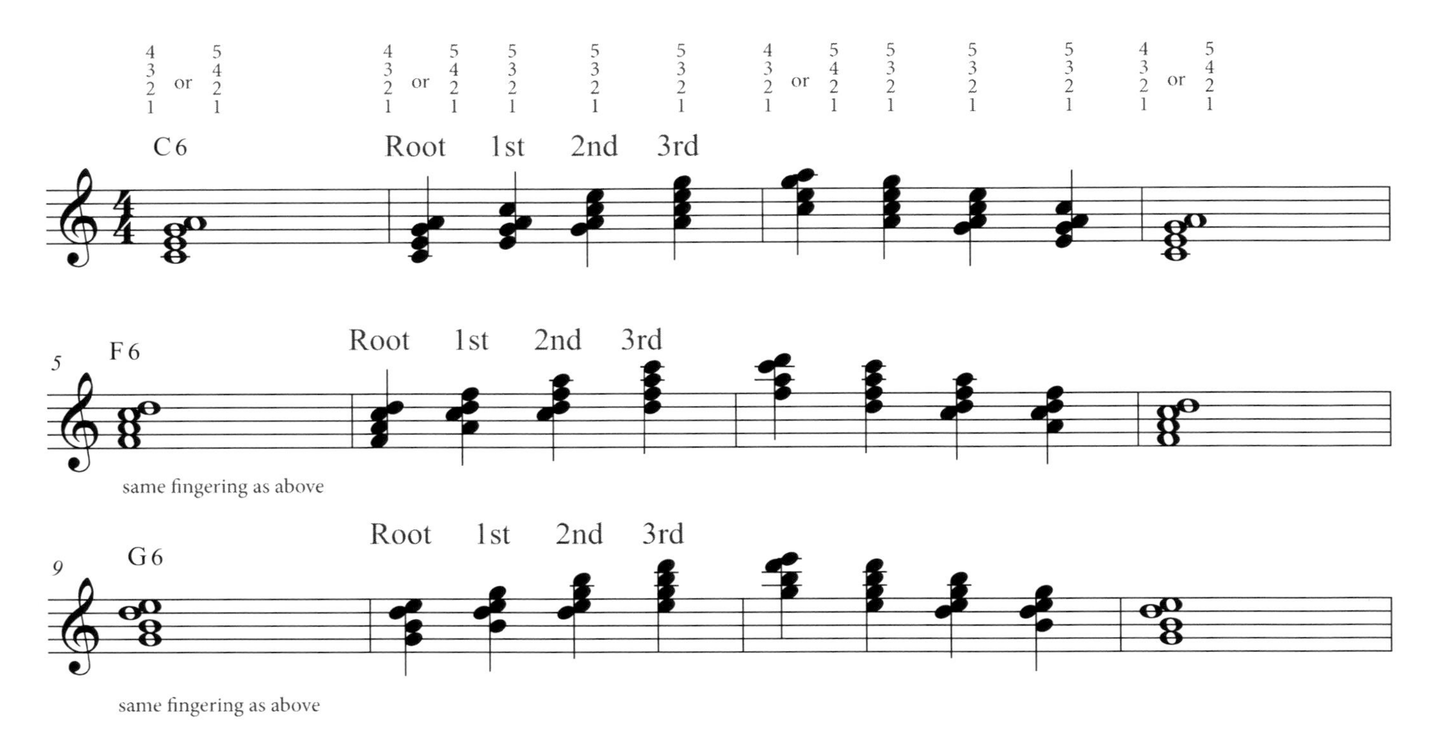

After you play this as written, try to break the notes apart in root position, 1st, 2nd, and 3rd inversions as well.

Even though we have only written out the right hand notes, try to do this with both hands.

ROCK 'N RAG

Pretend You Have a Rock in Your Rags (M.M. ♩ = c. 120)

BY JERALD SIMON

MM00001064

In this exercise, the left hand pattern uses the perfect 5th, major 6th, and minor 7th intervals. The right hand is a fun pattern created by playing the C Major Blues scale descending. Try playing this exercise in all key signatures by simply moving up in half steps through every key signature. It's simple to do and it can completely revolutionize your piano playing!

Now try to play this example in every key signature on the piano - C, C♯, D, E♭, E, F, F♯, G, A♭, A, B♭, and B.

On the next page, I have composed a simple piece where we use practical application...With the right hand, I have composed a simple melody. Have fun playing this simple jazz piece. After playing this in the key of C Major, try to play this jazz piece in every key signature on the piano - C, C♯, D, E♭, E, F, F♯, G, A♭, A, B♭, and B.

Junkyard Jive

MM0000106

Leftie

This piece was composed with the intention of allowing you to create a right hand melody. The left hand is mimicking the bass. With the right hand, first try to play the chord written above each measure. After playing the chords in root position, try playing those chords in root position, 1st, 2nd, and 3rd inversions blocked and broken. Come up with a simple jazzy melody that is catchy and easy to hum/sing.

By Jerald Simon

Homework Hangover

swing (♩ = c. 90)

By Jerald Simon

MM00001064

8va
15ma
15
3
3
3

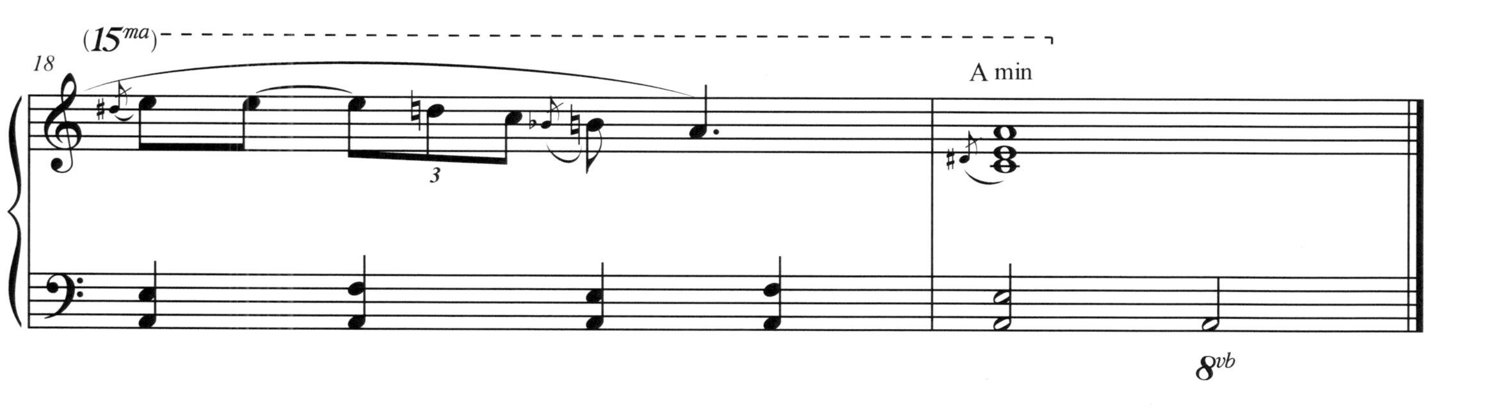
(15ma)
18
A min
3
8vb

Boot Camp Boogie

By Jerald Simon

left. left. left right left... (M.M. ♩ = c. 140)

C

2 3

mf

2 1
5 5

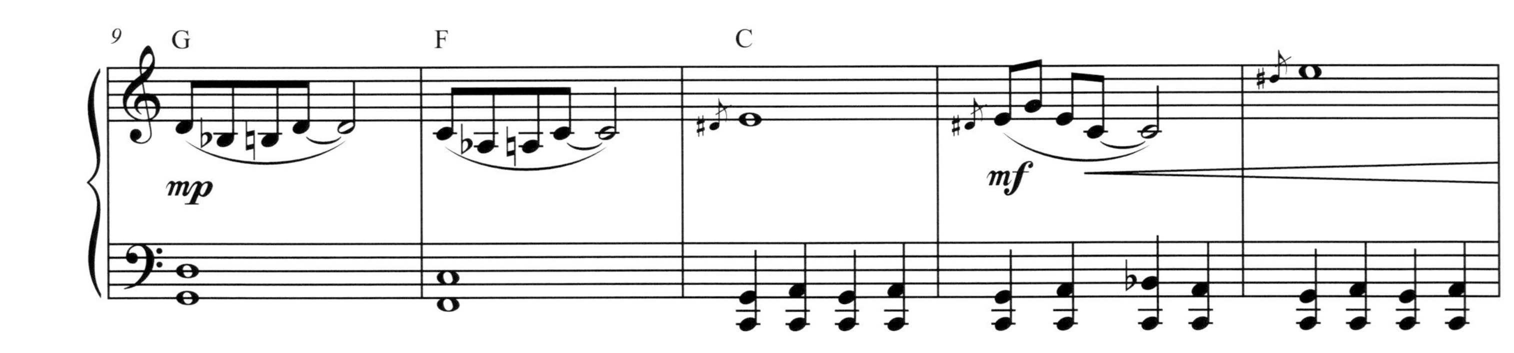

'Bored' Game Blues

By Jerald Simon

MM00001064

The Spy Kid

By Jerald Simon

22
mf
poco rit.
27
p pp

This exercise uses a familiar jazz left hand pattern that has been used in many jazz pieces and even video soundtracks (think Baby Elephant Walk and similar titles). I play this exercise straight without swinging the music, but you can play it both ways. Have fun playing this simple jazz piece. After playing this in the key of C Major, try to play this jazz piece in every key signature on the piano - C, C♯, D, E♭, E, F, F♯, G, A♭, A, B♭, and B.

MM00001064

The jazz piece on the next page features the left hand you learned on the previous page, but also features inverted sixth chords with the right hand and glissando. A glissando is when you slide from one note to another note - usually on white keys, but you can do glissandi on the black keys. When it is notated you will see a note up above and a note below that are connected with what appears to be a wavy line.

This is a simple Glissando where we slide up the keys playing all white keys from C2 - C6.

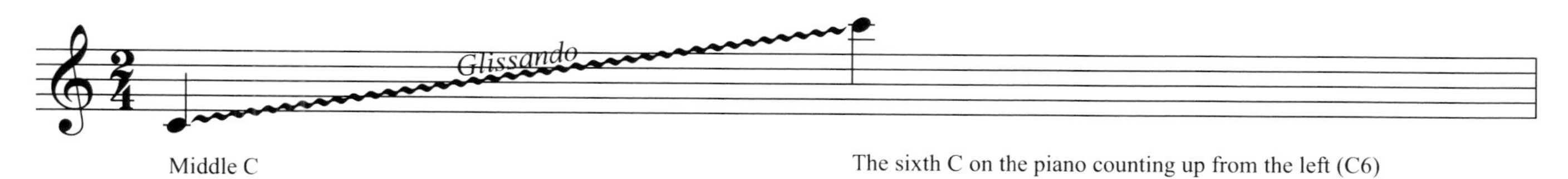

This is a simple Glissando where we slide down the keys playing all white keys from C6 - C2.

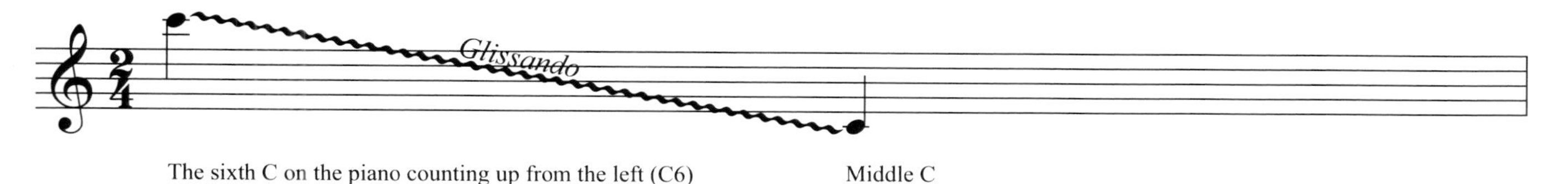

In this example, we slide up and down on the white keys.

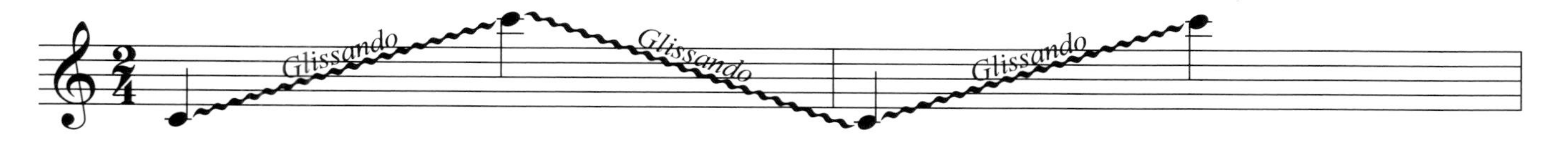

Practice sliding up and down the white keys on the piano. I usually tell piano students to slide up using the back of their right hand - only using the fingernails on the piano. The hand should be at a 45 degree angle with the fingernails touching the keys (palm side up). Don't slide up and down the keys using your skin as it will hurt.

When I slide down, I will usually use my entire right hand (palm side down) and use the fingers. This does require some practice and you need to build up calluses.

SLIP 'N SLIDE SUMMERTIME

BY JERALD SIMON

straight (M.M. ♩ = c. 120) **you can swing this song if you want to**

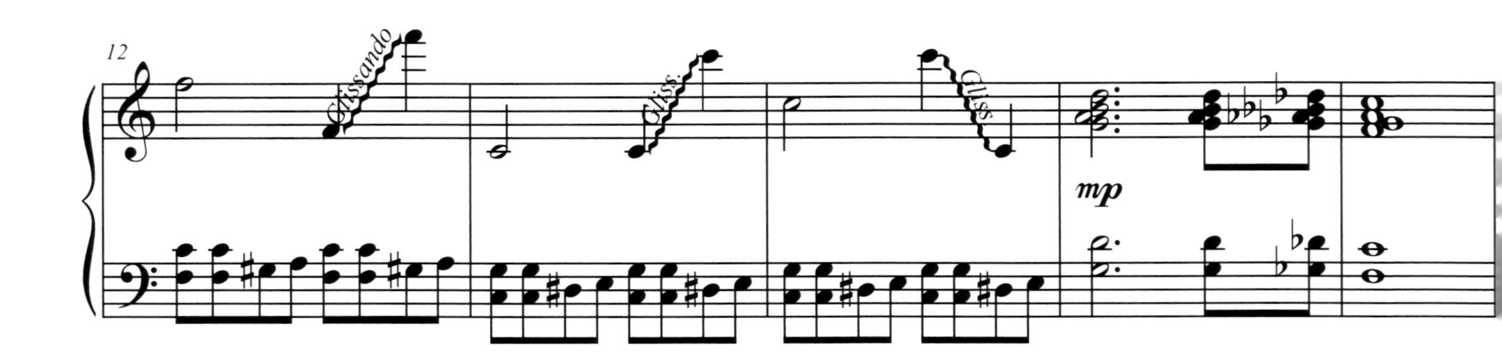

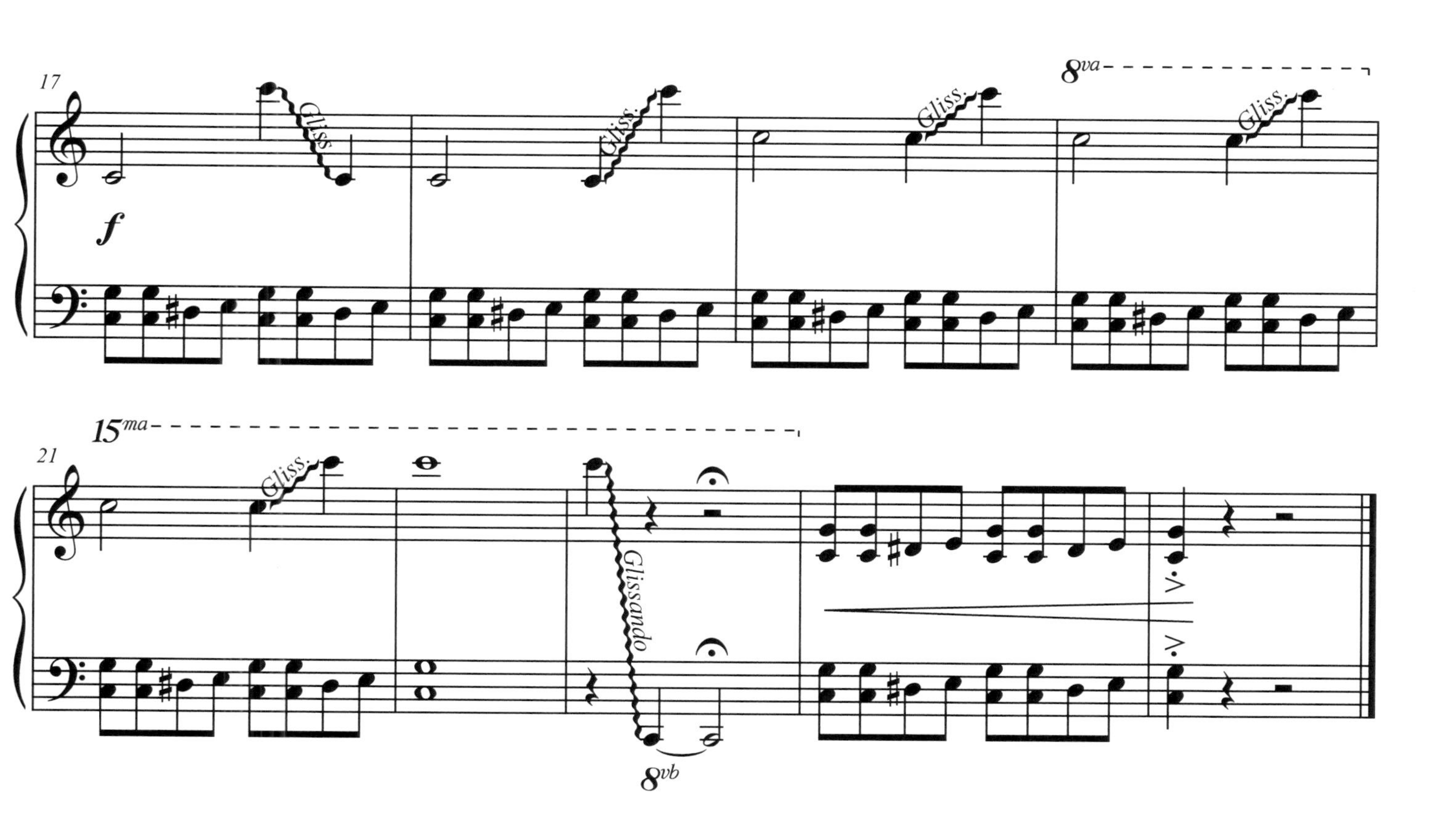
17
8va
Gliss.
Gliss.
Gliss.
Gliss.
f
21
15ma
Gliss.
Glissando
8vb

This exercise is to help you learn a simple left hand walking bass pattern created from a broken 6th chord with a minor 7th interval (i.e. the C6 chord is C E G A played together at the same time. If you break apart the C6 chord and add the minor 7th interval from C {B flat}, you then have a simple left hand walking bass pattern - C E G A B flat A G E). The right hand is playing a broken C6 chord (i.e. C E G A) - broken apart - one note played after the other. Have fun playing this simple jazz exercise. After playing this in the key of C Major, try to play this jazz exercise in every key signature on the piano moving up in half steps - C, C♯, D, E♭, E, F, F♯, G, A♭, A, B♭, and B.

Here you can improvise with your right hand. Play the corresponding 6th chord (notes from the 6th chord) any way you want! You can change the order of the notes or completely modify the rhythm (of the right hand notes). This is all about experimenting and playing around!

18 C6

22 F6 C6

26 G6 F6

This exercise is to help you learn a simple left hand walking bass pattern created from a broken 6th chord with a minor 7th interval (i.e. the C6 chord is C E G A played together at the same time. If you break apart the C6 chord and add the minor 7th interval from C {B flat}, you then have a simple left hand walking bass pattern - C E G A B flat A G E). The right hand is playing a broken C7 octave chord (i.e. C E G B flat C) - broken apart - one note played after the other. Have fun playing this simple jazz exercise. After playing this in the key of C Major, try to play this jazz exercise in every key signature on the piano moving up in half steps - C, C♯, D, E♭, E, F, F♯, G, A♭, A, B♭, and B.

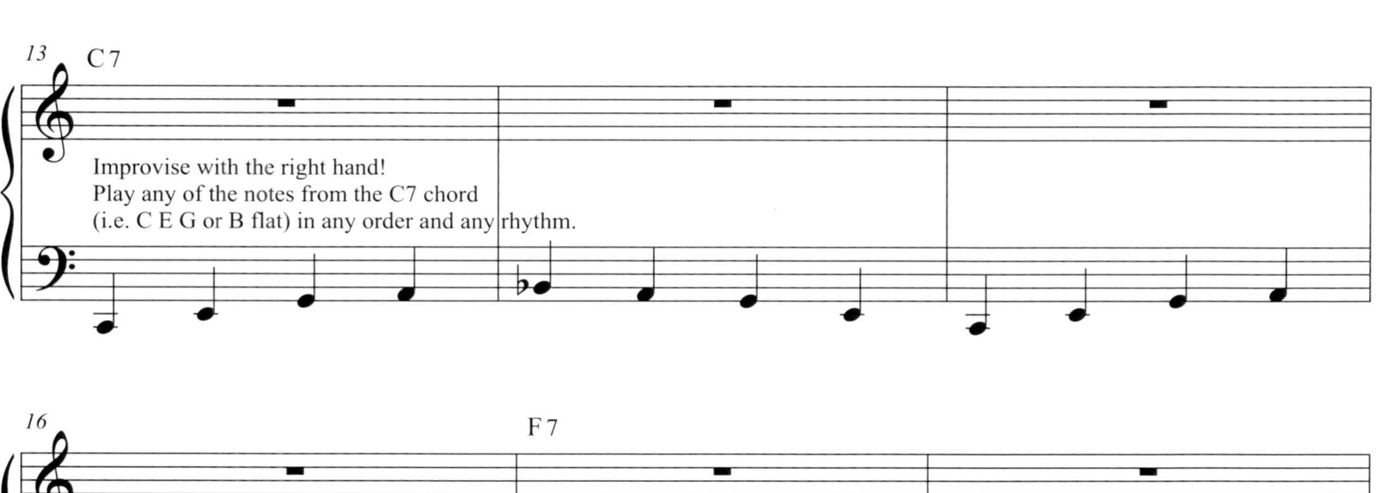
13
C 7
Improvise with the right hand!
Play any of the notes from the C7 chord
(i.e. C E G or B flat) in any order and any rhythm.

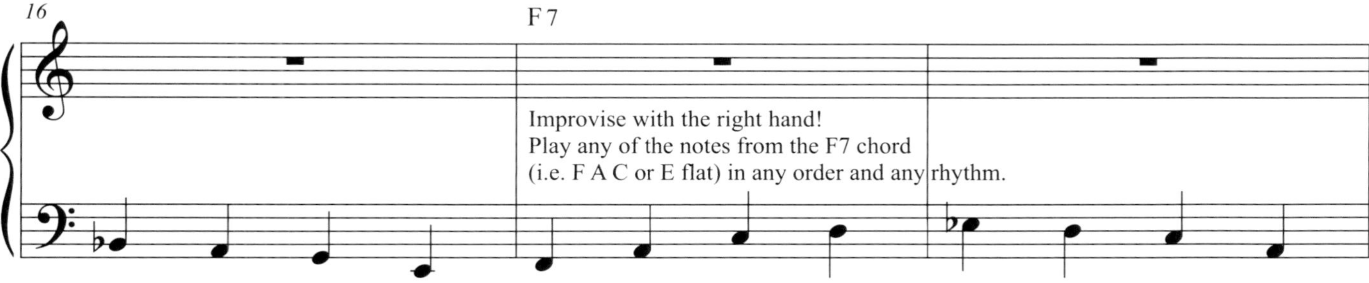
16
F 7
Improvise with the right hand!
Play any of the notes from the F7 chord
(i.e. F A C or E flat) in any order and any rhythm.

19
C 7
G 7
Improvise with the right hand!
Play any of the notes from the G7 chord
(i.e. G B D or F) in any order and any rhythm.

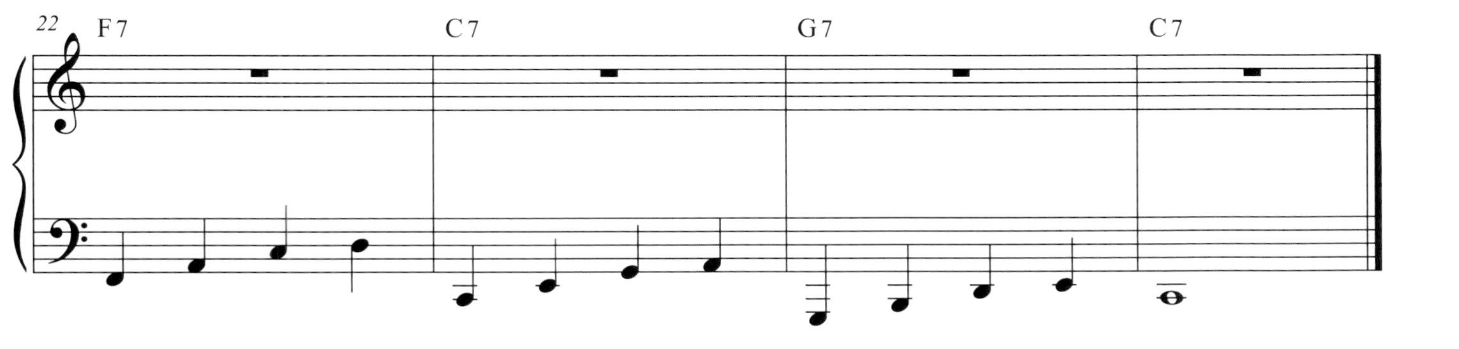
22
F 7
C 7
G 7
C 7

A Simple Walking Bass with a Major Blues Scale

Play this exercise in all key signatures moving up half a step each time through each key!

A Simple Walking Bass with a Major Blues Scale (variation)

Play this exercise in all key signatures moving up half a step each time through each key!

A Simple Walking Bass with a Major Blues Scale (variation)

This exercise is to help you learn a simple left hand walking bass pattern created from a broken 6th chord with a minor 7th interval (i.e. the C6 chord is C E G A played together at the same time. If you break apart the C6 chord and add the minor 7th interval from C {B flat}, you then have a simple left hand walking bass pattern - C E G A B flat A G E). The right hand is playing a descending major blues scale. Have fun playing this simple jazz exercise. After playing this in the key of C Major, try to play this jazz exercise in every key signature on the piano moving up in half steps - C, C♯, D, E♭, E, F, F♯, G, A♭, A, B♭, and B.

18
F6
C6
22
G6
F6
C6
26

Pogo Stick Punch Out

by Jerald Simon

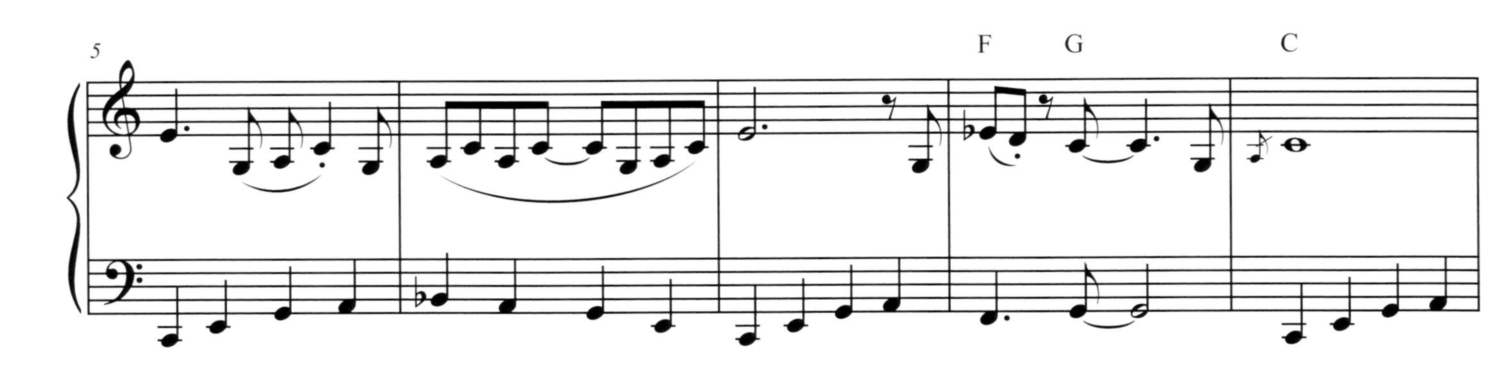

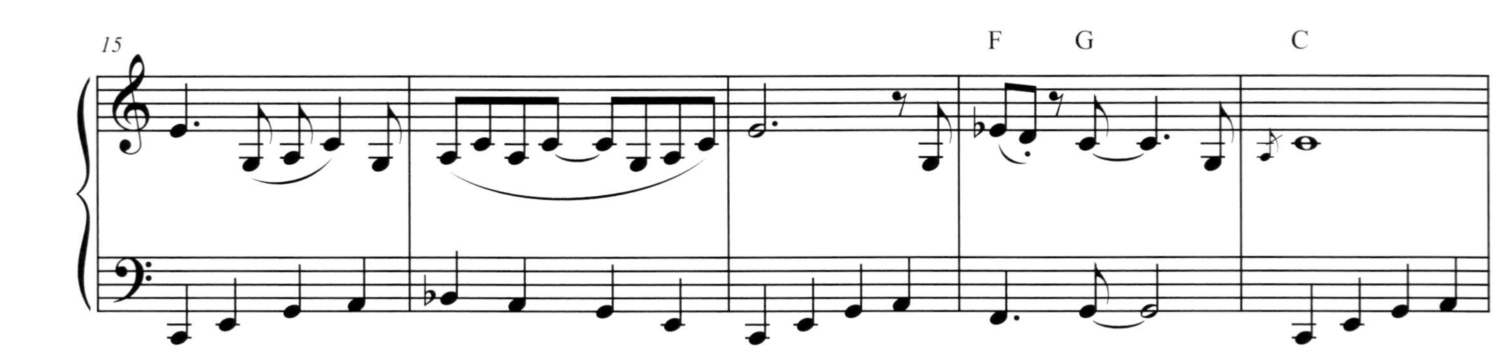

20
f
3
3
25
F
C
G
3
mf
30
F
C
3
mp
mf
35
F
G
C
40
f

Whole - Half - Half Walking Bass line

The right hand plays the Major and Minor Blues Scales

(ascending and descending)

In this exercise, I intentionally left off the chords because I don't want you to think about chords. The whole point of this exercise is to have you practice a whole - half - half walking bass pattern with the left hand and learn how to improvise with either the major or minor blues scale in the right hand. After playing this jazz exercise in the key of C Major, try to play it in every key signature on the piano moving up in half steps - C, C♯, D, E♭, E, F, F♯, G, A♭, A, B♭, and B.

17
Use the notes from the C Major or C minor Blues Scale to improvise with the right hand how you want to arrange it. Play around and have FUN!
21
25
29
33

The Gigabyte Guru

By Jerald Simon

19
23
27
31
f
35
8vb

On this page, we are going to play all of the 7th chords created from the notes of the C Major scale moving up diatonically (i.e. according to the C Major scale). First we play the chords blocked (together) and then we play the chords broken (one note played after another). Think of the C Major scale - C D E F G A B and C. Think of these as 1, 2, 3, 4, 5, 6, 7, and 8. You can also think of them as I - ii - iii - IV - V - vi - vii and VIII. The upper case Roman numerals are Major chords and the lower case Roman numerals are minor chords (the 7th is a diminished chord).

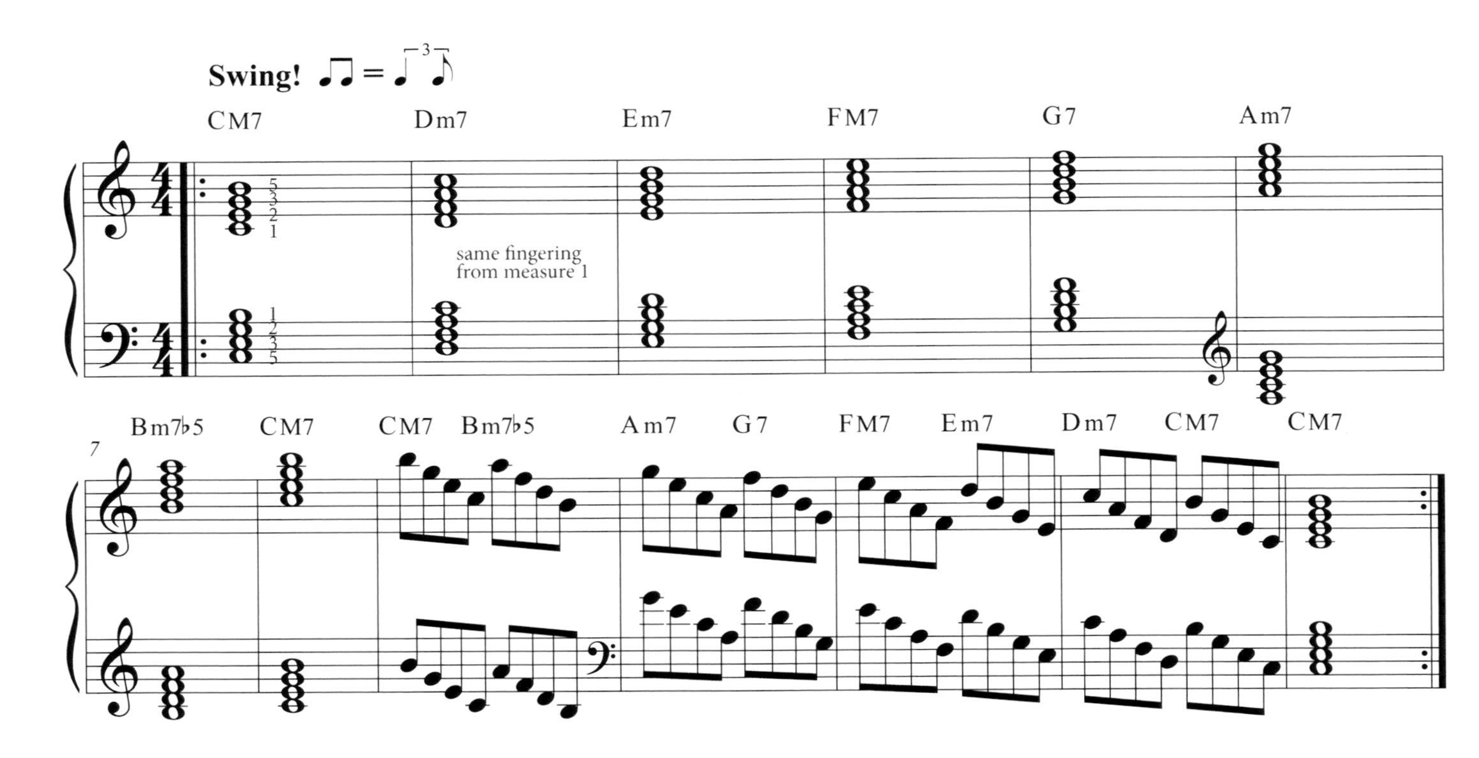

The right hand plays the broken 7th chords (bottom note moving up to the top note) while the left hand continues to play the blocked 7th chord. Swing this example like the previous one.

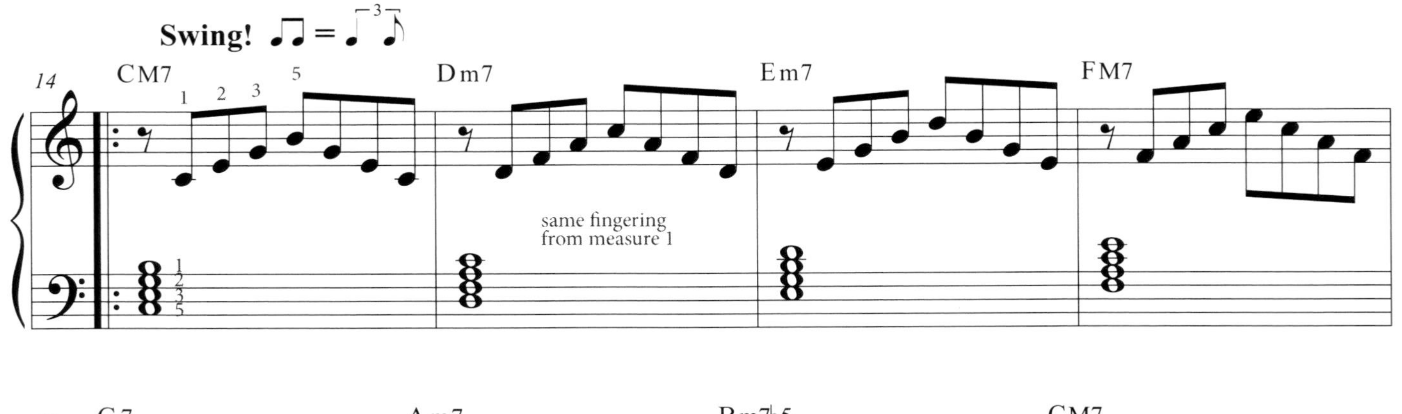

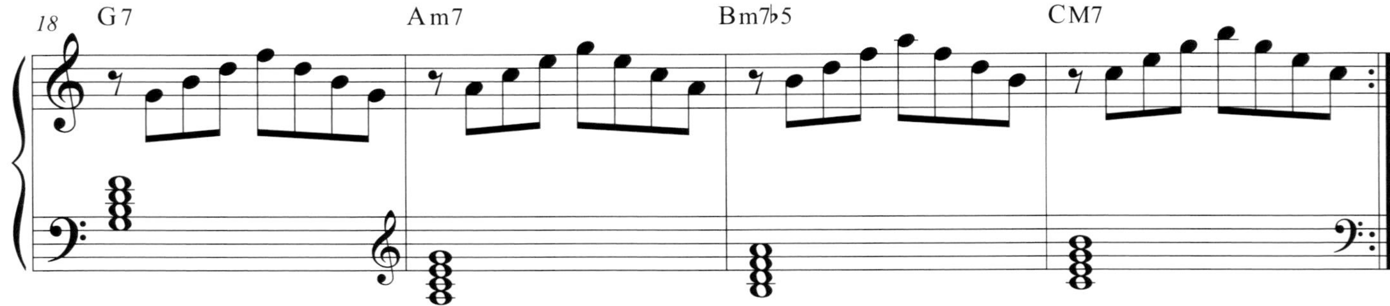

Try this variation as well!

Most jazz pieces are composed following various jazz chord progressions. We have a list of well-known jazz chord progressions in the appendix of this book, but on this page, we are going to learn how to create what is known as the **ii - V - I** jazz chord progression. It is very simple, especially after having played through the 7th chords on the previous page. The **ii - V - I** jazz chord progression, in its simplest form or pattern, is a ii (minor 7th chord), followed by a V (dominant 7th chord), and ending with a I (Major 7th chord). A simple example in the key of C Major is to play the Dm7 (ii), G7 (V), and CM7 (I) chord progression. In the example below, I show the simple ii - V - I jazz chord progression. First, I demonstrate it as half notes ending with a whole note, and then I modify the rhythms and show an 8th note followed by a quarter rest, then an 8th note tied with a half note. We follow this rhythm using the ii - V - I on Dm7 (ii), G7 (V), and CM7 (I). Try playing this example.

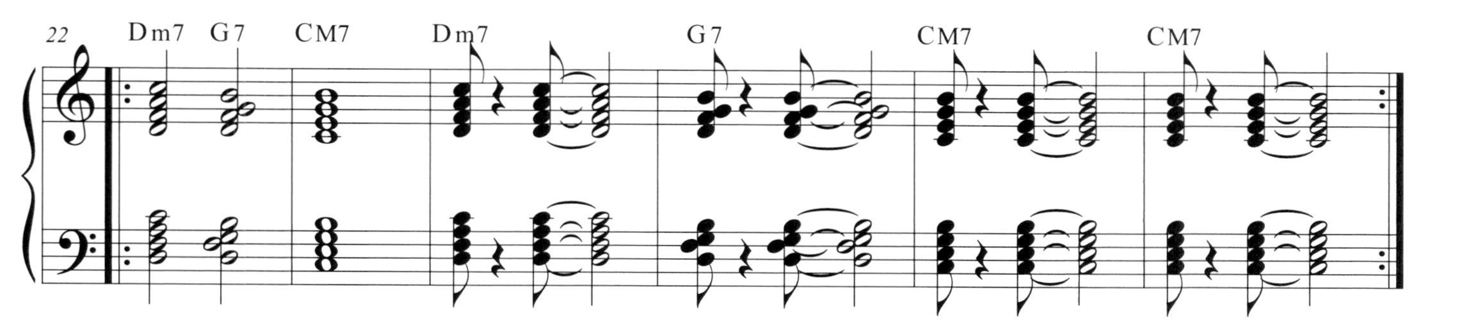

On the next two pages, I demonstrate the simple ii - V - I in every key signature following the circle/cycle of 4ths (the circle of 5ths follows the sharps clockwise to the right and the cycle of 4ths follows the flats counterclockwise to the left - see the circle of 5ths chart on page 9 of this book).

A Simple ii - V - I Chord Progression

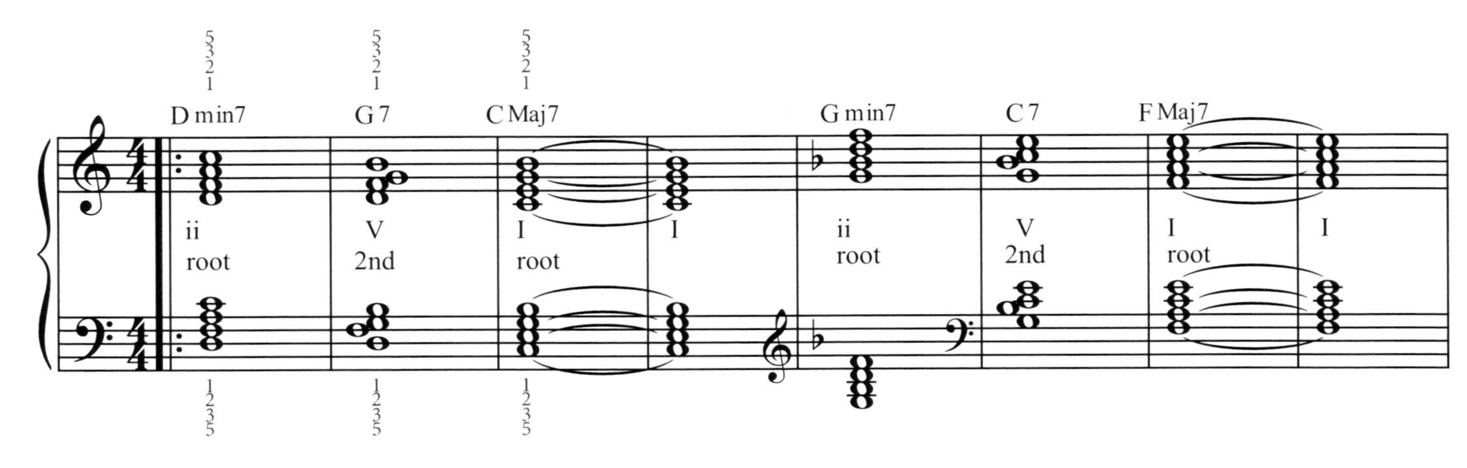

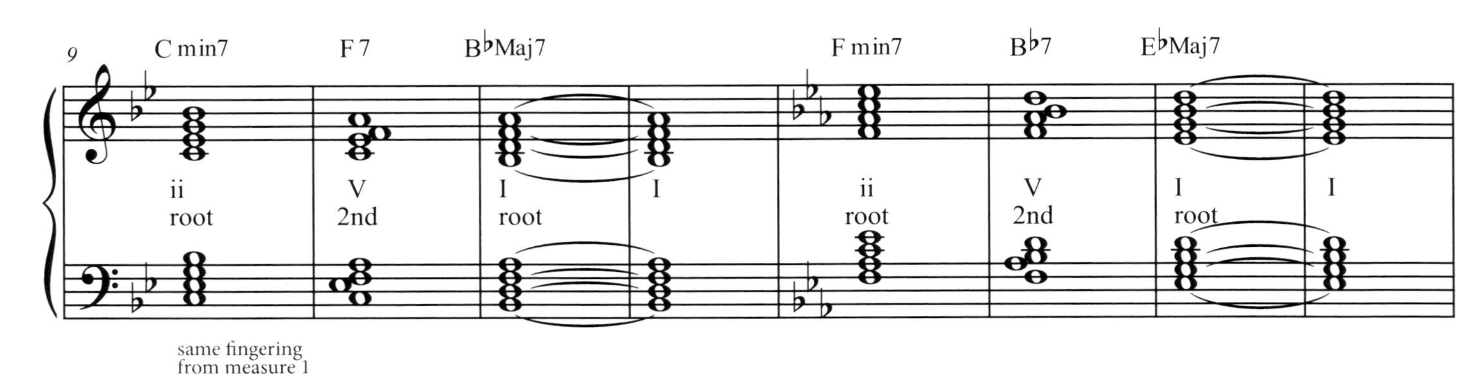

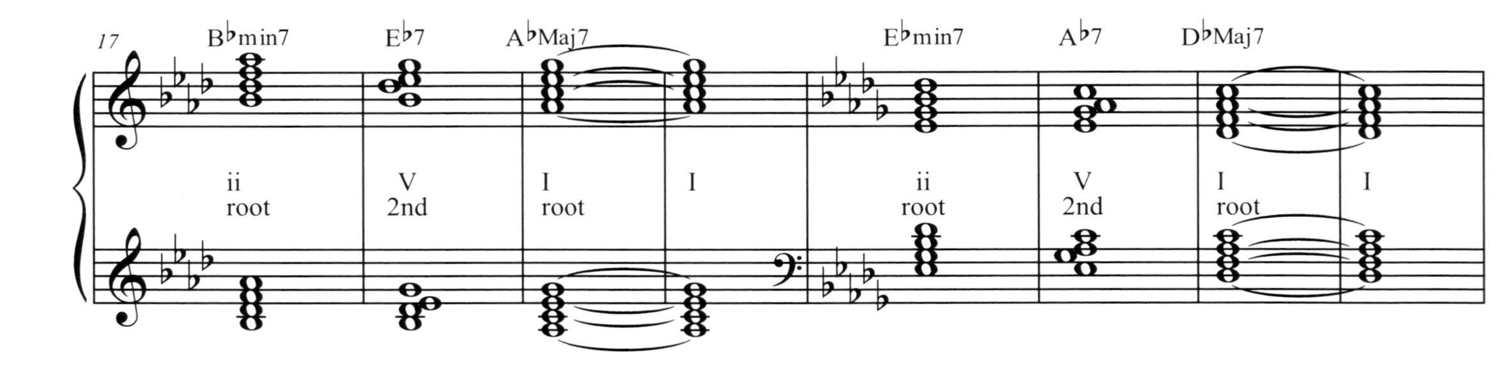

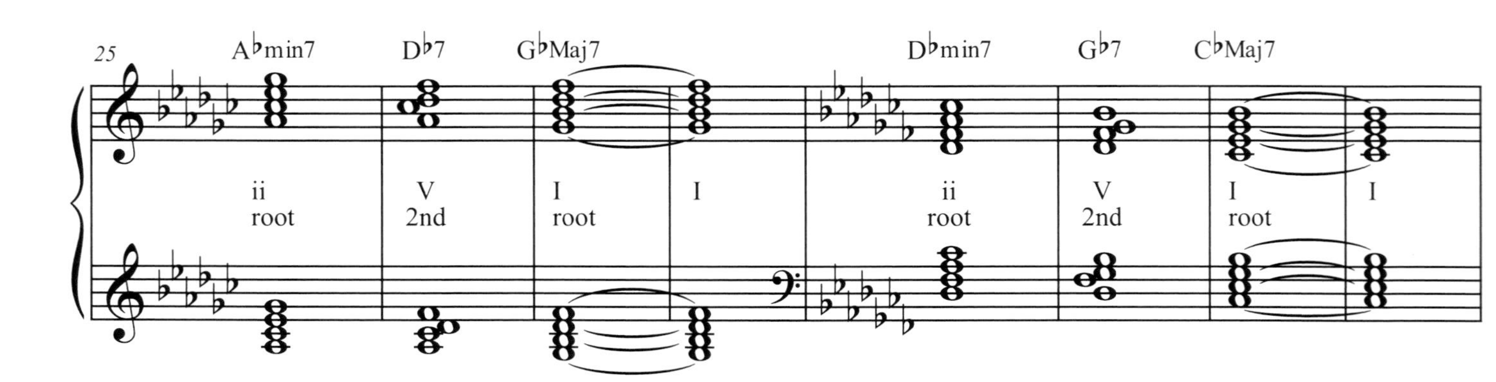

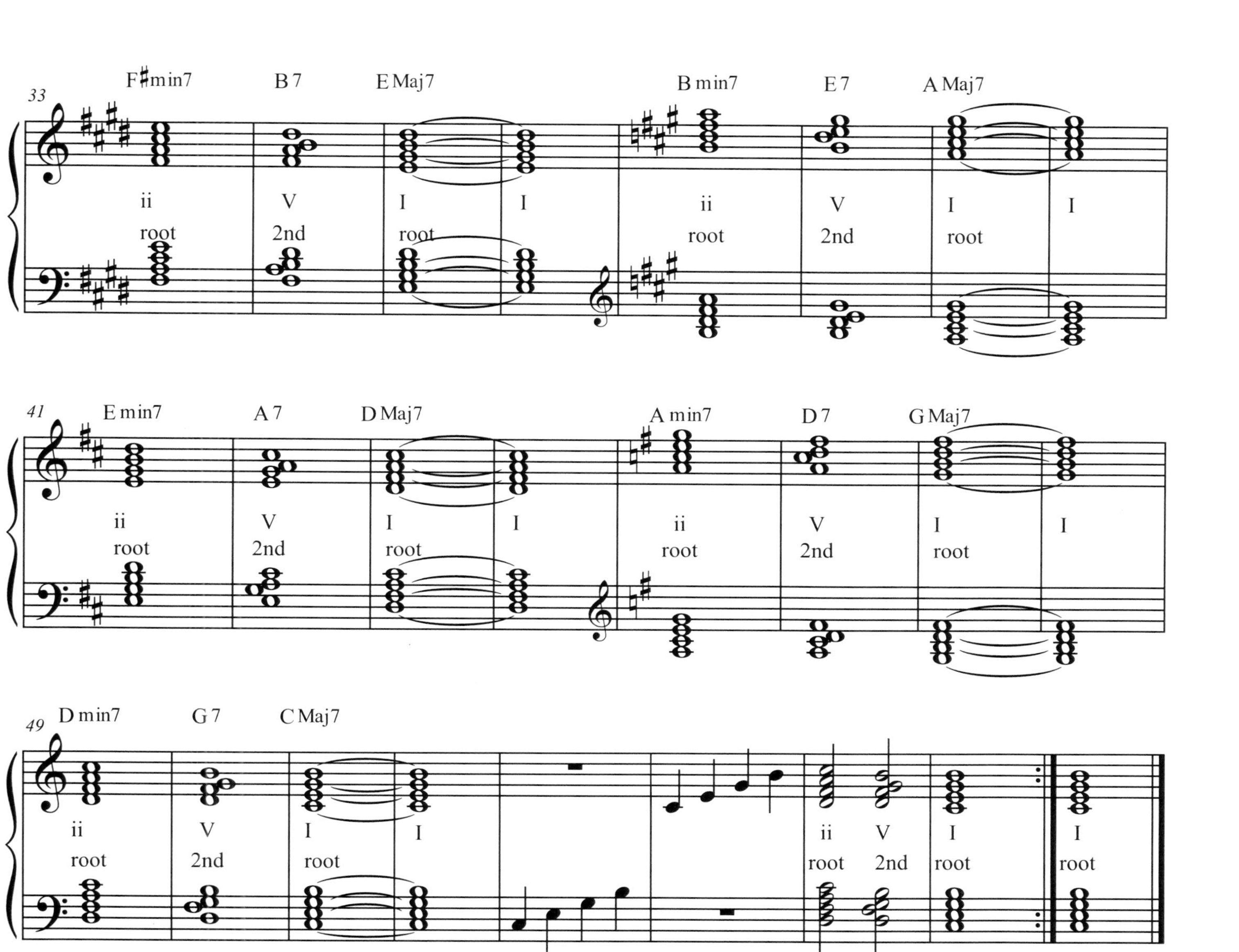
33
F♯min7
B 7
E Maj7
B min7
E 7
A Maj7
ii
V
I
I
ii
V
I
I
root
2nd
root
root
2nd
root
41
E min7
A 7
D Maj7
A min7
D 7
G Maj7
ii
V
I
I
ii
V
I
I
root
2nd
root
root
2nd
root
49
D min7
G 7
C Maj7
ii
V
I
I
ii
V
I
I
root
2nd
root
root
2nd
root
root

Now that you can play the simple ii - V - I jazz chord progression in all keys, try playing these few examples below to vary the rhythm of the chords played with both hands. In this example, I show you the key of C Major, F Major, and B flat Major. I did not want to write out every key signature, but after you can play these three examples as written, play them in every key signature following the cycle of 4ths. Notice how the left hand still plays the blocked progression, but the right hand now breaks the 7th chord apart. You can play the broken 7th chord notes in any order. This is just an example you can try.

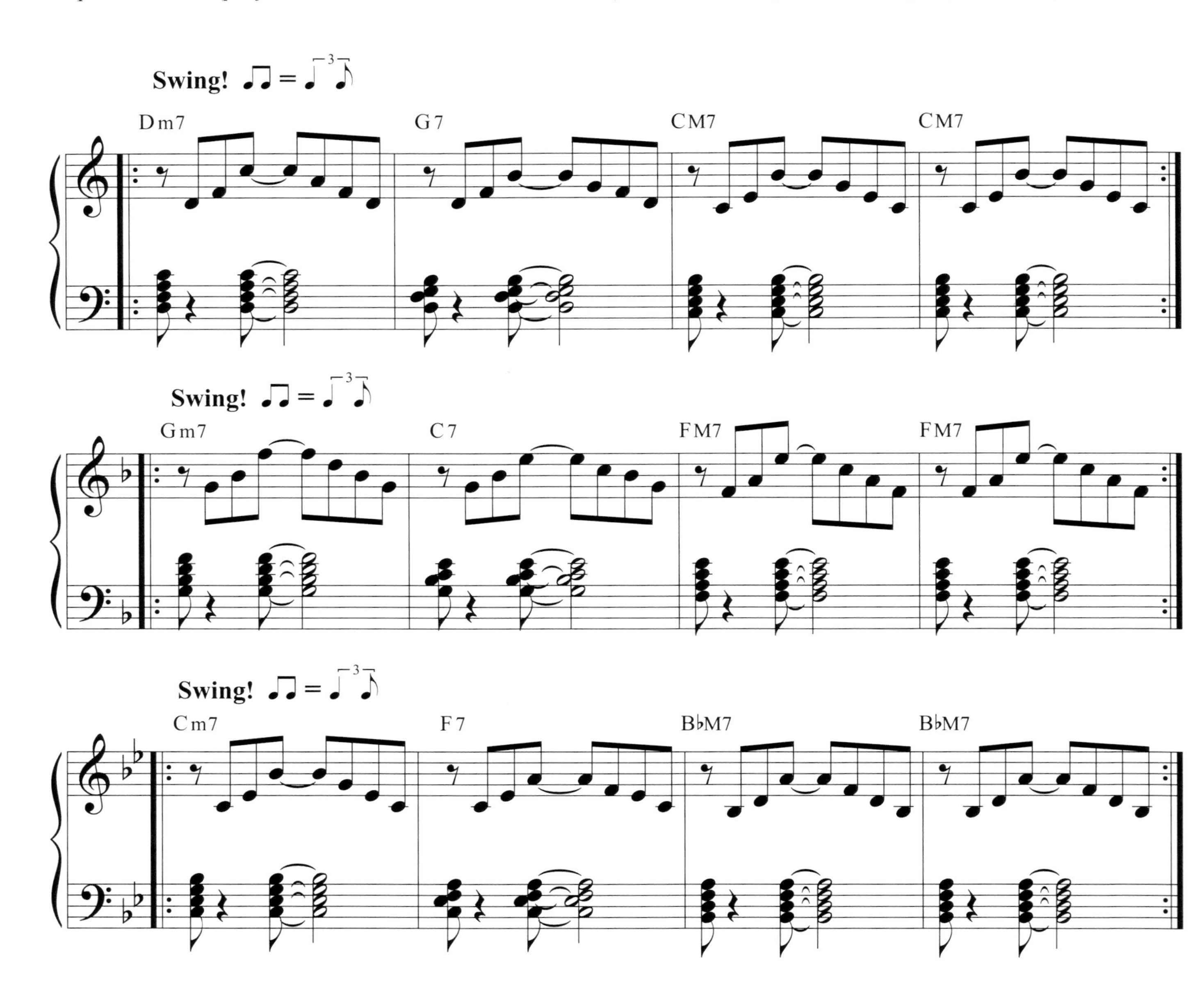

On the next three pages, you will try an exercise where you play the same ii - V - I chord progression from the previous two pages, but now you will play it in all inversions (root, 1st, 2nd, and 3rd inversions - in all key signatures). This is a very good exercise to learn and master in every key signature. Have fun playing this simple jazz exercise. After playing this in the key of C Major, try to embellish or play around with this chord progression using the notes from each chord. First play this jazz exercise in every key signature on the piano moving up in half steps - C, C♯, D, E♭, E, F, F♯, G, A♭, A, B♭, and B as written. Once you have mastered it as it is, modify the rhythm, change the order of the notes, add syncopation, varying rhythms, rests, etc. to make this unique and your own. Have fun playing this!

A II - V - I Chord Progression (All Keys) and also in All Inversions

33
B♭m7 E♭7/B♭ A♭M7
B♭m7/D♭ E♭7
A♭maj/G
B♭m7/F E♭7/D♭ A♭M7/C
B♭m7/D♭ E♭7
A♭maj/G
root 2nd root 1st 3rd 1st 2nd root 2nd 3rd 1st 3rd
41
E♭m7 A♭7/E♭ D♭M7
E♭m7/G♭ A♭7
D♭maj/C
E♭m7/B♭ A♭7/G♭ D♭M7/F
E♭m7/G♭ A♭7
D♭maj/C
root 2nd root 1st 3rd 1st 2nd root 2nd 3rd 1st 3rd
49
A♭m7 D♭7/A♭ G♭M7
A♭m7/B D♭7
G♭maj/F
A♭m7/E♭ D♭7/B G♭M7/B♭
A♭m7/B D♭7
G♭maj/F
root 2nd root 1st 3rd 1st 2nd root 2nd 3rd 1st 3rd
57
D♭m7 G♭7/D♭ BM7
D♭m7/E G♭7
B maj/B♭
D♭m7/A♭ G♭7/E BM7/E♭
D♭m7/E G♭7
B maj/B♭
root 2nd root 1st 3rd 1st 2nd root 2nd 3rd 1st 3rd
65
F♯m7 B7/F♯ EM7
F♯m7/A B7
E maj/D♯
F♯m7/C♯ B7/A EM7/G♯
F♯m7/A B7
E maj/D♯
root 2nd root 1st 3rd 1st 2nd root 2nd 3rd 1st 3rd

73
Bm7 E7/B AM7 Bm7/D E7 Amaj/G♯ Bm7/F♯ E7/D AM7/C♯ Bm7/D E7 Amaj/G♯
root 2nd root 1st 3rd 1st 2nd root 2nd 3rd 1st 3rd
81
Em7 A7/E DM7 Em7/G A7 Dmaj/C♯ Em7/B A7/G DM7/F♯ Em7/G A7 Dmaj/C♯
root 2nd root 1st 3rd 1st 2nd root 2nd 3rd 1st 3rd
89
Am7 D7/A GM7 Am7/C D7 Gmaj/F♯ Am7/E D7/C GM7/B Am7/C D7 Gmaj/F♯
root 2nd root 1st 3rd 1st 2nd root 2nd 3rd 1st 3rd
97
Dm7 G7/D CM7 Dm7/F G7 Cmaj/B Dm7/A G7/F CM7/E Dm7/F G7 Cmaj/B
root 2nd root 1st 3rd 1st 2nd root 2nd 3rd 1st 3rd root

TRY THESE II - V - I VARIATIONS

Play this in every key signature on the piano moving up in half steps - C, C♯, D, E♭, E, F, F♯, G, A♭, A, B♭, and B

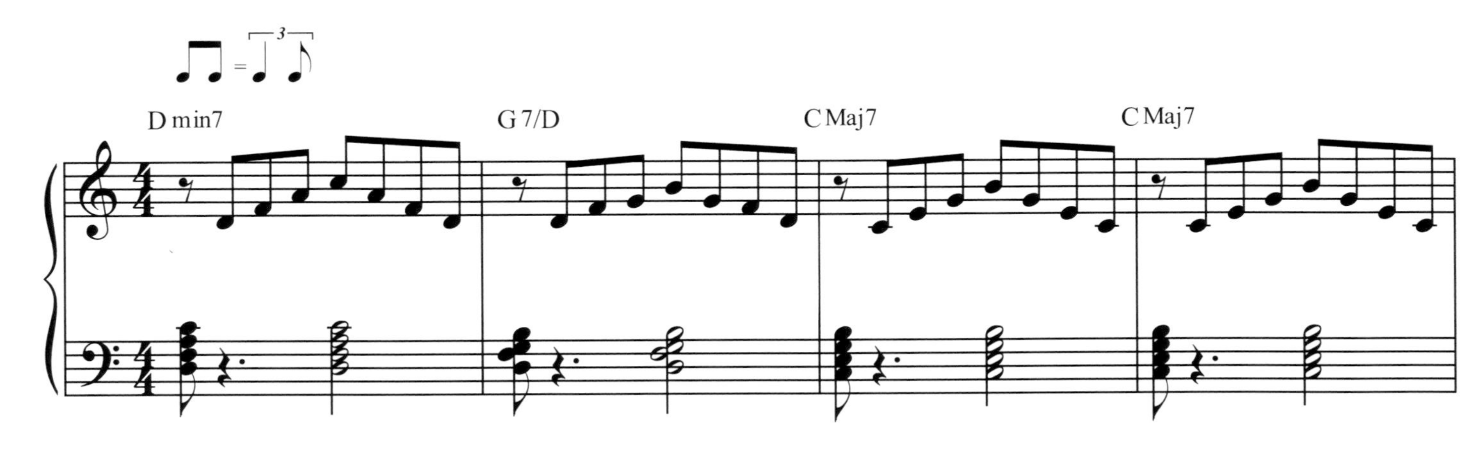

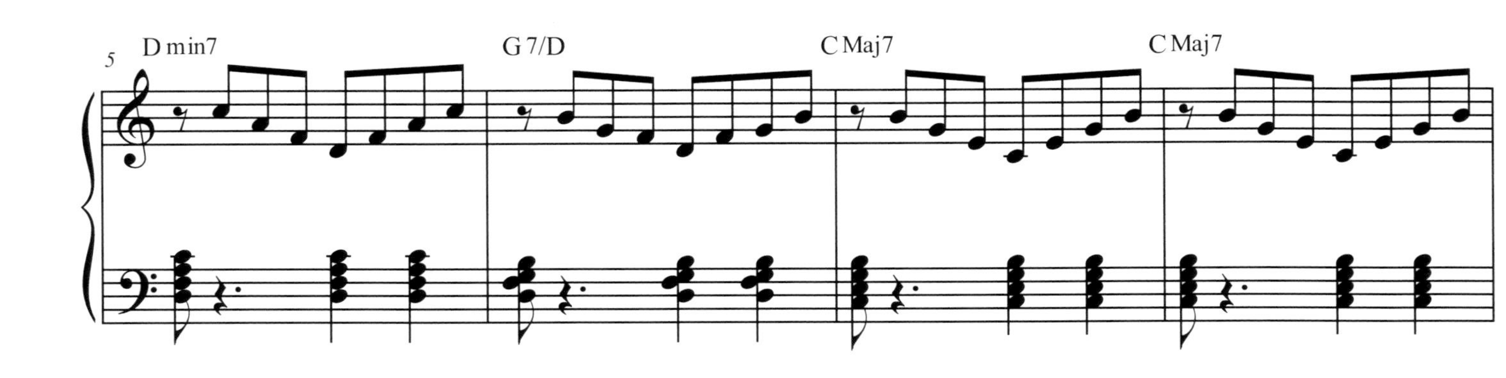

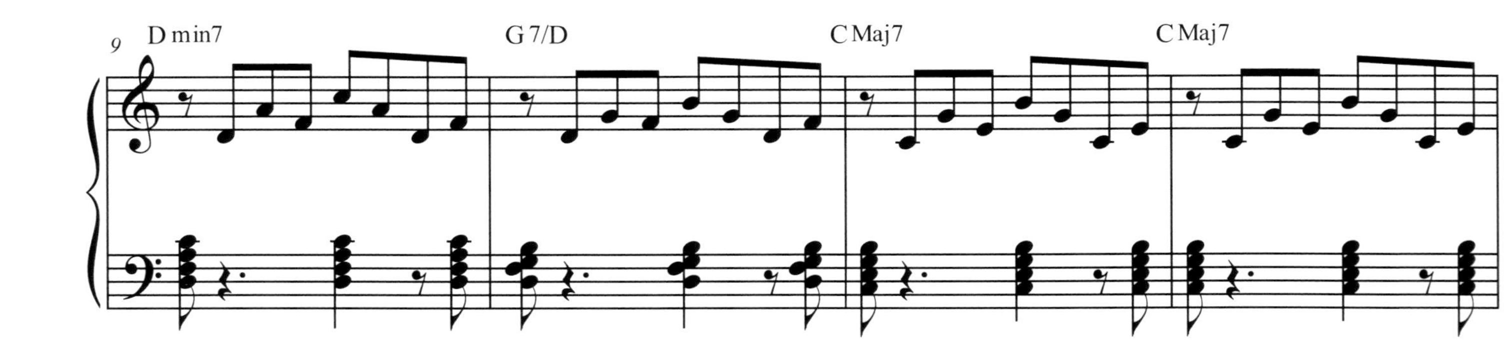

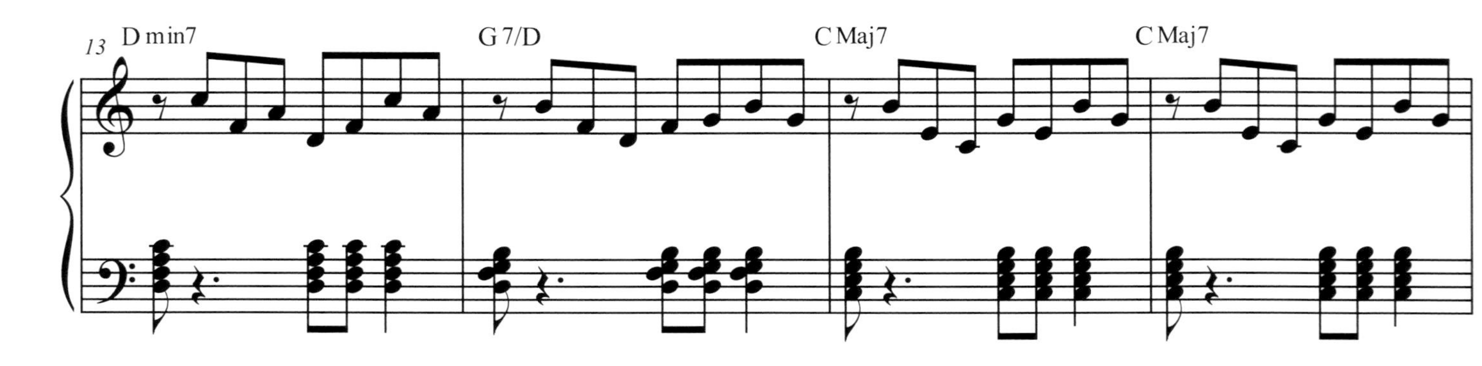

17
D min7
G 7/D
C Maj7
C Maj7
21
D min7
G 7/D
C Maj7
C Maj7
25
D min7
3
G 7/D
3
C Maj7
3
C Maj7
3
29
D min7
3
G 7/D
3
C Maj7
3
C Maj7
3
33
D min7
3
G 7/D
3
C Maj7
3
C Maj7
3

MM00001064

II - V - I Practical Application

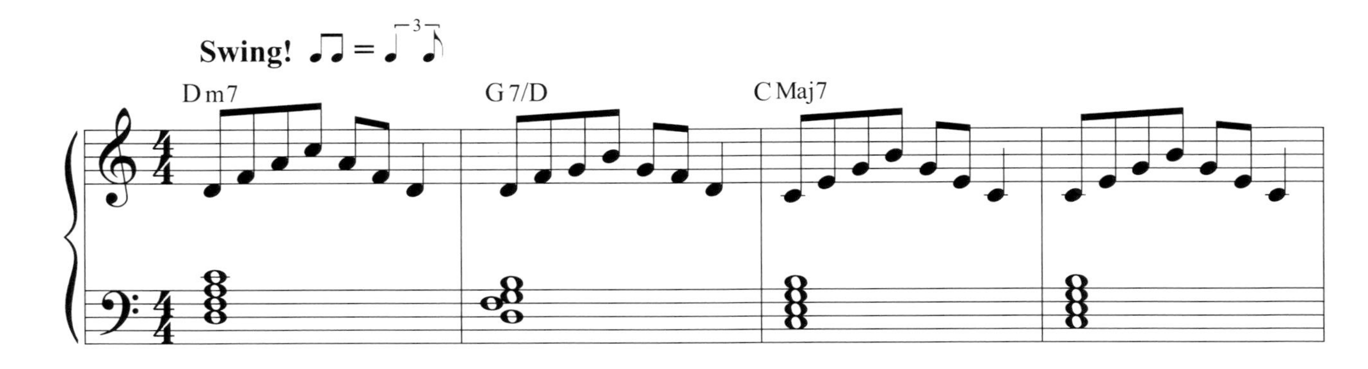

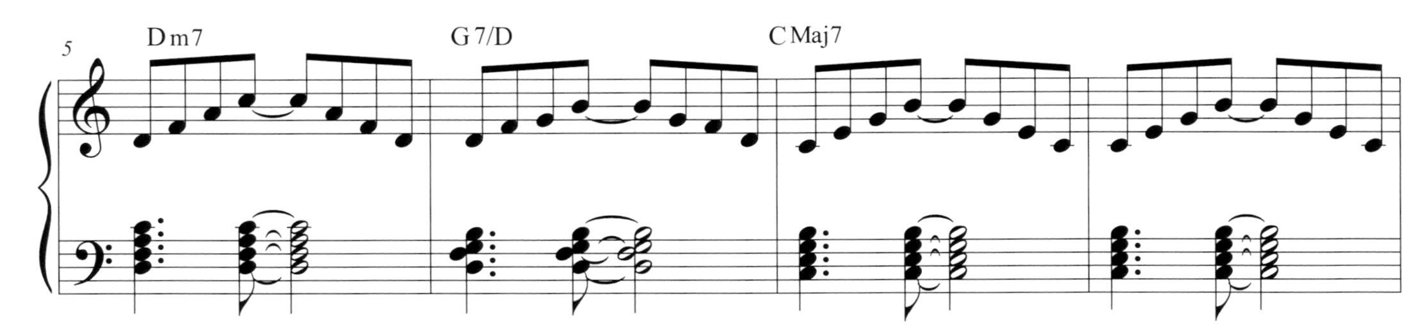

Create a right hand melody of your own. Try some of the right hand patterns from pages 72 and 73

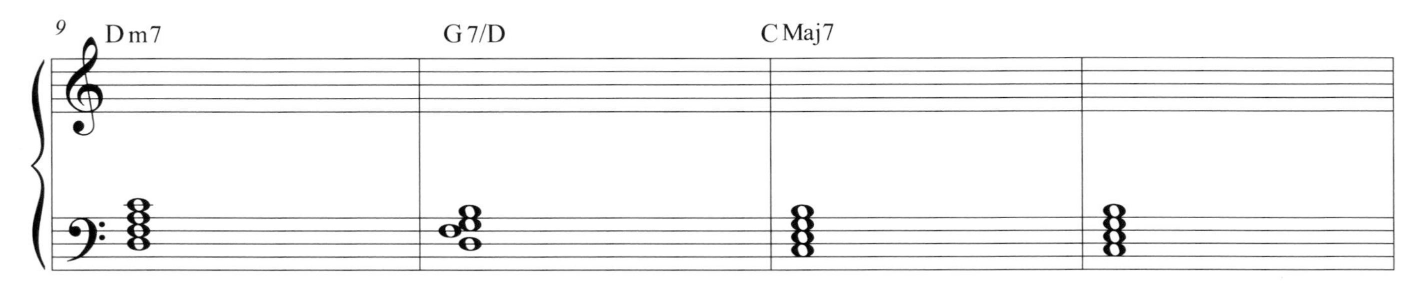

The right hand has intentionally been left blank so you can improvise
and create a right hand pattern of your own!

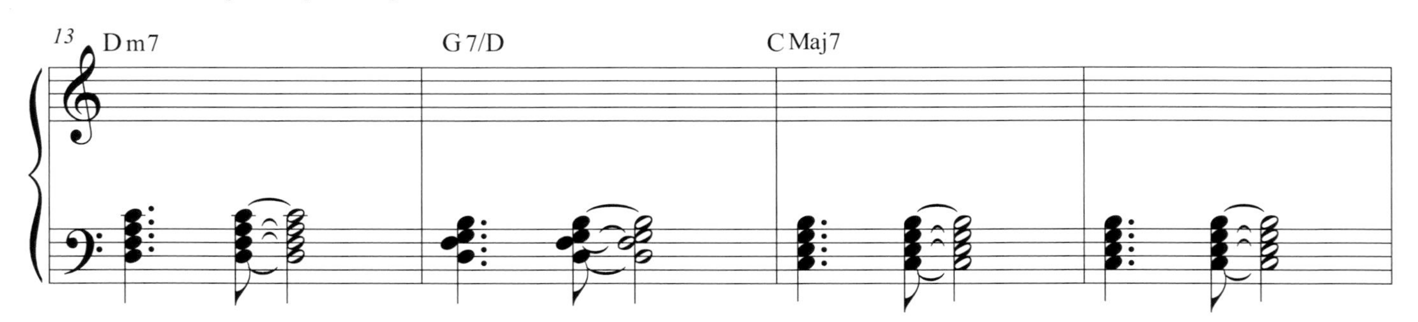

You've got this! Just have fun and play whatever comes to you!

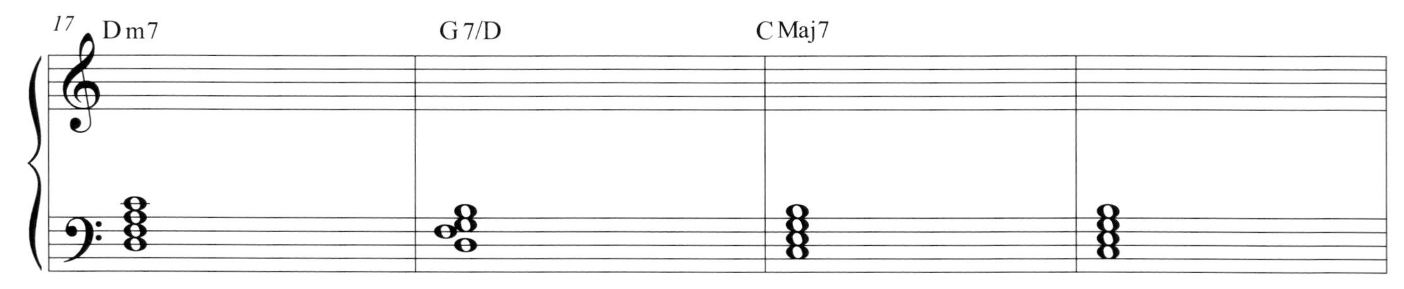

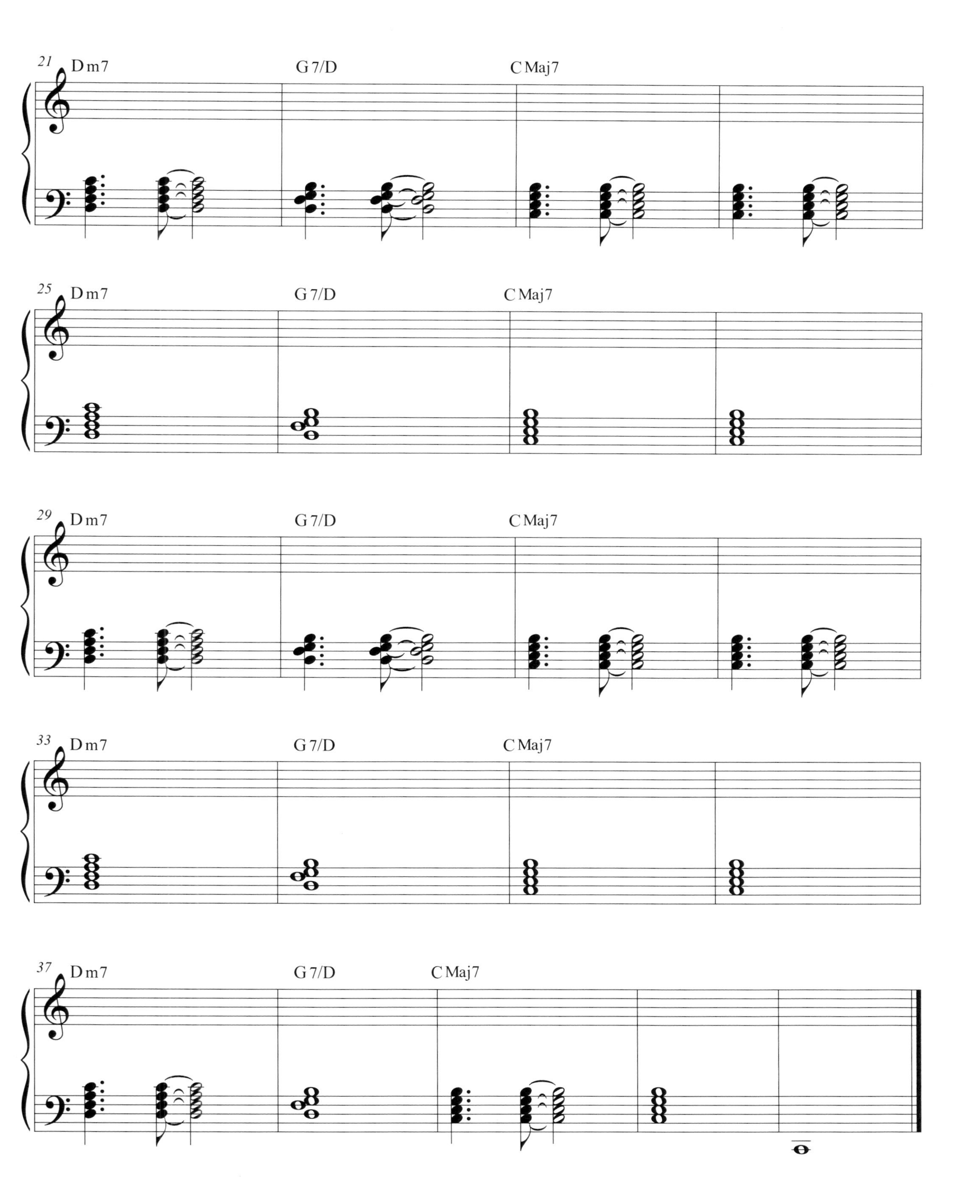

Play this in every key signature on the piano moving up in half steps - C, C♯, D, E♭, E, F, F♯, G, A♭, A, B♭, and B

In every scale there are different modes. An easy way to understand a mode is to think of it as a "**mood.**" We can be in good moods and in bad moods. When we play a song or piece in a different mode, a different mood is produced. It could be a happy, sad, strange, peaceful, violent, tired, or thoughtful mood, but with music it all depends on the modes. These modes have primarily been used in jazz and classical music, but we will learn how to use them with all types of music.

In this book, we will introduce seven different modes - each mode starting on one of the seven notes of the major scale (i.e. 1 = C, 2 = D, 3 = E, 4 = F, 5 = G, 6 = A, and 7 = B). To create the mode, you simply start on one of the notes and go until you play the same note an octave higher. As an example, there are eight notes from C - C, D - D, E - E, F - F, G - G, A - A, and B - B. All of these modes are played using the same sharps or flats in the key signature (in this case it would be the key of C - no sharps of flats).

First let me teach you a simple phrase: **"I Don't Play Like My Aunt Louise!"**

Memorize This! "**I** **D**on't **P**lay **L**ike **M**y **A**unt **L**ouise!"

Whenever I teach modes to my piano students or at workshops, seminars, and music camps, I have piano students learn and memorize this phrase. I have them repeat it five times. You'll be able to remember this phrase once you've repeated it five times to yourself. I have everyone pretend they have some aunt named Louise, who is a phenomenal pianist and travels all over the world performing. I then tell them to repeat the words, **"I Don't Play Like My Aunt Louise."** After I know they have the phrase memorized, I explain the reason they don't play like Aunt Louise is because they haven't learned the modes yet. As soon as they learn the modes they can be just as good - if not better than Aunt Louise.

Notice how there are seven words and each word is capitalized. If we take out those capitalized letters we have the first letters of the names of the modes. It is a helpful acronym.

"**I** **D**on't **P**lay **L**ike **M**y **A**unt **L**ouise!"

I	= Ionian	Ionian = W, W, H, W, W, W, H
D	= Dorian	Dorian = W, H, W, W, W, H, W
P	= Phrygian	Phrygian = H, W, W, W, H, W, W
L	= Lydian	Lydian = W, W, W, H, W, W, H
M	= Mixolydian	Mixolydian = W, W, H, W, W, H, W
A	= Aeolian	Aeolian = W, H, W, W, H, W, W
L	= Locrian	Locrian = H, W, W, H, W, W, W

Each of these modes is created from combining a series of Whole Steps (W), and Half Steps (H) in different orders. Look to the right above to see the whole and half steps used to create the scales. There are three major modes (**Ionian, Lydian, and Mixolydian**). I tell my students to say **"I Love Music"** to remember the major modes. There are four minor modes (technically three minor modes - **Dorian, Phrygian, Aeolian**, and one diminished mode - the **Locrian** mode). I tell my students to imagine they have a **"Depressed PAL"** to remember the minor modes.

Ionian, Dorian, Phrygian, Lydian, Mixolydian, Aeolian, and Locrian

If you look at each mode closely, you'll see a pattern. The sequence of whole and half steps shifts one to the left and then adds the beginning whole or half step at the end (Ionian mode has this pattern of whole and half steps: W, W, H, W, W, W, H and the Dorian mode has a different pattern of whole and half steps: W, H, W, W, W, H, W - the whole step (W) at the beginning was taken off and added to the end of the Ionian mode to create the Dorian mode). All of the modes follow this pattern.

Instead of memorizing the order of whole and half steps (which you can do if you really want to), here is an easier way to remember the modes.

Any major scale (like C major) is in the Ionian mode. Earlier we demonstrated how major scales are made (two tetrachords joined together by a whole step in between). Now let me show you how to create all of the other modes using the major scale.

"**I D**on't **P**lay **L**ike **M**y **A**unt **L**ouise!"

I = **Ionian** - the Major Scale

D = **Dorian** - take the major 3rd and major 7th down a half step

P = **Phrygian** - take the major 2nd, major 3rd, major 6th, and major 7th down a half step

L = **Lydian** - take the perfect 4th up a half step

M = **Mixolydian** - take the major 7th down a half step

A = **Aeolian** - take the major 3rd, major 6th, and major 7th, down a half step

L = **Locrian** - take the major 2nd, major 3rd, perfect 5th, major 6th, and major 7th down a half step

We will now go through every key signature (following the circle of fifths) and learn all of the scales and modes found in each key signature. You will learn the degree names, scale degrees, intervals, scale note names, one octave fingering, the major scale (contrary motion - 1 octave), the major scale (parallel motion - 1 octave), major scale intervals (harmonic and melodic), all triads built from the major scale, the primary chords built from the major scale (I - IV - V - V7 - I), and all seventh chords built from the major scale. On the opposite side of each key signature page, you will learn the modes.

C - Ionian
C - Ionian (Starting on C - Key of C Major)
D - Dorian
C - Dorian (Starting on C - Using the B♭ Major Key Signature)
E - Phrygian
C - Phrygian (Starting on C - Using the A♭ Major Key Signature)
F - Lydian
C - Lydian (Starting on C - Using the G Major Key Signature)
G - Mixolydian
C - Mixolydian (Starting on C - Using the F Major Key Signature)
A - Aeolian
C - Aeolian (Starting on C - Using the E♭ Major Key Signature)
B - Locrian
C - Locrian (Starting on C - Using the D♭ Major Key Signature)

To use a very simple explanation, an easy way to start doing modal jazz is to play a 7th chord with your left hand while your right hand plays the notes from a corresponding mode. For example, play a major 7th chord with your left hand while planing the Ionian or Lydian mode. Play a minor 7th chord with your left hand while the right hand plays a Dorian, Phrygian, or Aeolian mode. If you play a dominant 7th chord (7th) with your left hand, you can play a Mixolydian mode with your right hand. If you play a minor 7 (flat 5) chord with your left hand, for example, you can play a locrian mode with your right hand. The notes can be in any order and using any rhythm you want. Try this example below.

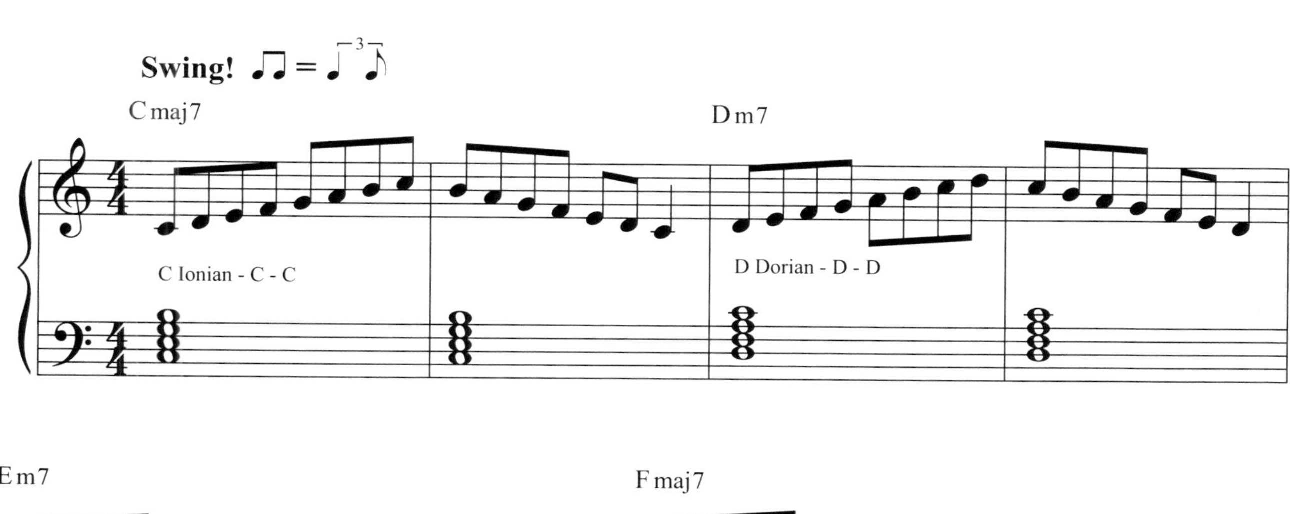

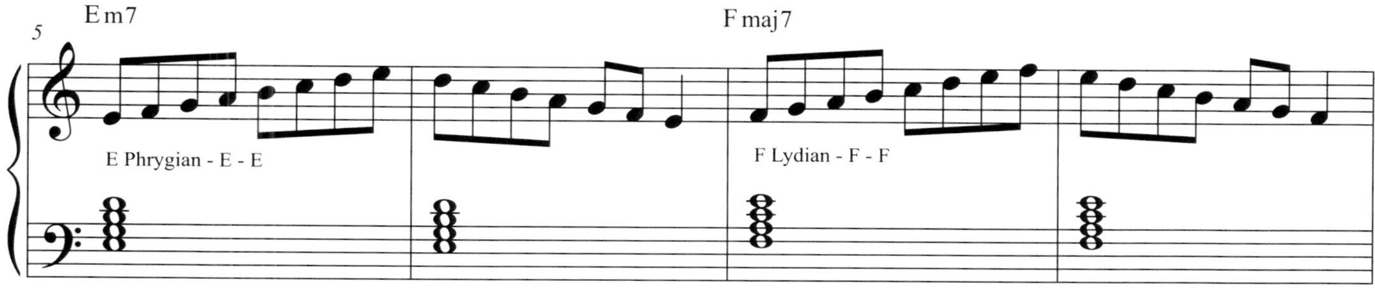

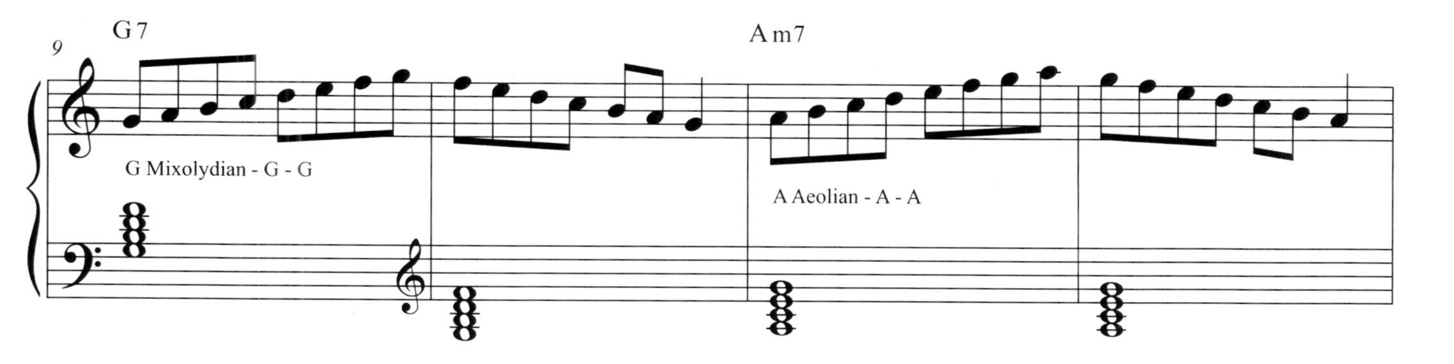

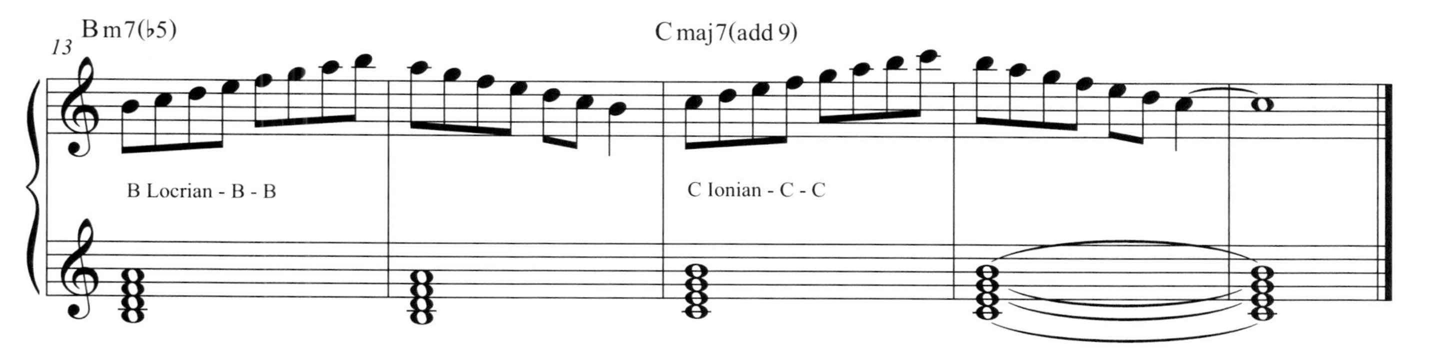

II - V - I Modal Jazz Practical Application

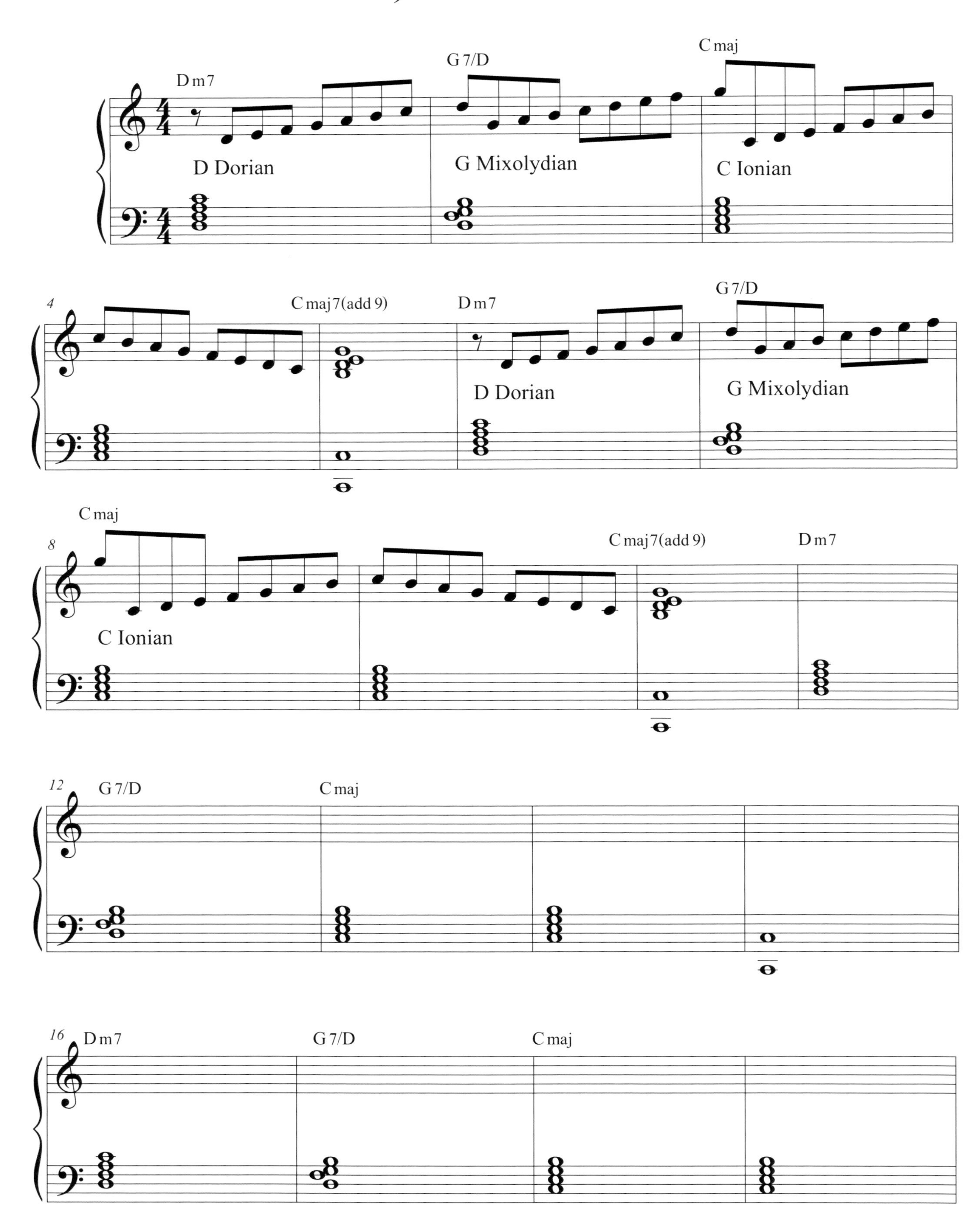

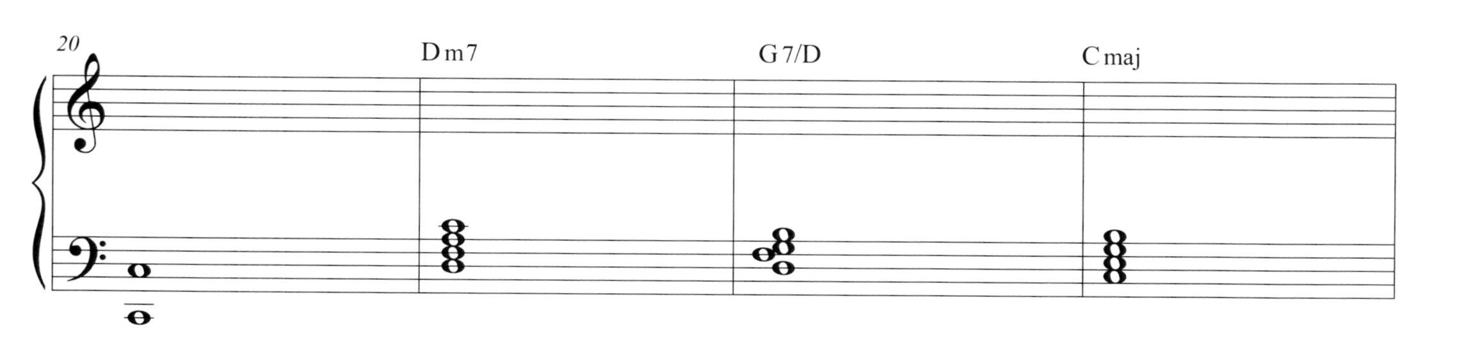
20
Dm7
G7/D
Cmaj

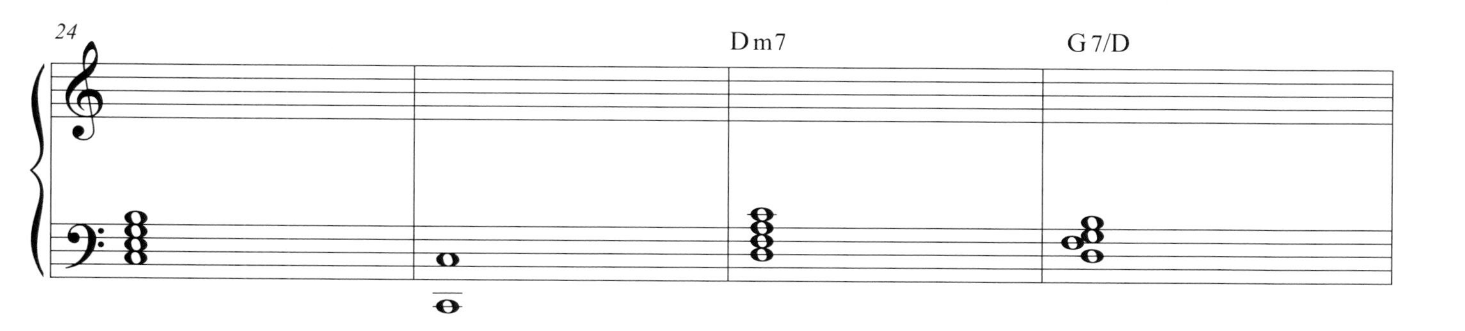
24
Dm7
G7/D

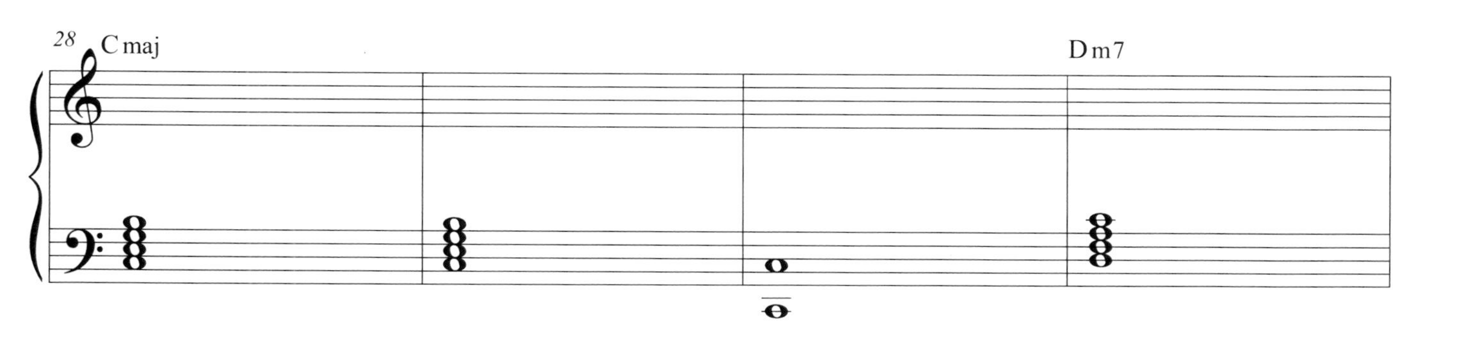
28
Cmaj
Dm7

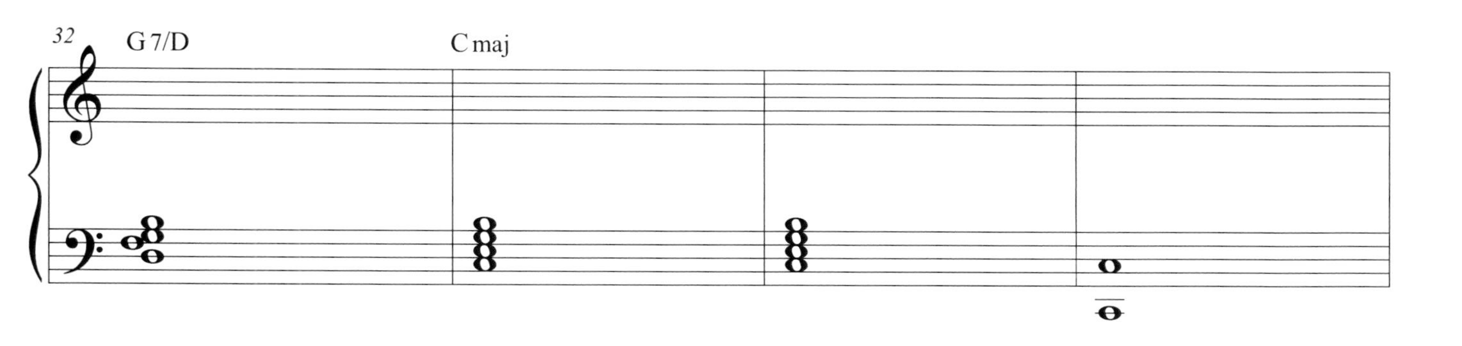
32
G7/D
Cmaj

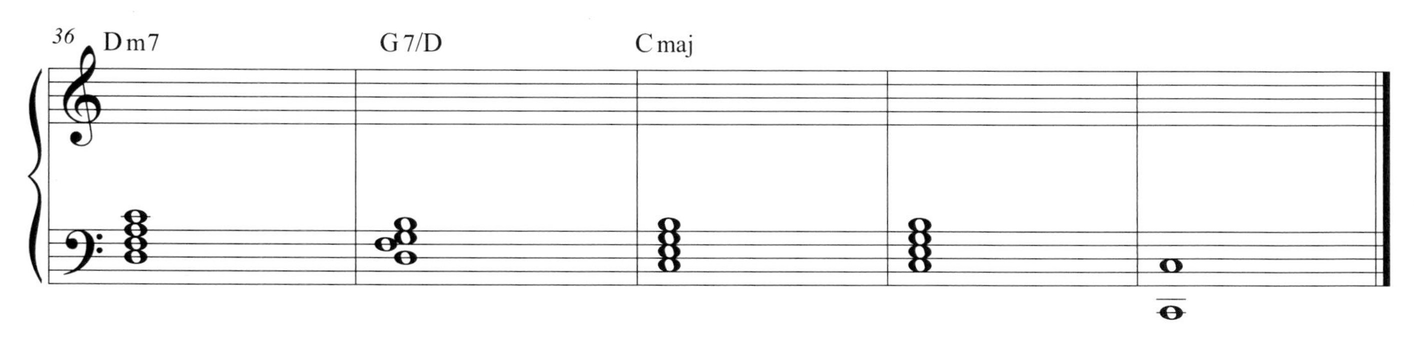
36
Dm7
G7/D
Cmaj

In this exercises, the left hand plays the accompanying 7th chord with the left hand that corresponds with the mode with the right hand. To simplify things, a bit, I only included the modes in pentascale format where you play the first five notes of each mode (Ionian, Dorian, Phrygian, Lydian, Mixolydian, Aeolian, and Locrian). After playing this jazz exercise in the key of C Major, try playing it in every key signature on the piano moving up in half steps - C, C♯, D, E♭, E, F, F♯, G, A♭, A, B♭, and B.

On the next page, I introduce you to a simple ii-V-I jazz chord progression where the left hand plays a simple whole - half - half walking bass pattern. You already played this back on page 84 of this book. You also learned the ii-V-I jazz chord progression back on pages 89 - 99.

Below I have notated C - D - E flat - and E natural. This is an example of the whole - half - half walking bass pattern starting on C. You can follow this pattern starting on any key on the piano black or white. Simply follow the pattern of Whole Step - Half Step - Half Step starting on any note you want.

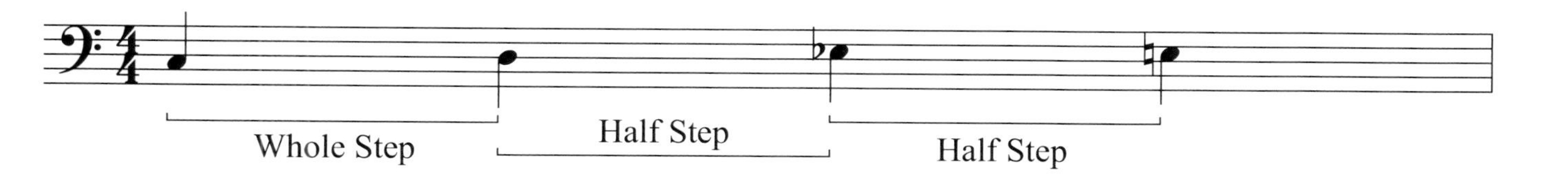

You have played the following example already, but you may not have realized what you were doing. In this example, I demonstrate the whole - half - half walking bass pattern starting on C, then moving to F, followed by D, and ending with G.

The right hand can play any of the notes from the chords written above each measure. As an example, I show the following chords played with the right hand: C7 - F7 - D7 - G7. You can play them blocked or broken.

Now that you have played through the whole - half - half walking bass pattern a few times, try to play it following a ii - V - I chord progression. We start with Dm7 (ii7), then we move to G7 (V7), and then we end by playing the C major 7 chord (IMaj7). We repeat the C major 7 chord and the accompanying whole - half - half left hand pattern two times. You can play the chords with the right hand as blocked or broken chords.

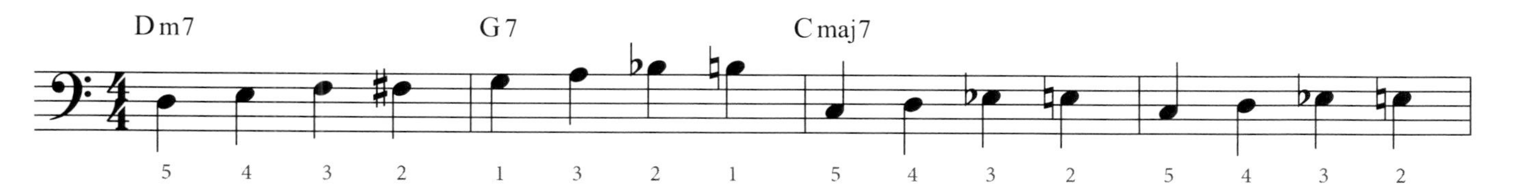

After playing the whole - half - half walking bass pattern as notated above, try to play it in every key signature on the piano moving up in half steps - C, C♯, D, E♭, E, F, F♯, G, A♭, A, B♭, and B.

II - V - I Whole, Half, Half Improv
Practical Application

Try to play it in every key signature on the piano moving up in half steps - C, C♯, D, E♭, E, F, F♯, G, A♭, A, B♭, and B.

swing it! (M.M. ♩ = c. 120)

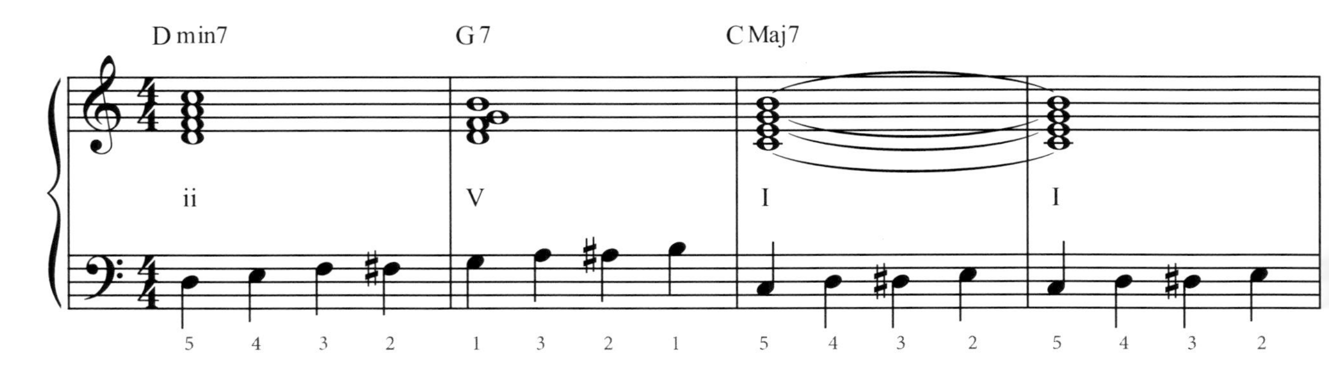

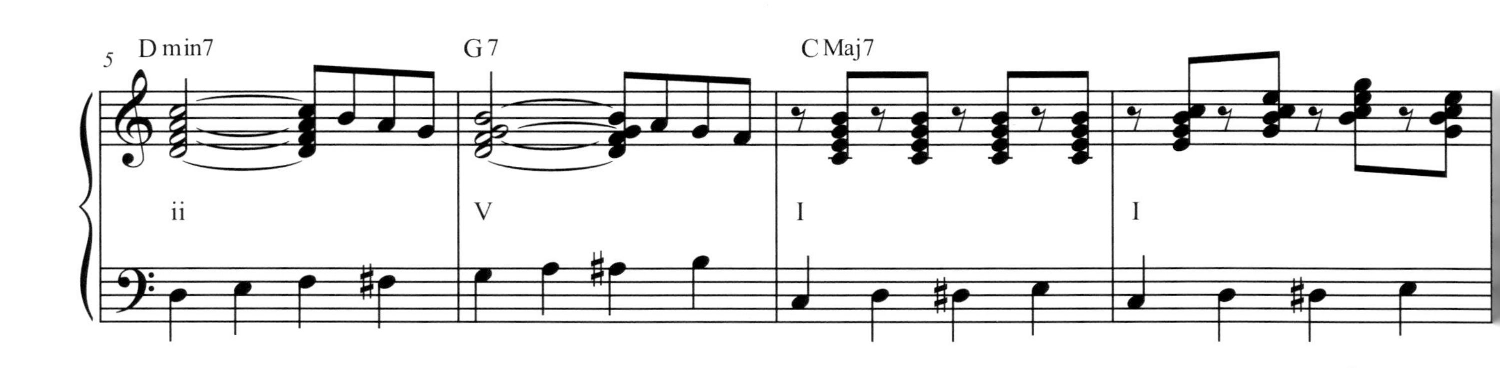

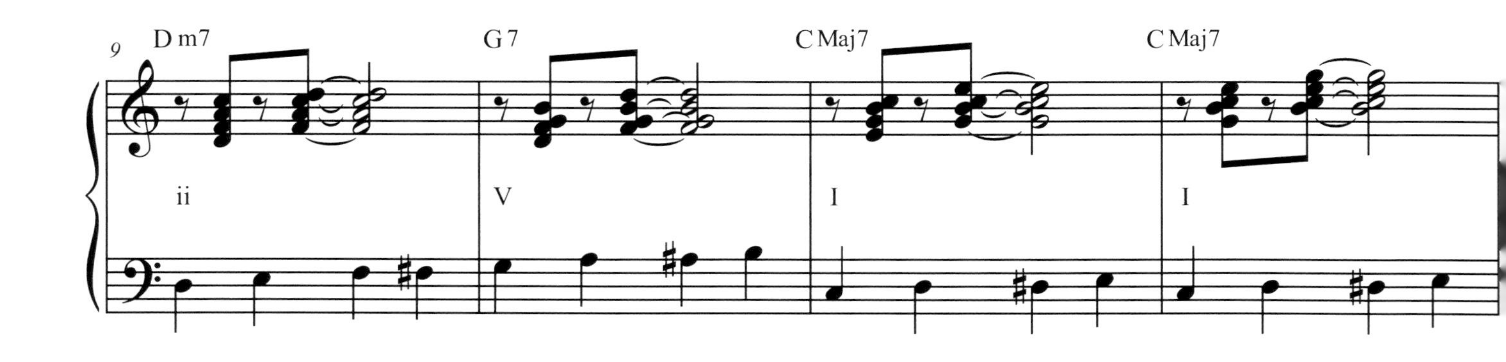

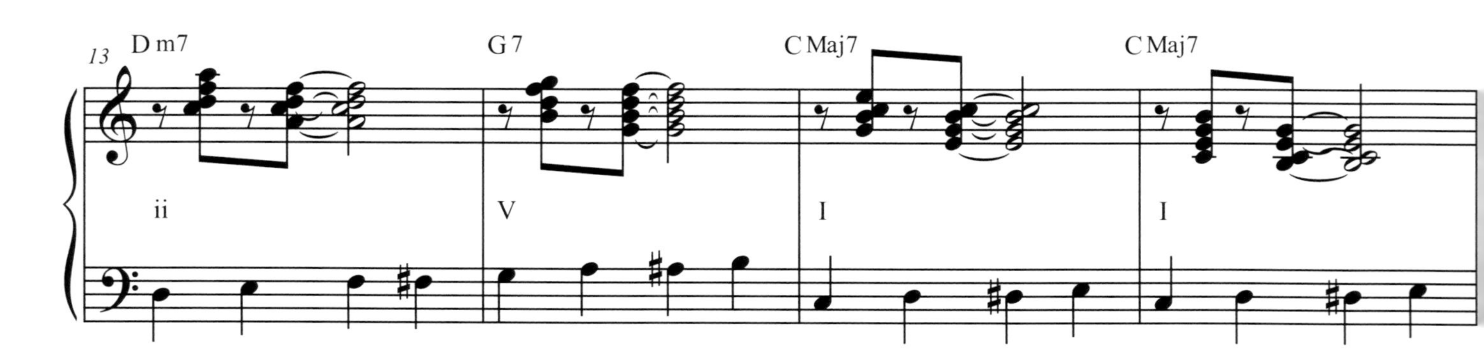

17
D m7
G 7
C Maj7
C Maj7
ii
V
I
I
21
D m7
G 7
C Maj7
ii
V
I
I
25
D m7
G 7
C Maj7
ii
V
I
I
29
D m7
G 7
C Maj7
3
ii
V
I
I
33
D min7
G 7
C Maj7
ii
V
I
I

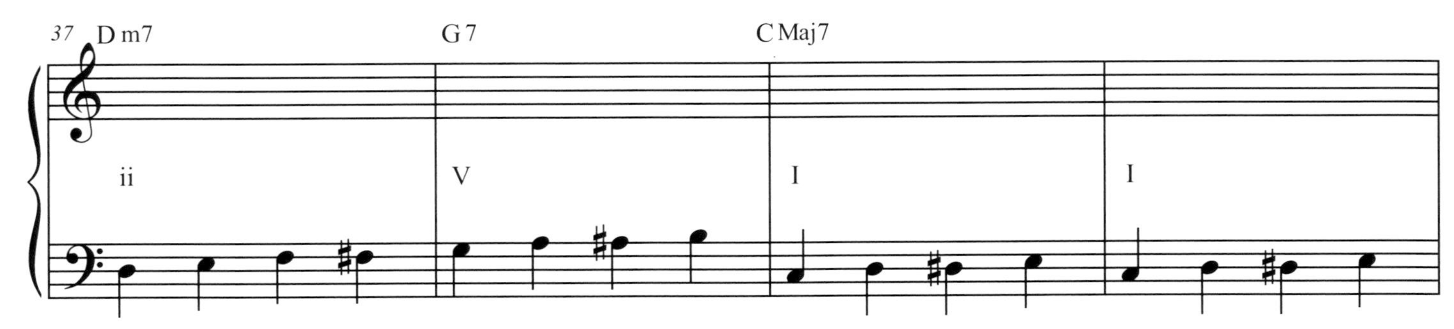

On this page and the next, I would like you to create your own right hand patterns. Feel free to use any of the right hand patterns I used on the previous two pages or create your own. Simply take the notes from the Dm7, G7, and C Maj7 chords and break them apart in any order and any rhythm. Have FUN!

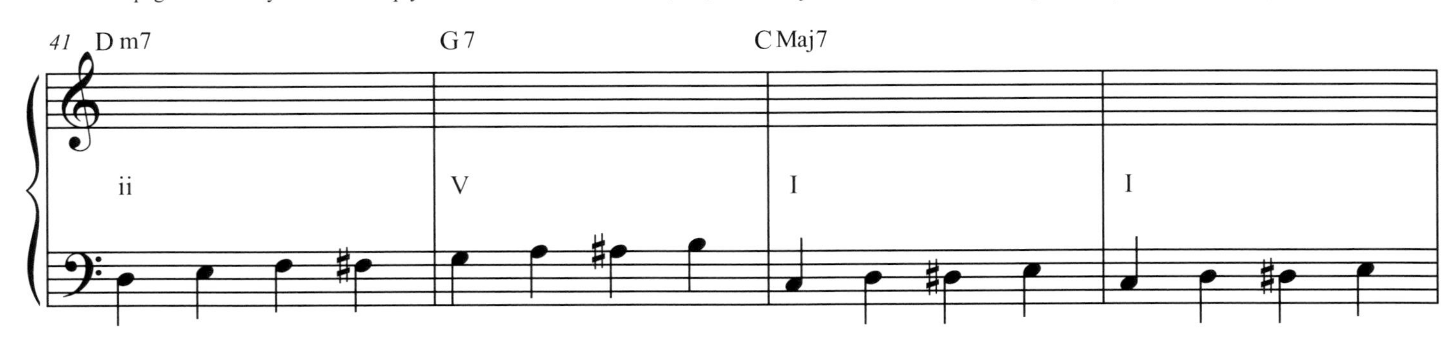

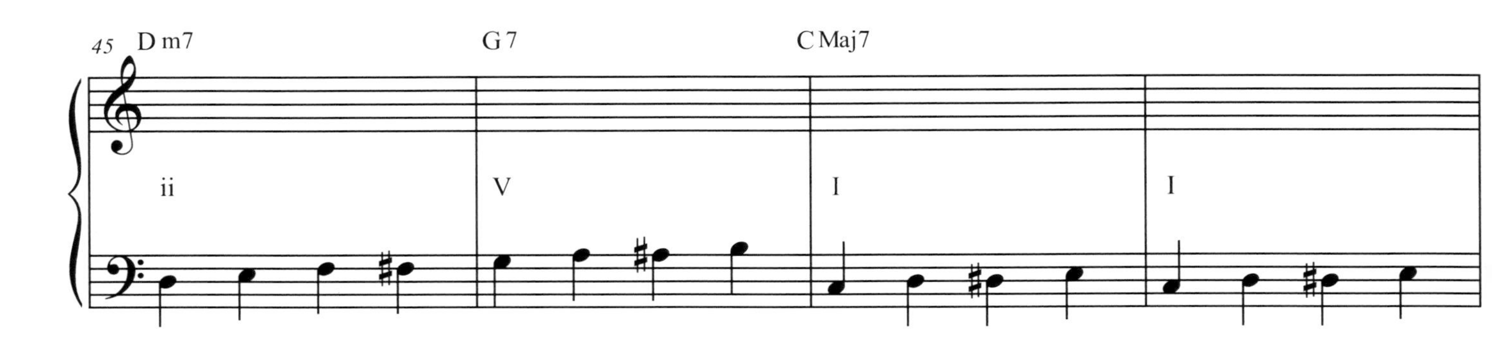

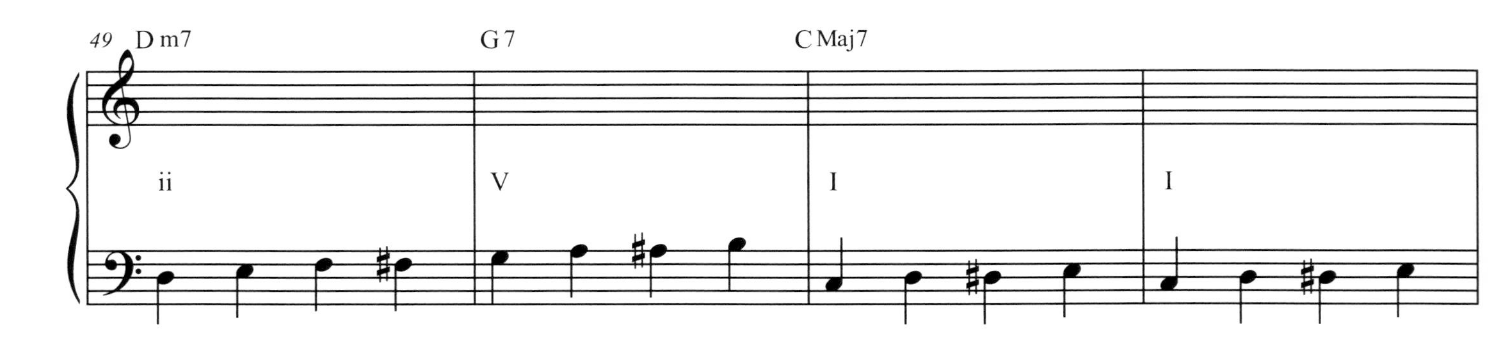

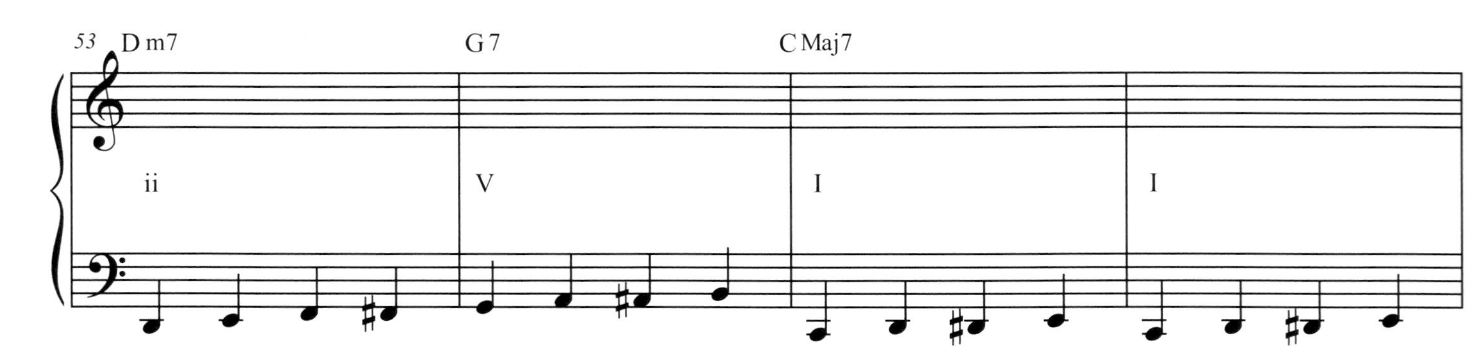

57
D m7
G 7
C Maj7
ii
V
I
I
61
D m7
G 7
C Maj7
ii
V
I
I
65
D m7
G 7
C Maj7
ii
V
I
I
69
D m7
G 7
C Maj7
ii
V
I
I

On this page I would like to explain a little about the chromatic scale. This may be a refresher for those who have already learned the chromatic scale.

Essentially, the chromatic scale is the half step scale. Simply start on C and move up in half steps (also known as chromatically).

Here is the general rule for the fingering of the right hand:

RH - **Thumb (1)** plays white keys (*except C and F*), **Middle Finger (3)** plays black keys up and down the piano, and the **Pointer Finger (2)** plays C and F

First, let's play the chromatic scale going up the piano (to the right). This is also known as the *ascending chromatic scale.*

Now play the chromatic scale going backwards. This is also known as the *descending chromatic scale.*

Now we are going to swing the 8th notes. Since we are learning jazz patterns, chords, and rhythms, it is essential to learn how to improvise with the chromatic scale moving up and down on the piano - especially when swinging the 8th notes. Remember to keep the feeling of the long - short - long - short - long - short - long - short jazz feeling when swinging the 8th notes (1 & 2 & 3 & 4 &).

After playing the chromatic scale starting on C, try to play it starting on every key on the piano moving up in half steps - C, C♯, D, E♭, E, F, F♯, G, A♭, A, B♭, and B. The chromatic scale is the same, but it is good to practice starting on different notes and moving up and down the piano. Try to play it one, two, and even three octaves up and down the piano.

Chromatically Sound

By Jerald Simon

II - V - I Whole, Half, Half Chromatic Scale Improv

Practical Application

RH - Thumb (1) plays white keys (except C and F), Middle Finger (3) plays black keys up and down the piano, and the pointer finger (2) plays C and F

13
Dm7
G7
Cmaj7
16
Dm7
3
18
G7
Cmaj7
20
Dm7
22
G7
Cmaj7

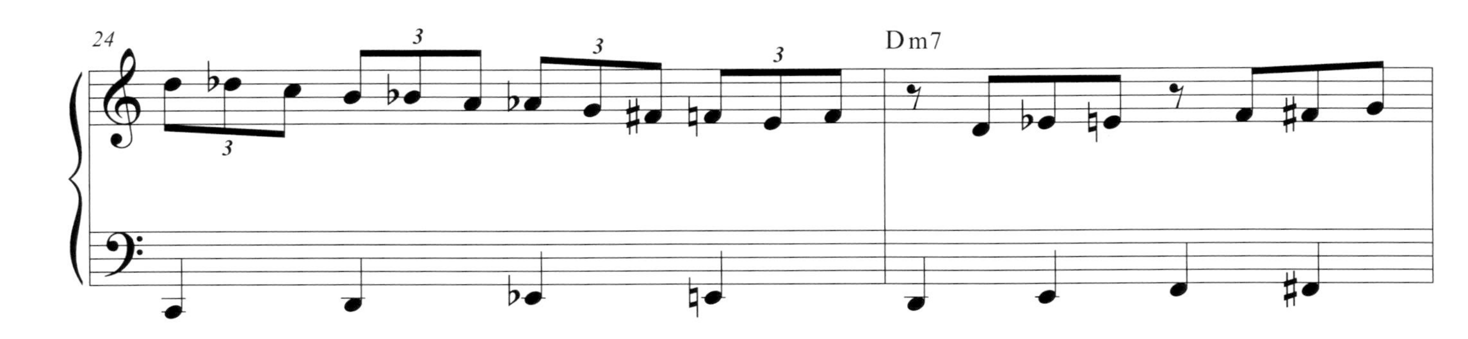

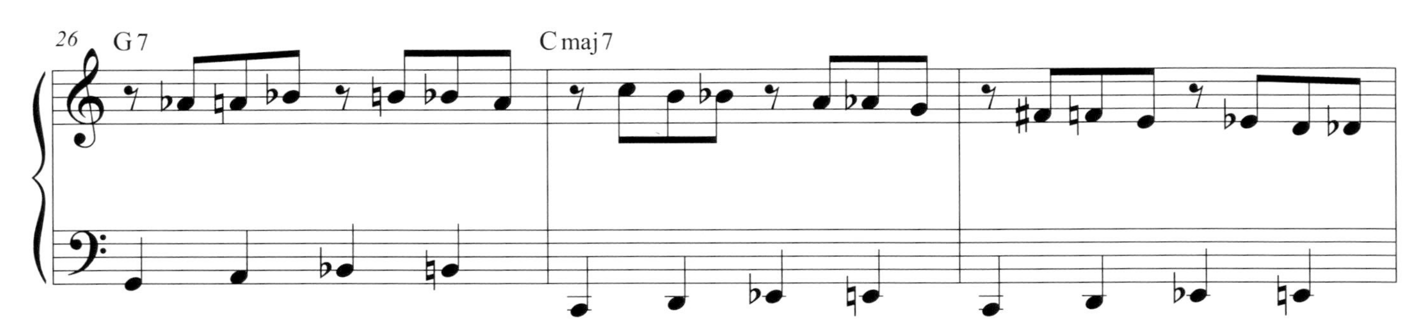

Improvise with the Chromatic Scale up and down the piano. If it helps, start on the note of the chord shown within each measure and move up or down according to the chormatic scale as demonstrated on the previous two pages.

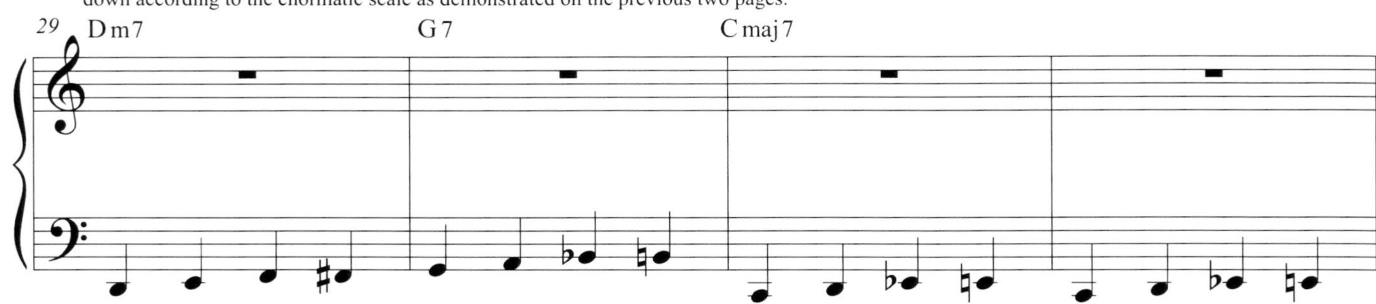

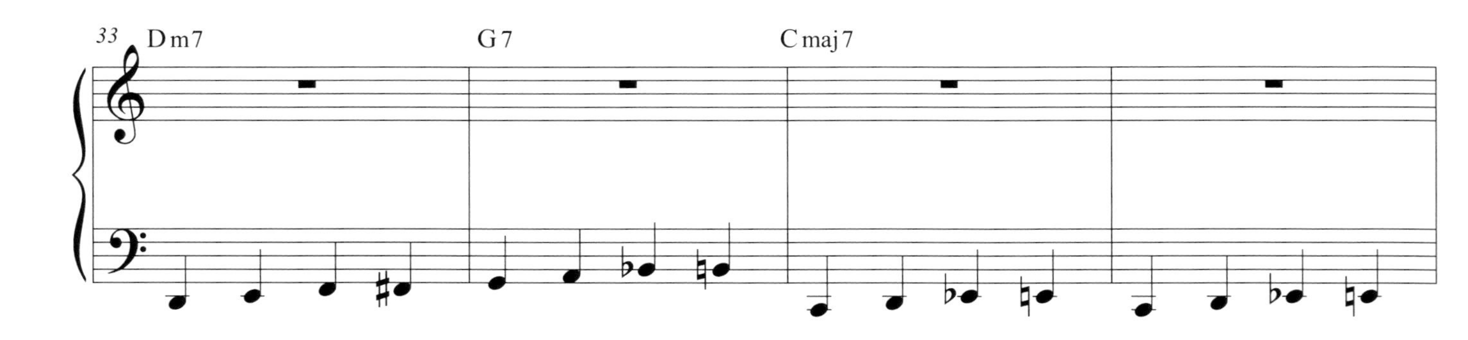

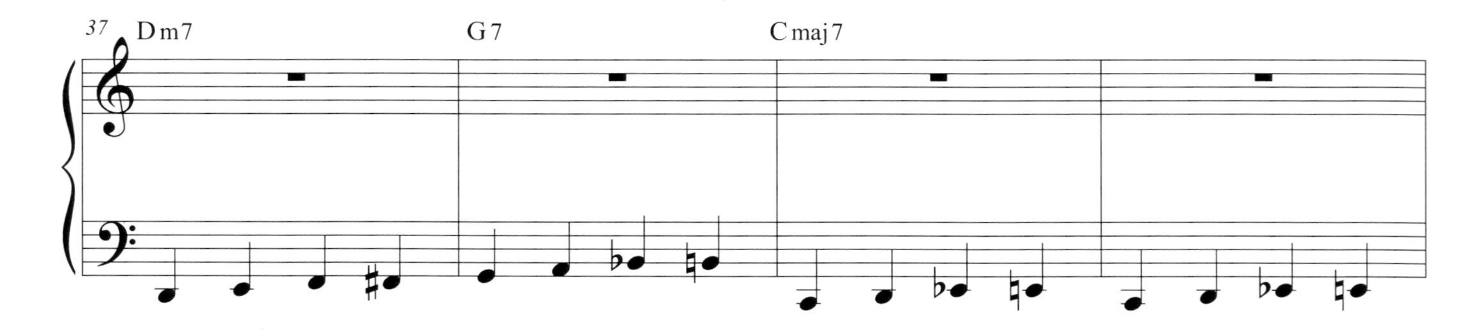

41
Dm7
G7
Cmaj7
45
Dm7
G7
Cmaj7
49
Dm7
G7
Cmaj7
53
Dm7
G7
Cmaj7
57
Dm7
G7
Cmaj7

This exercise is to help you learn the C6, C minor 6 (Cm6), C Major 7 (CM7), C minor major 7 (CmM7), C7, C minor 7 (Cm7), C minor 7 flat 5 (Cm7♭5), C minor 7 sharp 5 (Cm7♯5), and the C diminished 7 chord (Cdim7). First we play both hands together (blocked), and then we play the left hand blocked while the right hand breaks apart the notes from the chord (broken). Have fun playing this simple jazz exercise. After playing this in the key of C Major, try to play it in every key signature on the piano moving up in half steps - C, C♯, D, E♭, E, F, F♯, G, A♭, A, B♭, and B.

C7
Cm7
Cm7♭5
Cm7♯5
Cdim7

6th Chord Jazz Exercise

21
25
8va
1
5
etc.
29
33

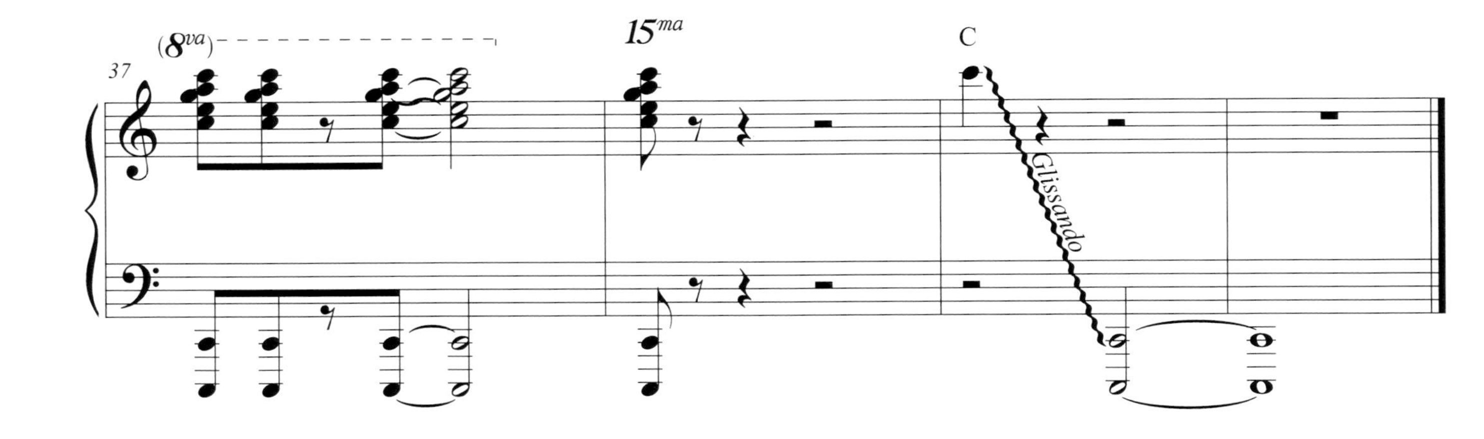

After playing this in the key of C Major, try to play this jazz exercise in every key signature on the piano moving up in half steps - C, C♯, D, E♭, E, F, F♯, G, A♭, A, B♭, and B.

Octave 6th Chord Jazz Exercise

After playing this in the key of C Major, try to play this jazz exercise in every key signature on the piano moving up in half steps - C, C♯, D, E♭, E, F, F♯, G, A♭, A, B♭, and B.

6TH CHORD BOOGIE WOOGIE EXERCISE

Have fun playing this simple jazz exercise. We are working on playing 6th chords with the right hand while the left hand plays a boogie - woogie pattern. After playing this in the key of C Major, try to play this jazz exercise in every key signature on the piano moving up in half steps - C, C♯, D, E♭, E, F, F♯, G, A♭, A, B♭, and B.

16
G6
F6
C6
20
F6
24
C6
G6
28
F6
C6

7th Chord Boogie Woogie Exercise

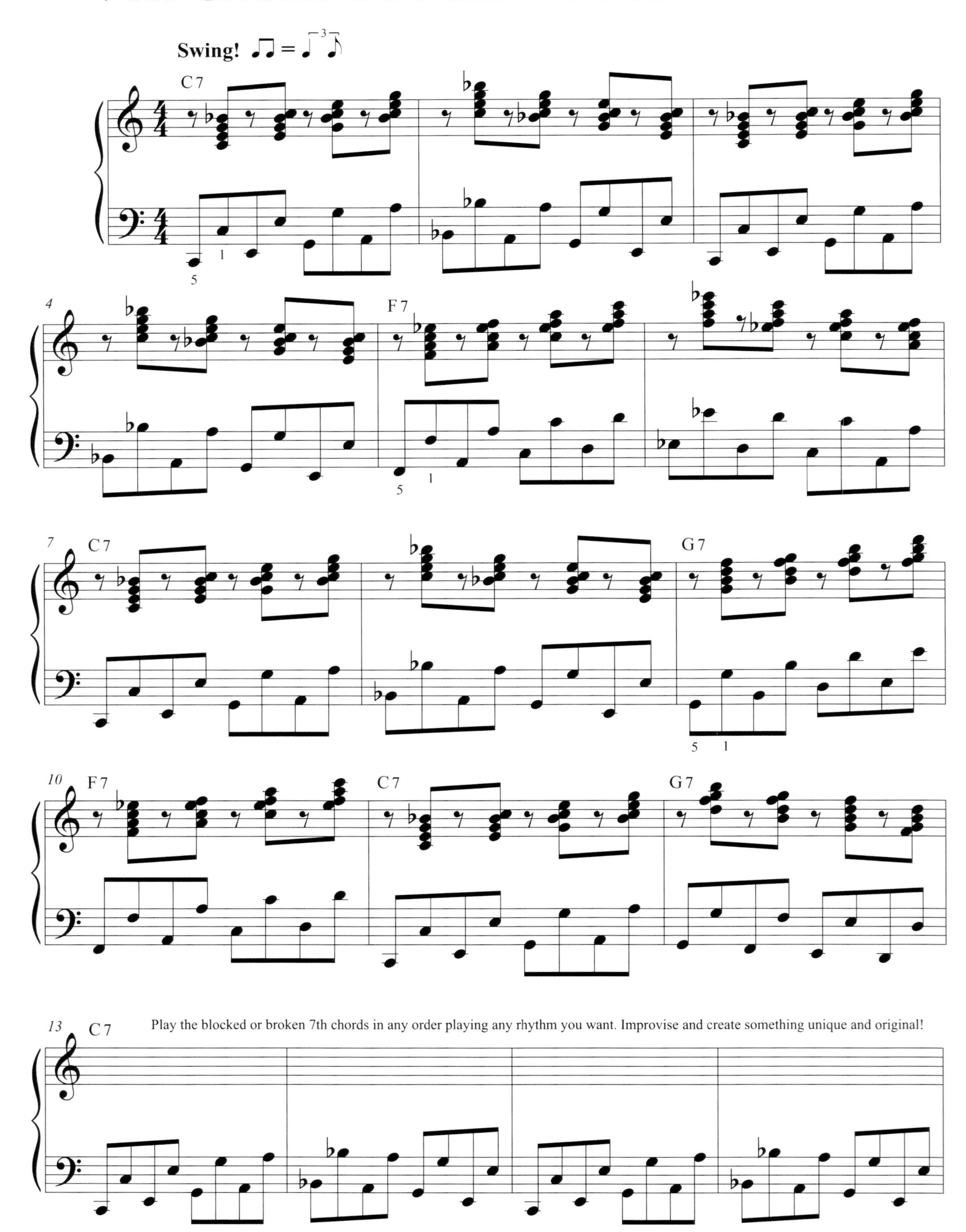

Have fun playing this simple jazz exercise. After playing this in the key of C Major, try to play this jazz exercise in every key signature on the piano moving up in half steps - C, C♯, D, E♭, E, F, F♯, G, A♭, A, B♭, and B.

6th or 7th Chord Walking Bass Improv

Have fun playing this simple jazz exercise. You can improvise with 6th or 7th chords in the right hand. I have written 6th chords above each measure, but you can just as easily use 7th chords as well. After playing this jazz exercise in the key of C Major, try to play it in every key signature on the piano moving up in half steps - C, C♯, D, E♭, E, F, F♯, G, A♭, A, B♭, and B.

18
C 6
G 6
22
F 6
C 6

In this exercise, we will essentially be combining everything we have been learning on the past several pages, but instead of following a ii - V - I jazz chord progression, we will instead follow a I - IV - ii - V chord progression and use 7th chords with the right hand. We will play blocked and broken 7th chords with the right hand, and improvise and create musical patterns of our own using chords and scales. Have fun playing this simple jazz exercise. After playing this jazz exercise in the key of C Major, try to play it in every key signature on the piano moving up in half steps - C, C♯, D, E♭, E, F, F♯, G, A♭, A, B♭, and B.

MM0000106

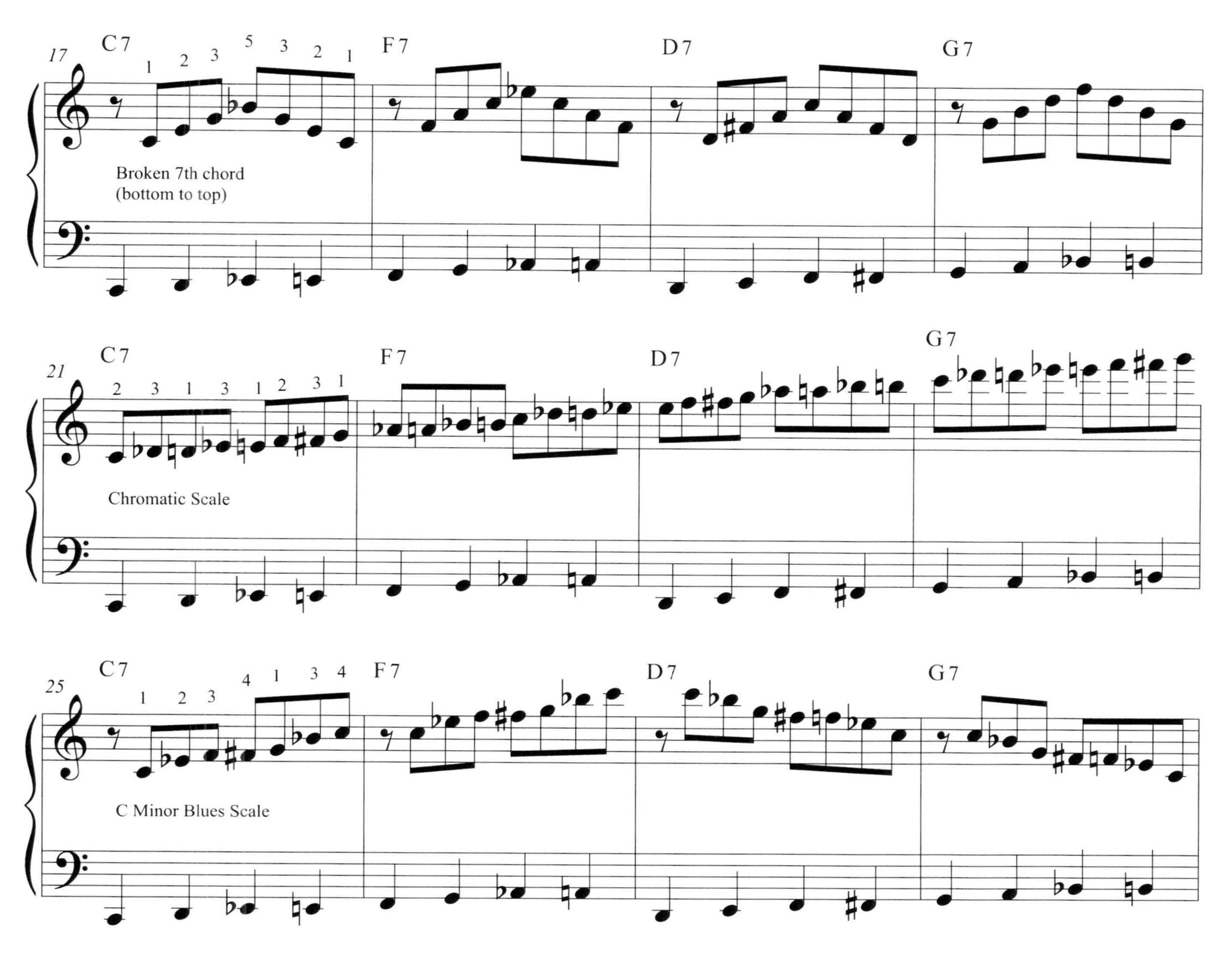

Try to figure out which inversion of each chord I have written out below. This will help you better learn your chords in their various inversions.

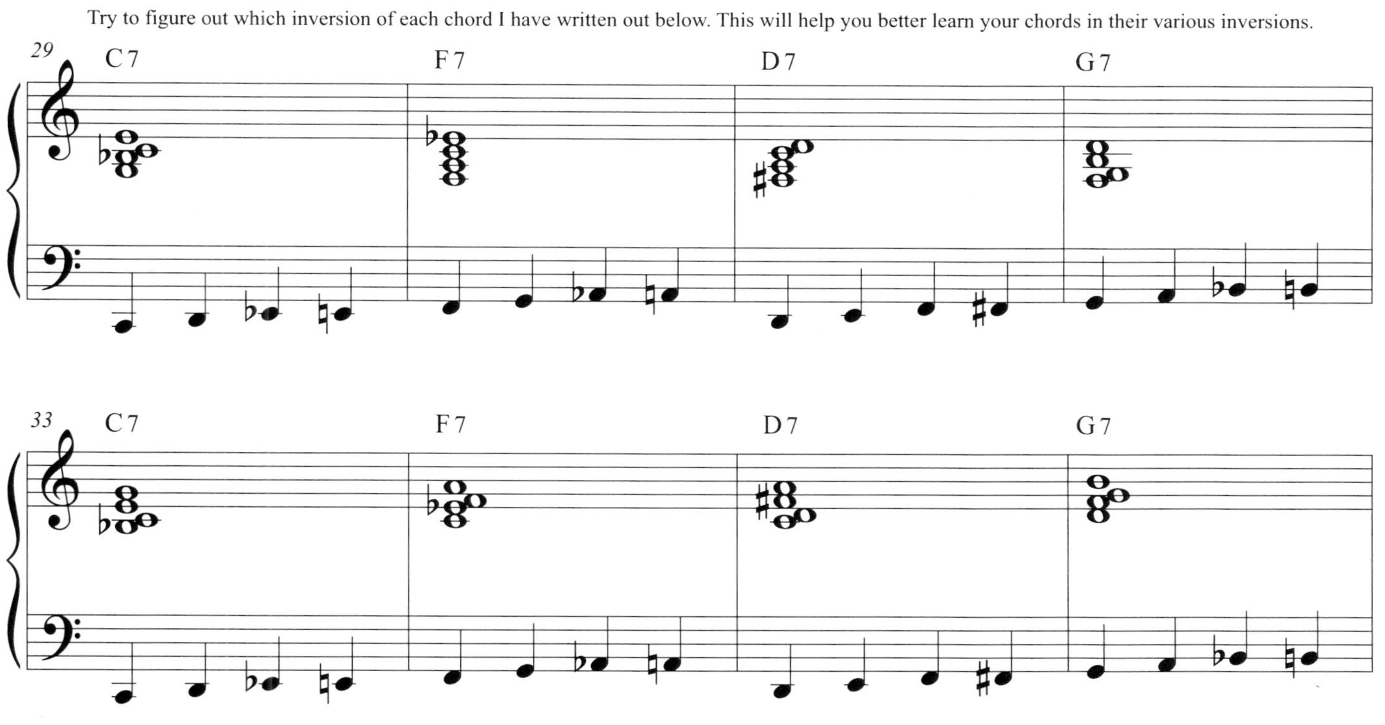

Right hand improvises using the all of the examples from this exercise. Have fun with this section - be creative and play around!

57
C7
F7
D7
G7
61
C7
F7
D7
G7
65
C7
F7
D7
G7
69
C7
F7
D7
G7
C7

In this exercise, we play descending octave intervals with the left hand while the right hand plays different inversions of 7th chords. The left hand is descending following a Whole - Half - Whole step walking bass pattern. After playing this jazz exercise in the key of C Major, try to play it in every key signature on the piano moving up in half steps - C, C♯, D, E♭, E, F, F♯, G, A♭, A, B♭, and B.

In this exercise we are playing a combination of theory concepts we have learned in this book so far. The left hand plays 7th chords, minor 7th chords, various left hand patterns from a barrel house blues left hand pattern to a Whole - Half - Half walking bass pattern. All of this is done while the right hand is given the freedom to improvise and experiment with either the notes from the chords written above each measure or any other right hand pattern you have learned from any of the previous pages. Have fun playing this simple jazz exercise. After playing this in the key of C Major, try to play this jazz exercise in every key signature on the piano moving up in half steps - C, C♯, D, E♭, E, F, F♯, G, A♭, A, B♭, and B.

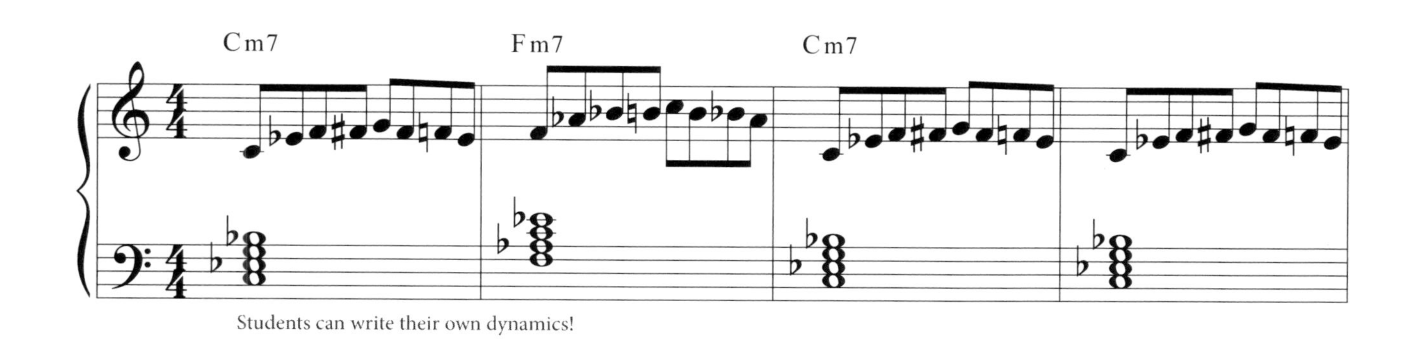

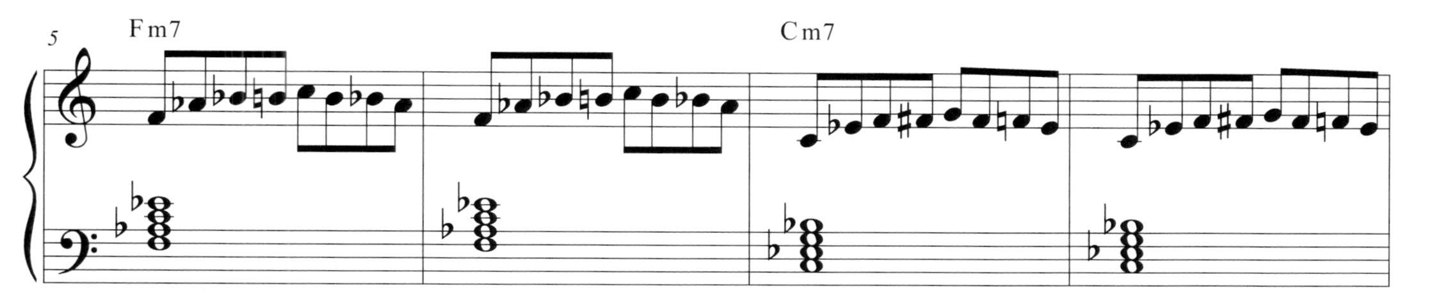

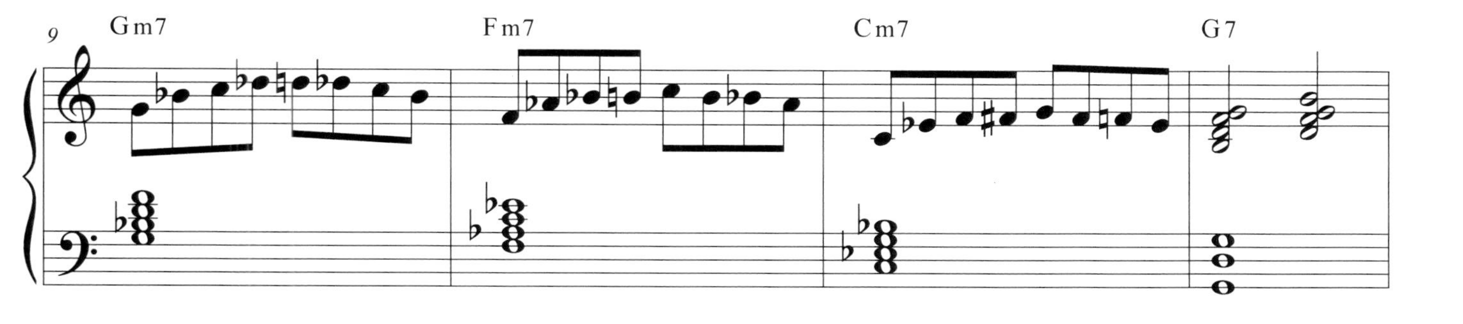

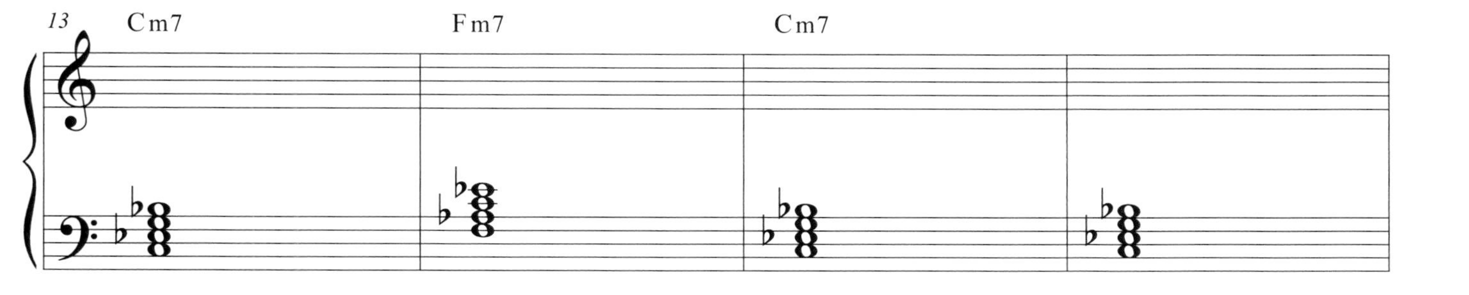

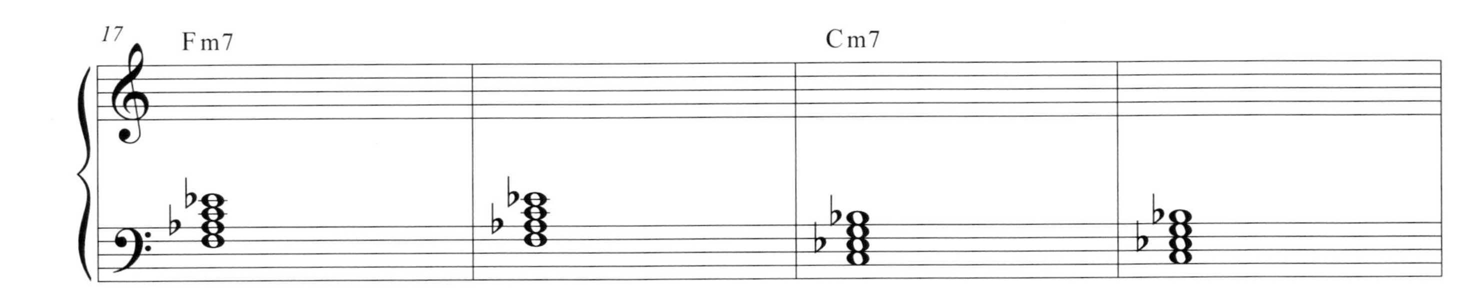
17
Fm7
Cm7

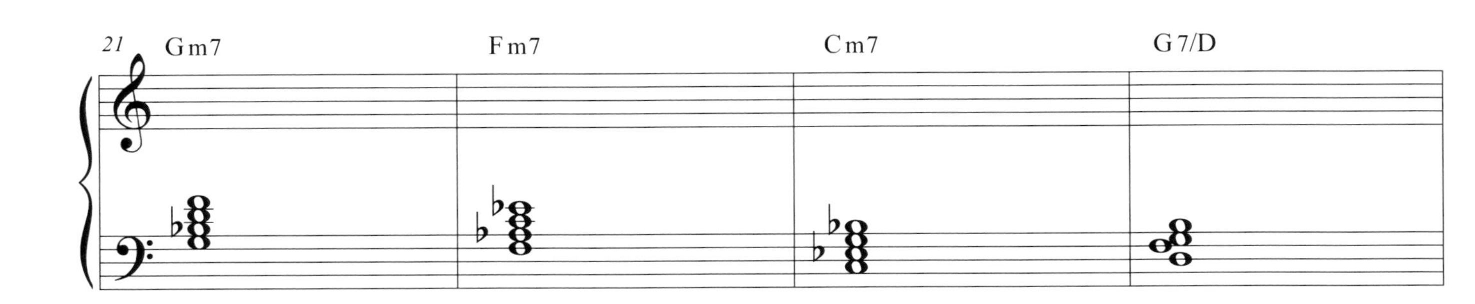
21
Gm7
Fm7
Cm7
G7/D

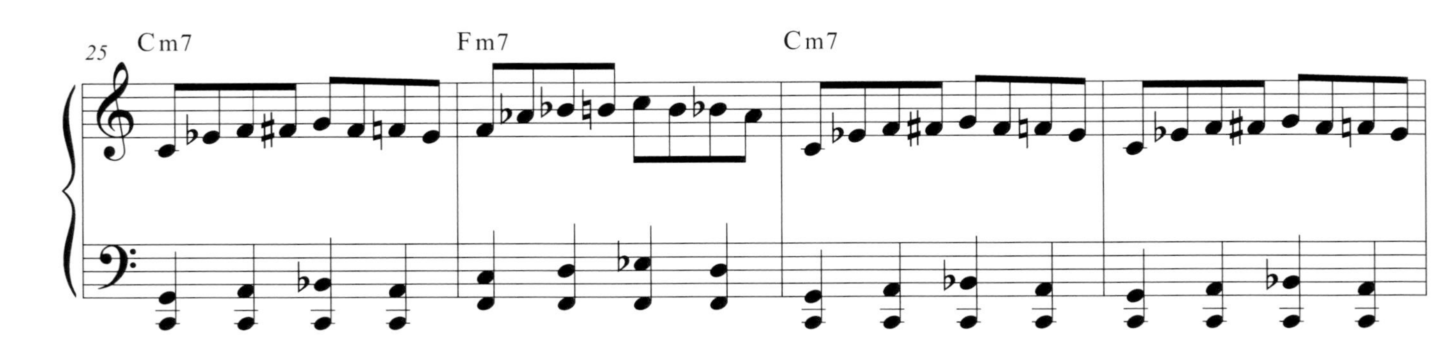
25
Cm7
Fm7
Cm7

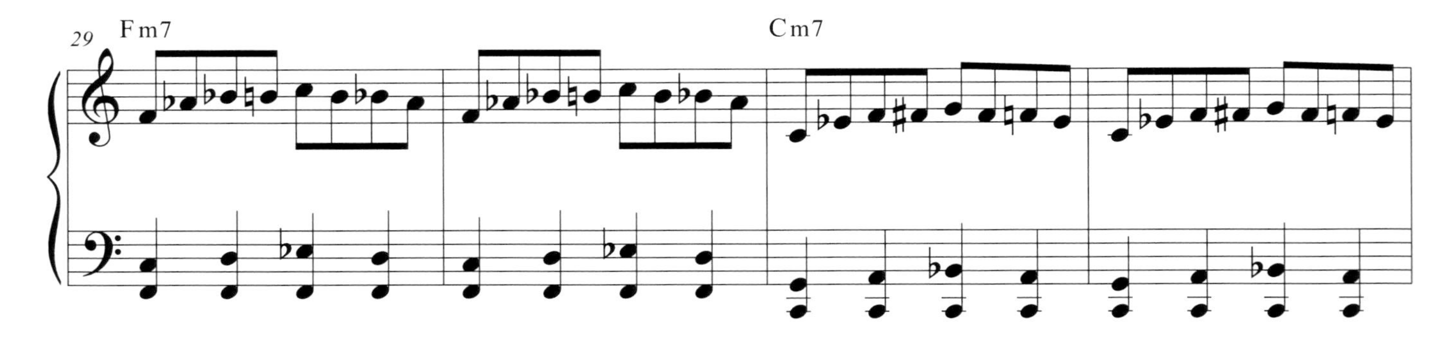
29
Fm7
Cm7

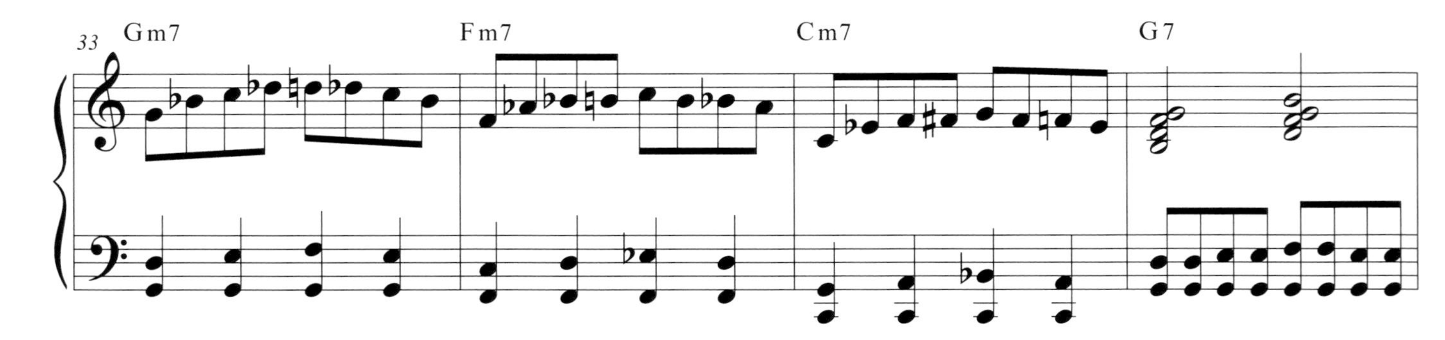
33
Gm7
Fm7
Cm7
G7

37
C7
F7
C7
41
F7
C7
45
G7
F7
C7
G7
49
C7
F7
D7
G7
53
C7
F7
D7
G7

57
C7
F7
D7
G7
61
C7
F7
D7
G7
65
C7
F7
D7
G7
69
C7
F7
D7
G7
73
Cm7
Fm7
Cm7

77
Fm7
Cm7
81
Gm7
Fm7
Cm7
G7
85
Cm7
Fm7
Cm7
89
Fm7
Cm7
93
Gm7
Fm7
Cm7
G7
C7

A Few Left Hand Patterns

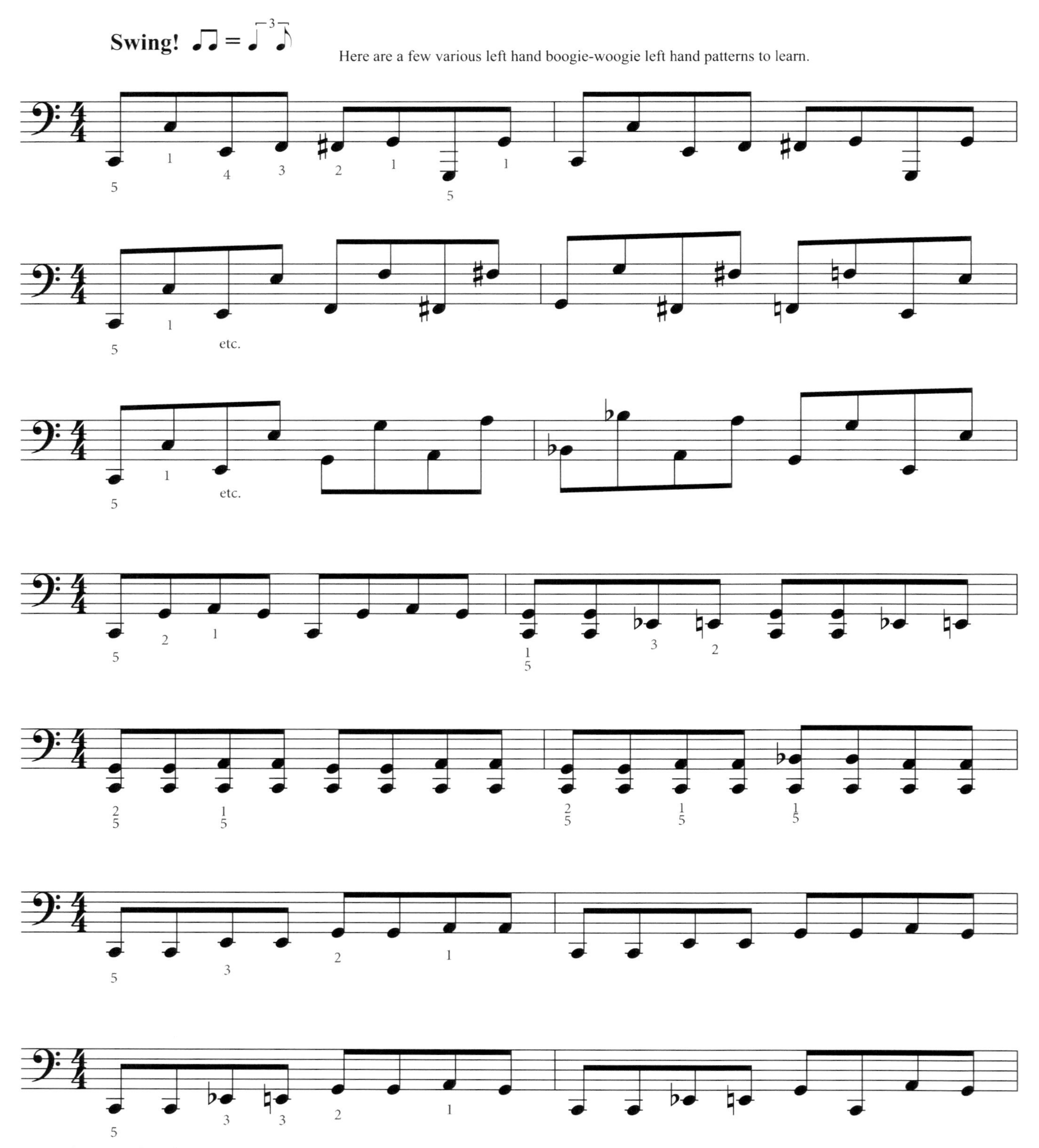

These are a few of the left hand patterns from my best-selling book, "100 Left Hand Patterns Every Piano Player Should Know" - The "100 Left Hand Patterns" PDF book is already included within my Essential Piano Exercises Course for those who are already members of the course.

On the next few pages we will be working on playing a boogie-woogie left hand pattern while the right hand plays the blues pentascale. The blues pentascale contains the first five notes from the complete minor blues scale (i.e. C, E flat, F, F sharp, G, F sharp, F natural, E flat, C).

Blues Pentascale Boogie Woogie Exercise

First play this exercise as written. Then try to play the right hand as written, but play each of the left hand patterns found on the previous page (and then play everything in every key signature - moving up in half steps).

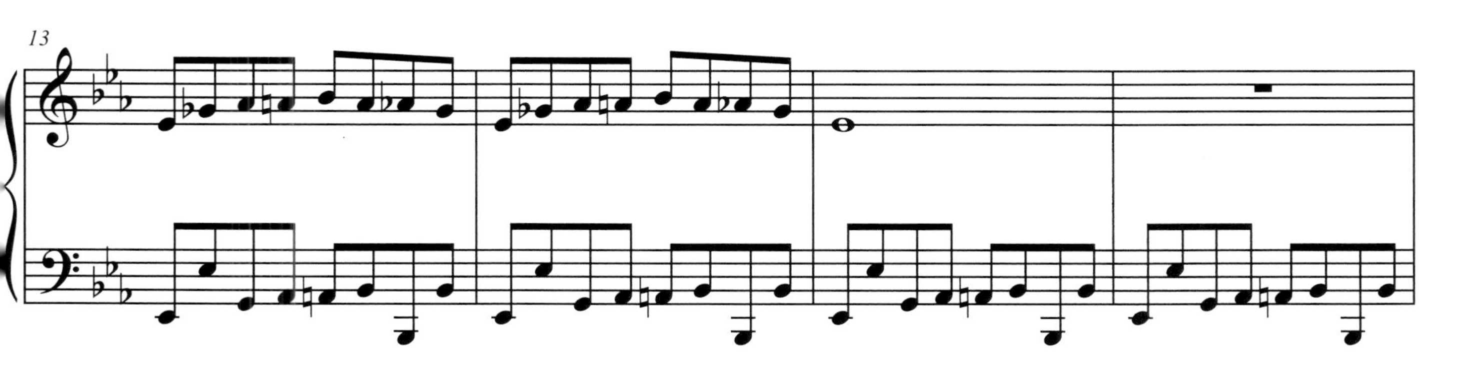

17
21
25
29
33

37
41
45
49

Simple Jazz Chord Progression
(with the Minor Blues Scale)

Have fun playing this simple jazz exercise. After playing this in the key of C Major, try to play it in every key signature on the piano moving up in half steps - C, C♯, D, E♭, E, F, F♯, G, A♭, A, B♭, and B.

Lesson for Boomerang Boogie

A 'boogie' is often thought of as a set of swung notes that are repeated in a pattern (generally played on the piano in boogie-woogie music). Merriam-Webster defines boogie - woogie music as "a percussive style of playing blues on the piano characterized by a steady rhythmic ground bass of eighth notes in quadruple time and a series of improvised melodic variations." (For more information visit The Boogie Woogie Foundation online at www.bowofo.org)

There are two main left hand boogie-woogie patterns used in "Boomerang Boogie." Play each example below several times with the left hand until you feel comfortable playing the boogie woogie patterns. The notes are all eighth notes. They are called eighth notes because in common time (𝄴 or 4/4 time signature - 4 beats per measure) there are eight notes that fit in each measure. The counting is **1** & **2** & **3** & **4** &.

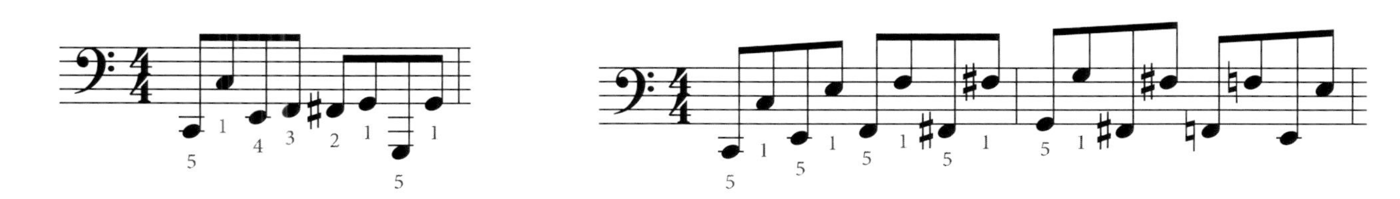

Generally, the boogie-woogie patterns shown above are played beginning on the tonic (1), the sub-dominant (4), and the dominant (5) degrees of the scale. In the song "Boomerang Boogie," the left hand plays each boogie-woogie on the tonic note (which in this case happens to be C because the song is in the key of C) (for a fun exercise, try playing both boogie-woogie left hand patterns in every key moving up chromatically in half steps).

A good understanding of 7th chords will help in playing "Boomerang Boogie." It is very helpful and important to understand intervals when creating chords. Intervals can be diminished, minor, major, perfect, or augmented. In the major scale think of the numbers 1 - 8 (1 = C, 2 = D, 3 = E, 4 = F, 5 = G, 6 = A, 7 = B). The numbers 1, 4, and 5 are called perfect intervals (C, F, and G). The numbers 2, 3, 6, and 7 are called major intervals (D, E, A, and B).

To create a major 7th chord, simply play the perfect 1st (i.e. C), major 3rd (i.e. E), perfect 5th (i.e. G) and major 7th (i.e. B) intervals from the scale at the same time. This is the C major 7th chord (CEGB). To create the dominant 7th chord (sometimes called the 7 chord) simply play the perfect 1st (i.e. C), major 3rd (i.e. E), perfect 5th (i.e. G) and minor 7th (i.e. B♭) intervals from the scale at the same time. This is the C dominant 7th chord (CEGB♭). To create the minor 7th chord simply play the perfect 1st (i.e. C), minor 3rd (i.e. E♭), perfect 5th (i.e. G), and minor 7th (i.e. B♭) intervals from the scale at the same time. This is the C minor 7th chord (CE GB♭). To create the diminished 7th chord simply play the perfect 1st (i.e. C), minor 3rd (i.e. E♭), diminished 5th (i.e. G♭), and diminished 7th (i.e. B𝄫 or A). This is the C diminished 7th chord (C E♭ G♭ B𝄫).

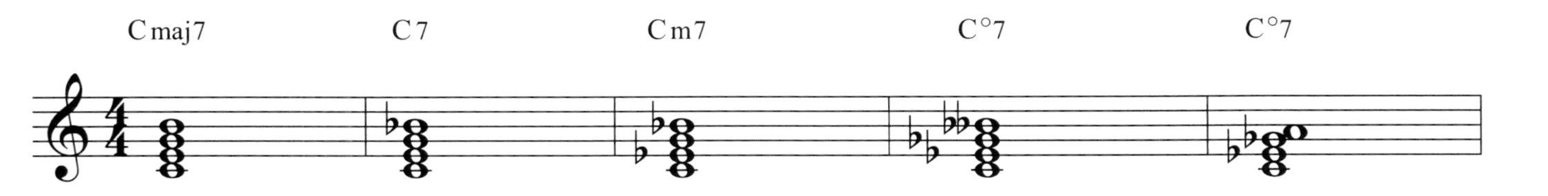

The "Boomerang Boogie" uses several variations and segments from the blues scale. The blues scale is created using the root/perfect first (i.e. C), a minor 3rd or flat the 3rd (i.e. E♭), a perfect 4th (i.e. F), an augmented 4th or sharp the 4th (i.e. F♯), a perfect 5th (i.e. G), a minor 7th or flat the 7th (i.e. B♭) and ending with the tonic (i.e. C). The C blues scale is C - E - F - F♯- G - B♭- C.

Boomerang Boogie

Once you feel comfortable playing this scale one octave try two, three and four octaves up and down the keyboard. Then, for fun try playing the blues scale in every key moving up chromatically in half steps.

MM0000106

16
F min
A♭Maj7
C
20
A m7(♭5)/C
C
24
F 9
G 7
F 9
G 7
C
8vb
28
(8vb)
C m7
32
C
(8vb)

36
C min7
8vb
40
F m9
G min7
A♭Maj7
B♭7
F m9
G min7
(8vb)
44
A♭Maj7
B♭7
C
8vb
48
F m9
G min7
(8vb)
52
A♭Maj7
B♭7
F m9
G min7
A♭Maj7
B♭7
C min7

56
A °7/C
F min7/C
60
F min
A♭Maj7
F min
64
A♭Maj7 B♭7
A♭min7/B A 7 D♭7/A♭
F 9
E 7(♯9)
8vb
68
C
rit.
15ma
Glissando
(8vb)

Below, I have included 7th Chords that move up a 4th following the 7th chords found in the C Major scale (i.e. CMaj7 - FM7 - Bm7 flat 5 - Em7 - Am7 - Dm7 - G7 - CMaj7 - or - I - IV - vii - iii - vi - ii - V - I). First play them in root position and then try the various voicings. After playing this jazz exercise in the key of C Major, try to play it in every key signature on the piano moving up in half steps - C, C♯, D, E♭, E, F, F♯, G, A♭, A, B♭, and B.

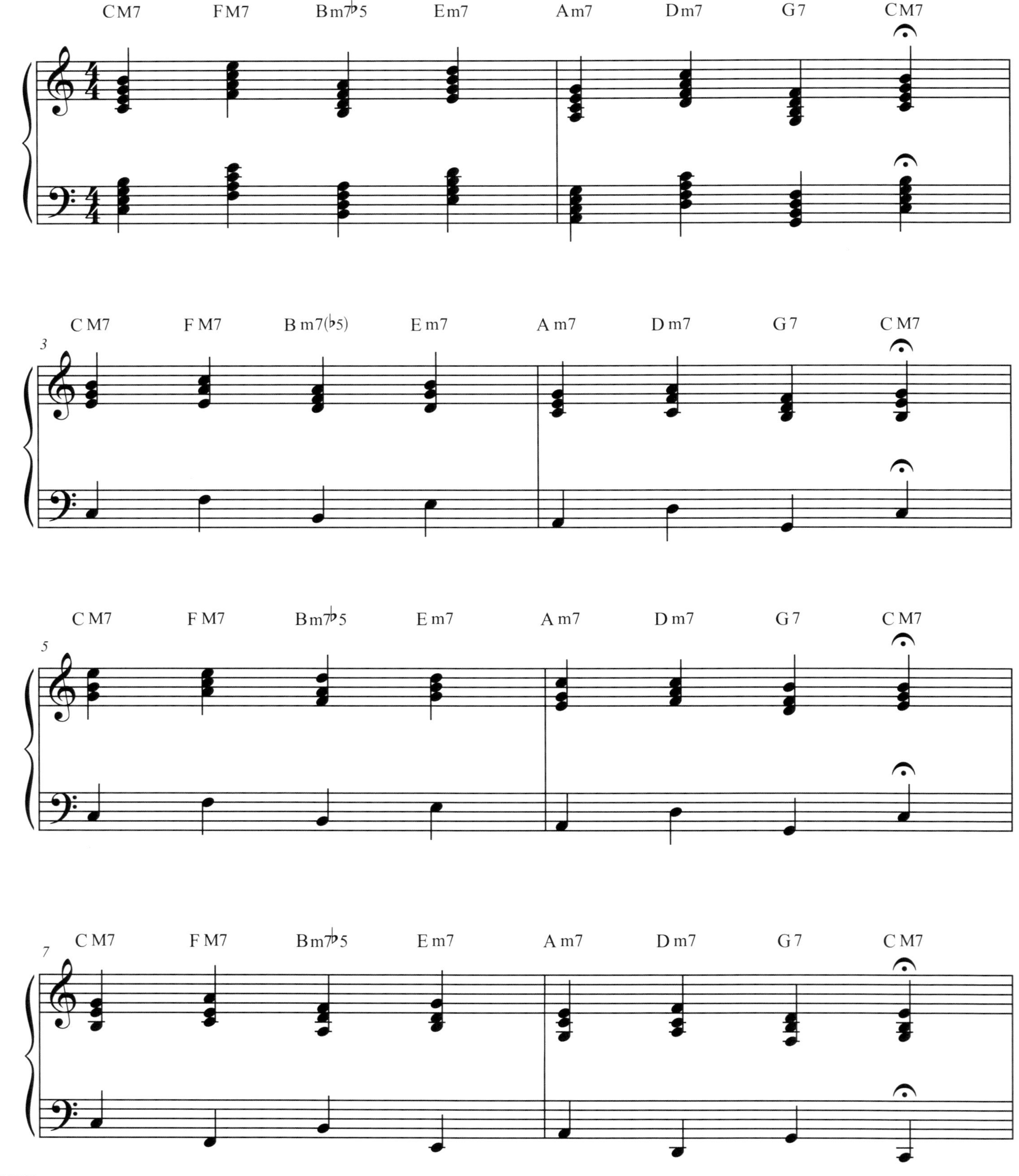

In this example, we follow the same chord progression as before but we are using open voicing. Notice how there are only two notes for each hand. You can try to play other 7th chords like this by separating the notes from the chords as shown. After playing this jazz exercise in the key of C Major, try to play it in every key signature on the piano moving up in half steps - C, C♯, D, E♭, E, F, F♯, G, A♭, A, B♭, and B.

Blocked and Broken 7th Chords

Below, I have included blocked and broken 7th Chords that move up according to the C Major scale (i.e. CM7 - Dm7 - Em7 - FM7 - G7 - Am7 - Bm7 flat 5 and CM7). After playing this jazz exercise in the key of C Major, try to play it in every key signature on the piano moving up in half steps - C, C♯, D, E♭, E, F, F♯, G, A♭, A, B♭, and B.

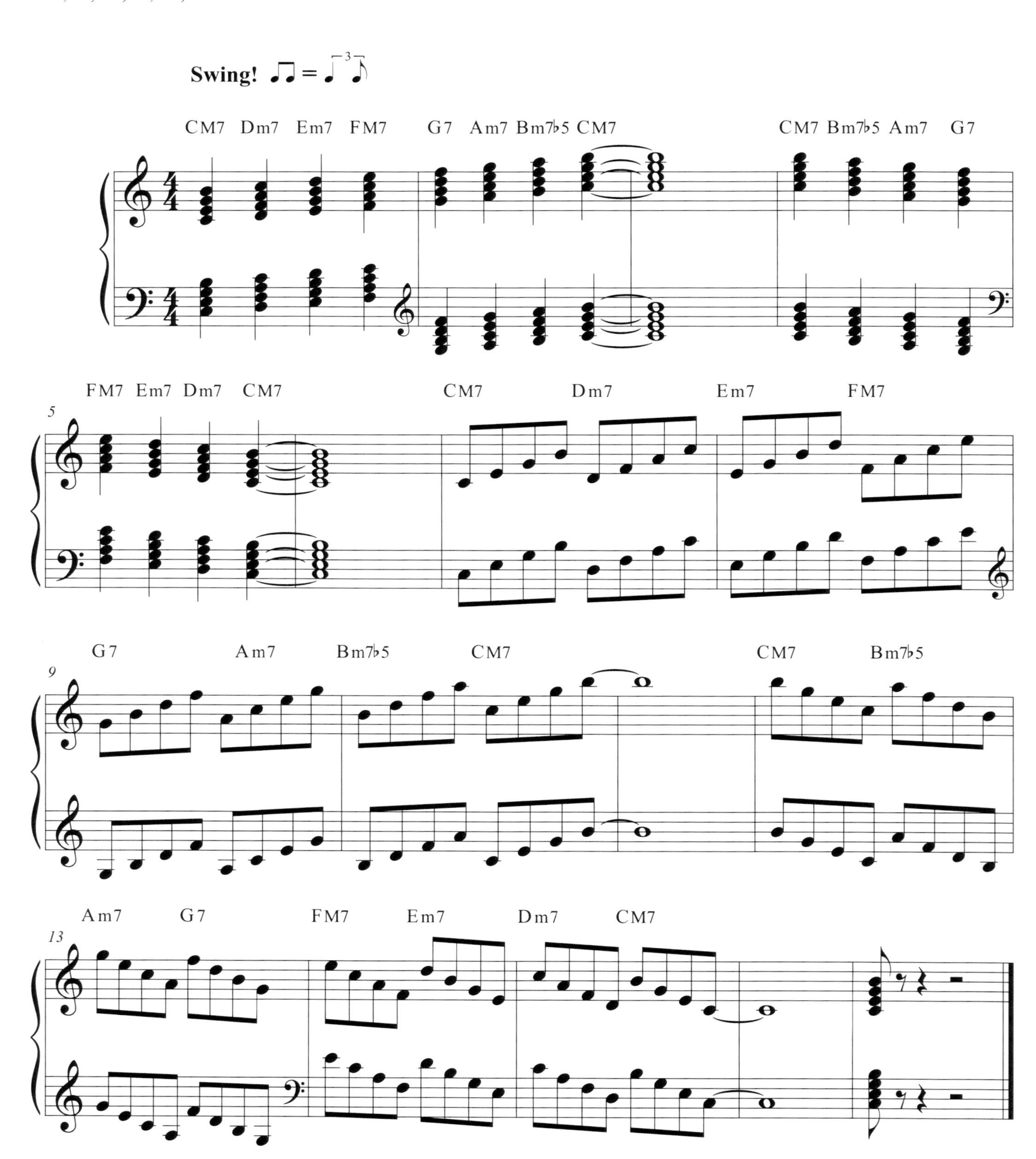

Lesson for Skippin' Along

"Skippin' Along" follows a progression of 7th chords descending in 5ths (you can think of the chords descending in 5ths or ascending in 4ths - either way the same notes are played). The song begins with a C major 7th chord then proceeds to the F major 7th, B minor 7th flat the 5th, E minor 7th, A minor 7th, D minor 7th and G 7th chords. This is what the chord progression looks like when notated on the staff. Each chord below is shown in root position.

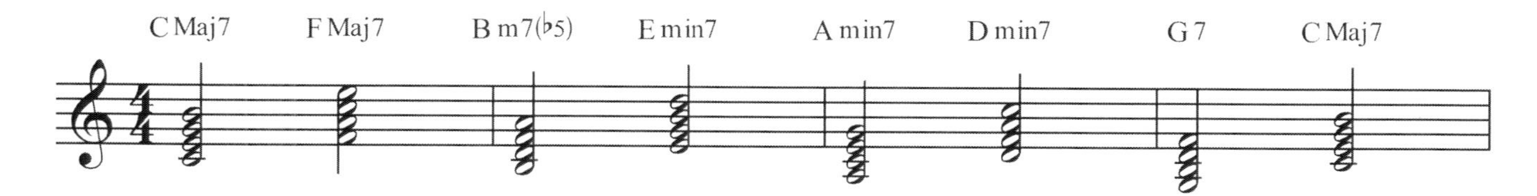

Now that you've tried this progression of descending 7th chords in root position, try playing each of the chords in root position, first, second, and third inversions. Root position is where the tonic note (or the note after which the chord is named) is on the bottom (i.e. C E G B). The "first inversion" of the chord is where the root note has been removed from the bottom and placed on top of the chord (i.e. E G B C). The "second inversion" is where the bottom note from the first inversion chord has been removed from the bottom and placed on top of the chord (i.e. G B C E). The "third inversion" is where the bottom note from the second inversion chord has been removed from the bottom and placed on top of the chord (i.e. B C E G). Try each example below (for fun play with both hands at the same time).

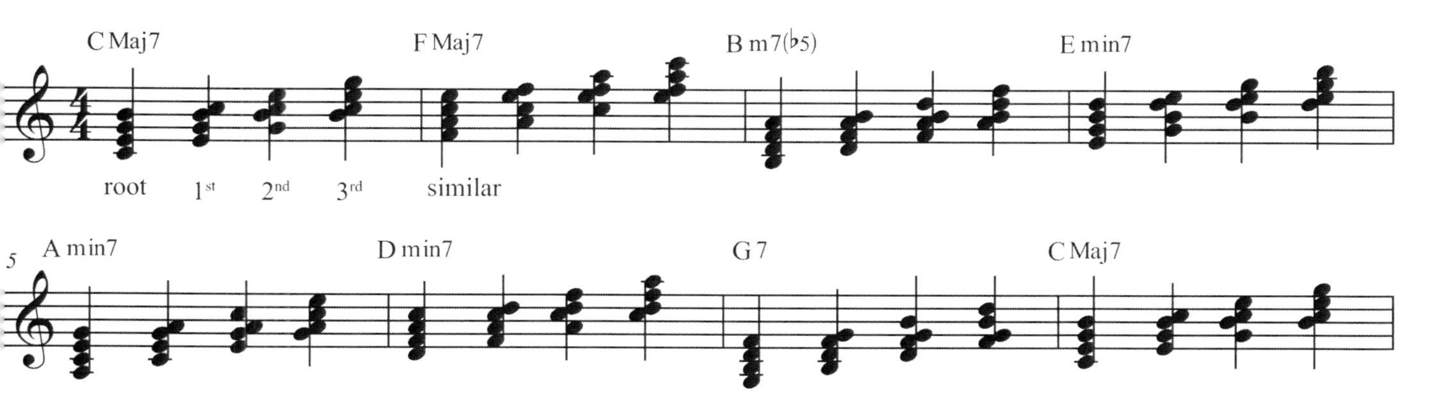

As a fun challenge, try playing every major 7th, dominant 7th, minor 7th, and diminished 7th chord in root position, first, second, and third inversions in every key signature (moving up chromatically in half steps) with both hands (for a reminder on how to create these chords refer to pg. 5).

"Skippin' Along" uses several combinations of various 7th chords in root position, first, second, and third inversions. Try these examples below (for fun, try playing the progressions in every key moving up chromatically in half steps).

This example shows the chord progression descending in 5ths while the chords rotate repeatedly between the root position and the third inversion.

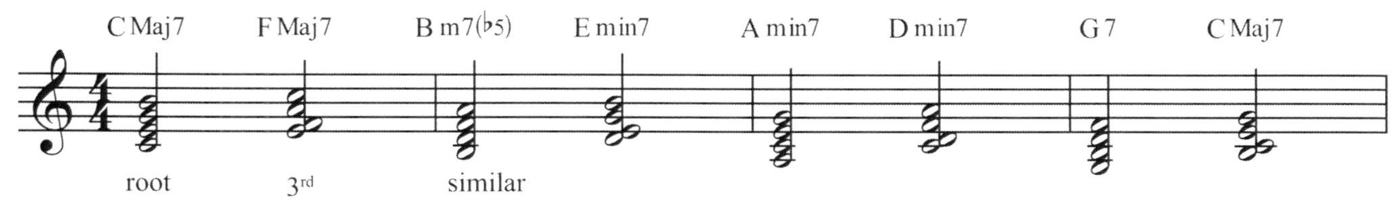

This example shows the chord progression descending in 5ths while the chords rotate repeatedly between the third inversion and the second inversion.

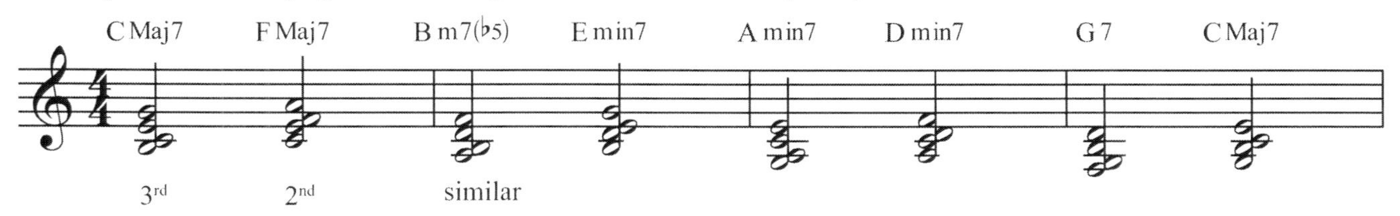

Skippin' Along

Review the chord progression from page 120 (i.e. CMaj7 - F Maj7 - B flat minor 7 flat 5 - Emin7 - Amin7 - Dmin7 - G7 - CMaj7 - or - I - IV - vii - iii - vi - ii - V - I).

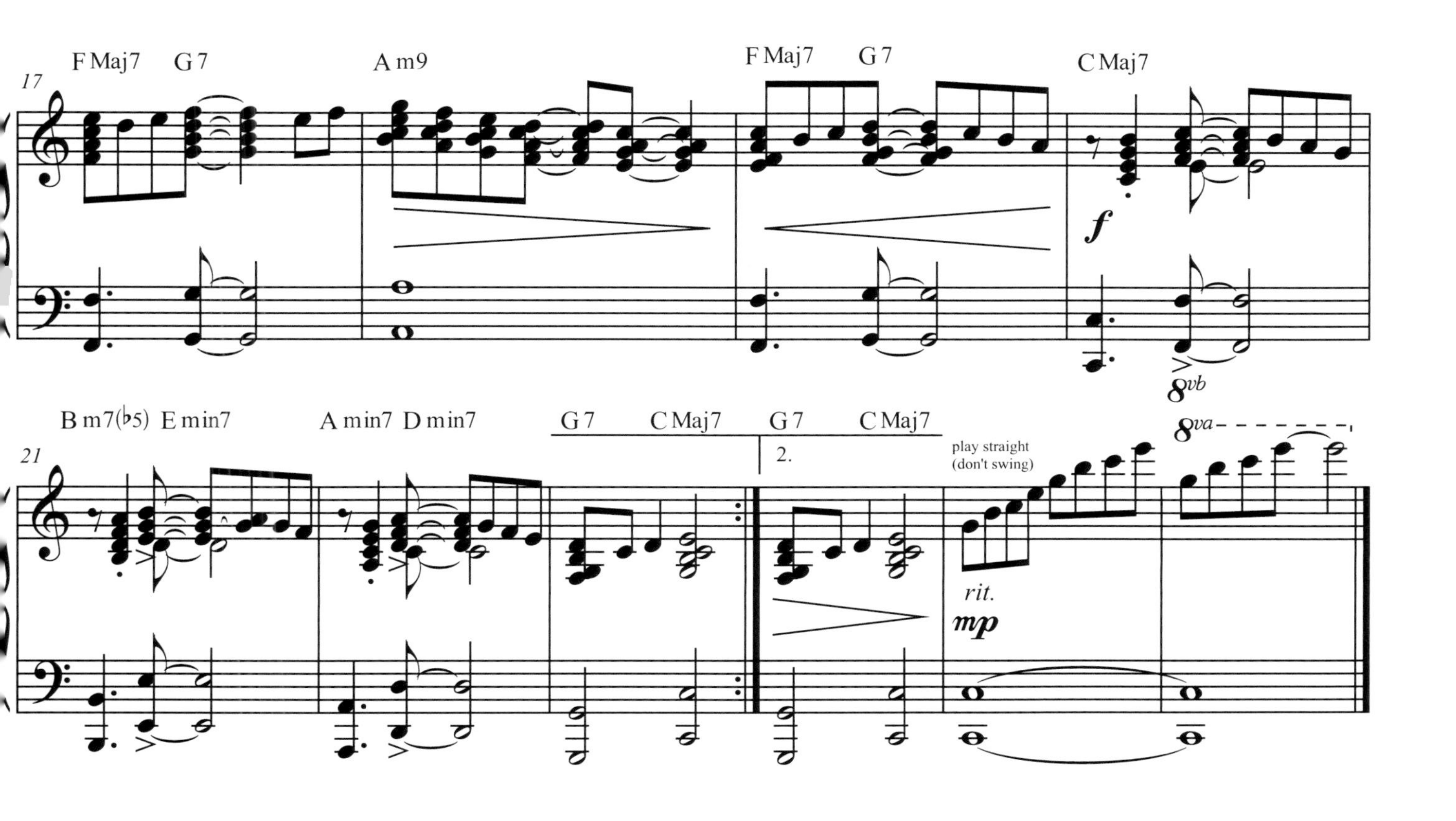
17
F Maj7
G 7
A m9
F Maj7
G 7
C Maj7
f
8vb
B m7(♭5)
E min7
A min7
D min7
G 7
C Maj7
G 7
C Maj7
21
2.
play straight
(don't swing)
8va
rit.
mp

Lesson for The Sidewalk Shuffle

Merriam-Webster defines a "shuffle" as "moving (the feet) by sliding along or back and forth without lifting: to perform (as a dance) with a dragging, sliding step." Webster also refers to shuffle as a "lazy nonchalant manner with sliding and tapping motions of the feet." The dictionary's definition is primarily referring to movement when walking and dancing, but the same definition can be applied to a shuffle feel when playing the piano. The rhythmic device (known as a shuffle) is created by holding the first note in a pair of notes longer than the second note. A swing or shuffle rhythm is the rhythm produced by playing repeated pairs of notes in this way. Try playing the notes below. They are swung and create a shuffle feel. Play the first example and then try each of the following examples from the song *(once again play each exercise in every key moving up chromatically in half steps).*

Once you feel comfortable playing this example in the key of C major, try playing it in every key signature moving up chromatically in half steps. Once you play in one key, you should always try to play in every key.

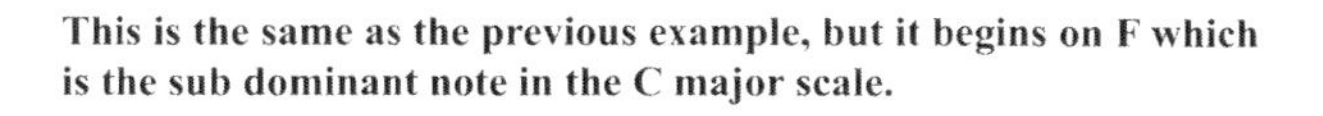

This is the same as the previous example, but it begins on F which is the sub dominant note in the C major scale.

This example shows a shuffle left hand pattern created with two perfect 5th intervals (C and G), the two major 6th intervals (C and A), two minor 7th intervals (C and B flat), and returning to the two major 6th intervals again (C and A).

This example shows a shuffle left hand pattern created with two perfect 5th intervals (F and C), the two major 6th intervals (F and D), two minor 7th intervals (F and E flat), and returning to the two major 6th intervals again (F and D).

This example shows a shuffle left hand pattern created by playing the Tonic note two times (C), the augmented Super Tonic note once (D sharp or E flat), the Mediant note once (E), the Dominant note two times (G), the Sub Mediant note once (A), and the Dominant note again (G).

This example shows a shuffle left hand pattern created by playing the Tonic note two times (F), the augmented Super Tonic note once (G sharp or A flat), the Mediant note once (A), the Dominant note two times (C), the Sub Mediant note once (D), and the Dominant note again (C).

The Sidewalk Shuffle also has several measures of the chromatic scale (created by playing every half step). This scale moves up and down according to half steps (every note on the piano is played one after another). As a helpful hint for the fingering, only the thumb (1) the index finger (2), and the middle finger (3) are used when playing this scale. The middle finger (3) plays all of the black keys, the thumb (1) plays all of the white keys except for C and F, and the index finger (2) plays C and F. Try this example below.

Once you feel comfortable playing this scale one octave, try two, three and four octaves up and down the keyboard.

The Sidewalk Shuffle

17
G 7
C 7
21
25
F 7
C 7
29
G 7
C 7
33

37
F7
C7
41
G7
C7
45
D7/C
C7
50
D7/C
C7
mp
8vb

JAZZY

BY JERALD SIMON

You can improvise from measures 21-28
17
22
8va
3
You can improvise any right hand pattern you'd like for these few measures. I included a combination of 8th notes and triplets, but you can do anything.
26
(8va)
30
34

Blocked and Broken 7th Chord Exercises following the C Major Scale

After playing this in the key of C Major, try to play this jazz exercise in every key signature on the piano moving up in half steps - C, C♯, D, E♭, E, F, F♯, G, A♭, A, B♭, and B.

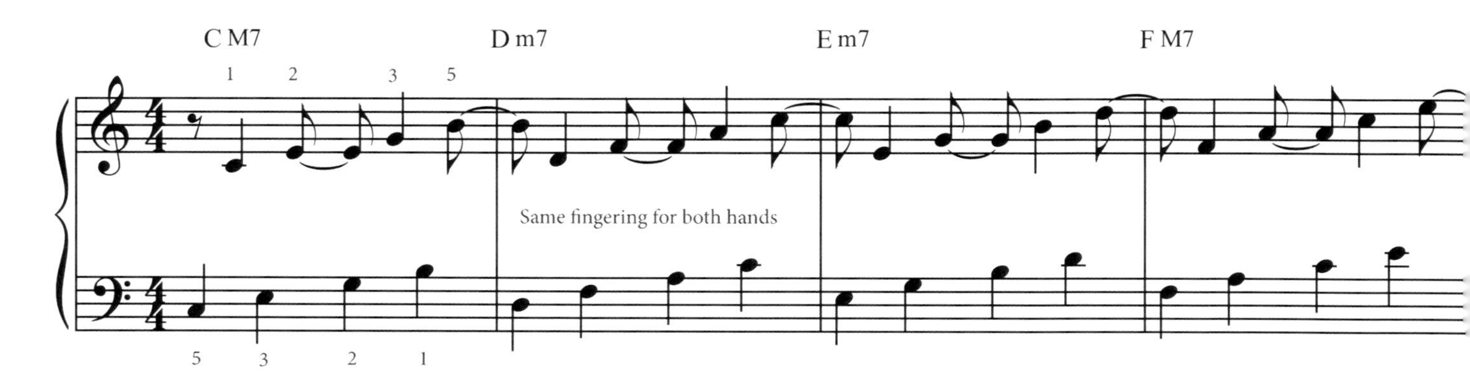

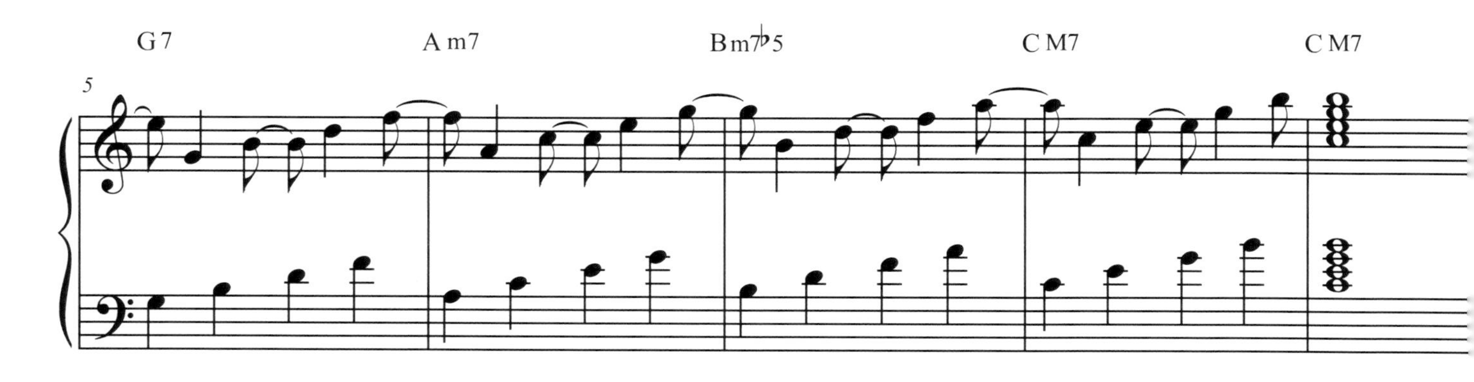

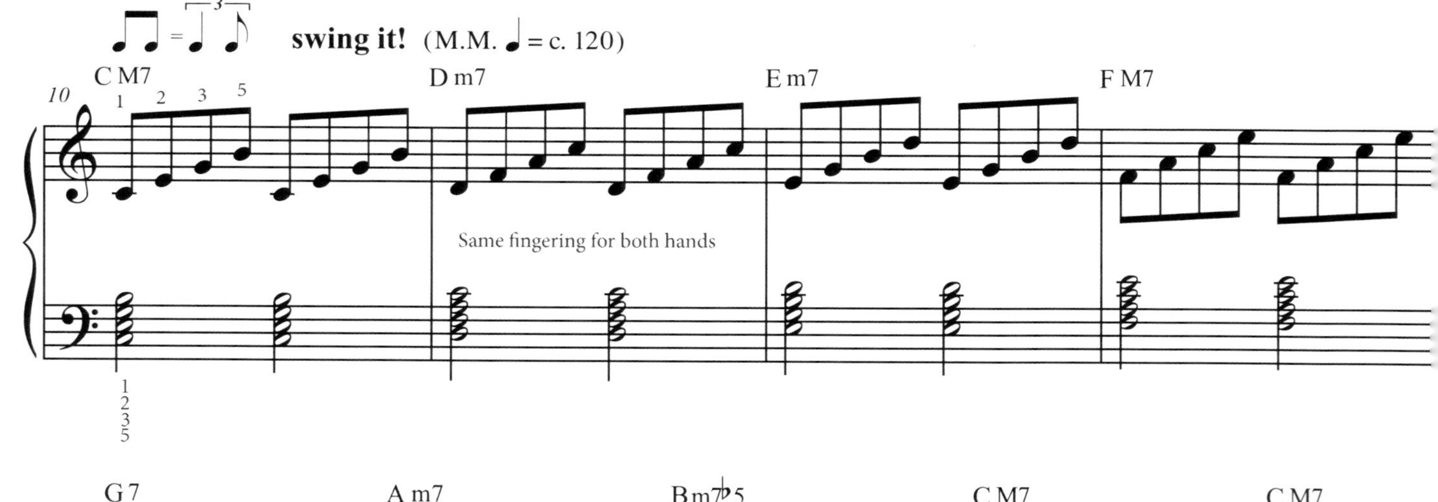

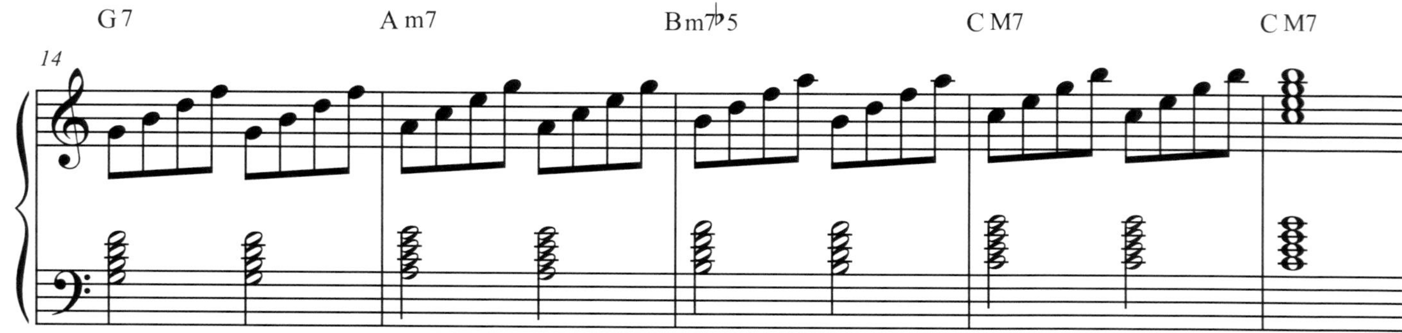

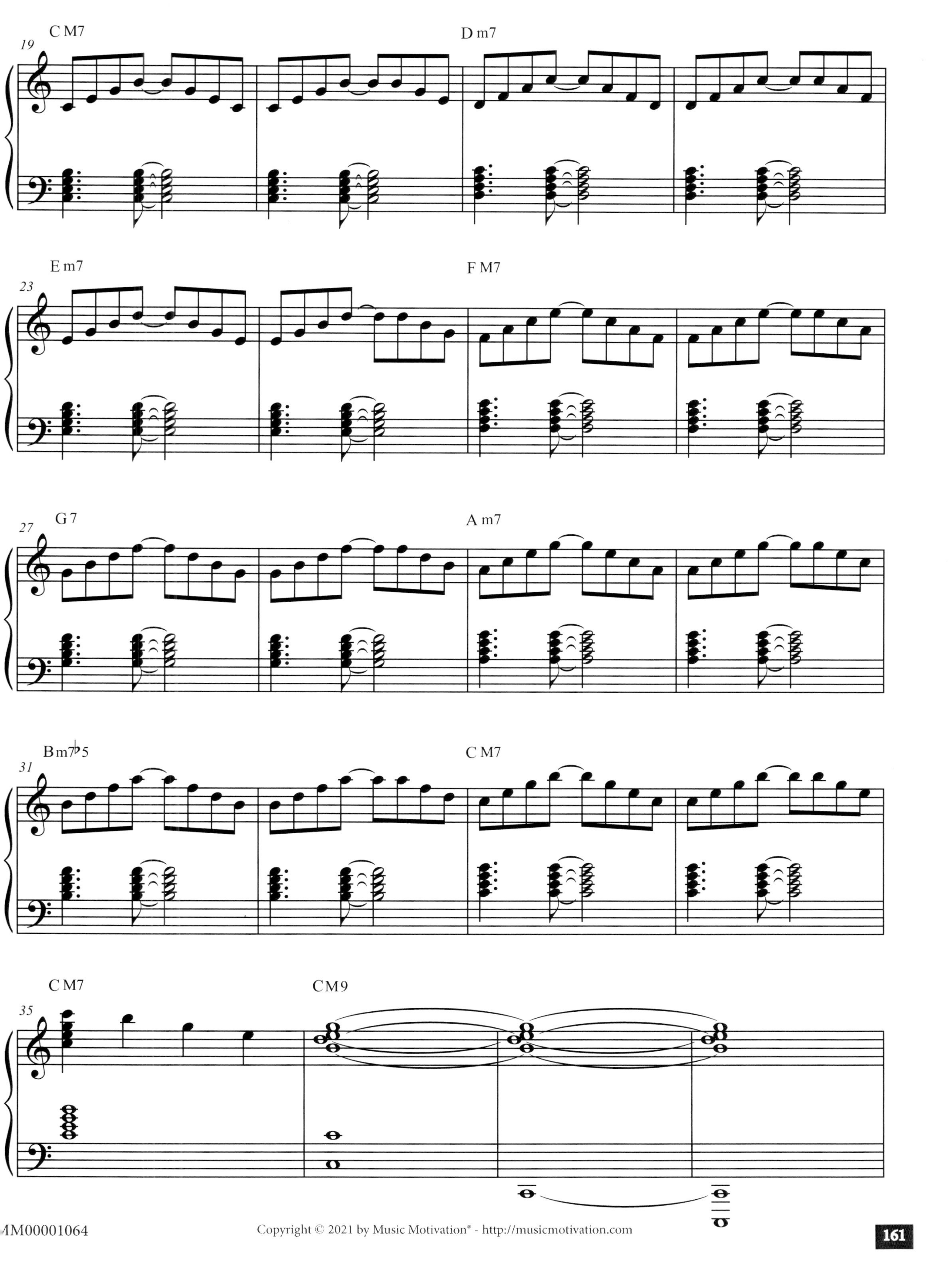
C M7
19
D m7
E m7
23
F M7
G 7
27
A m7
Bm7♭5
31
C M7
C M7
35
C M9

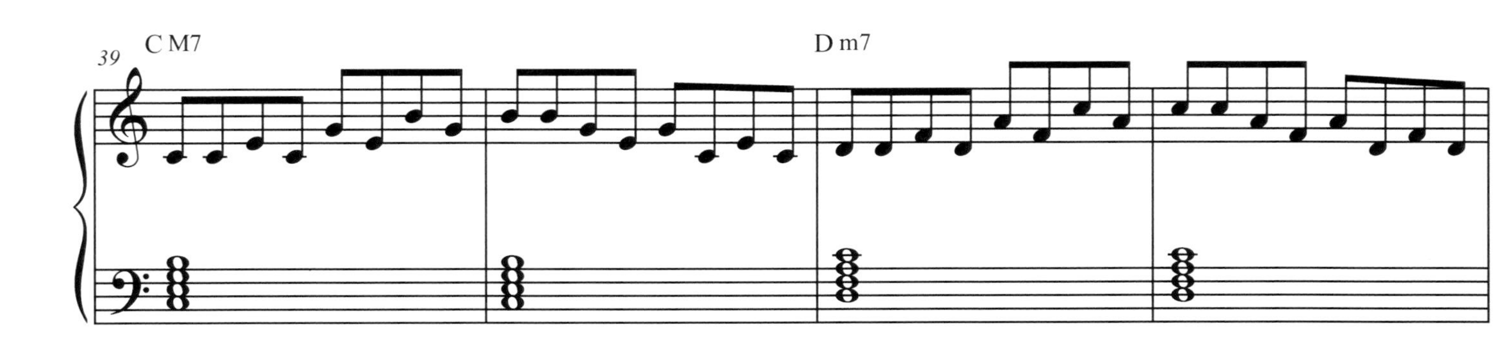
39
C M7
D m7

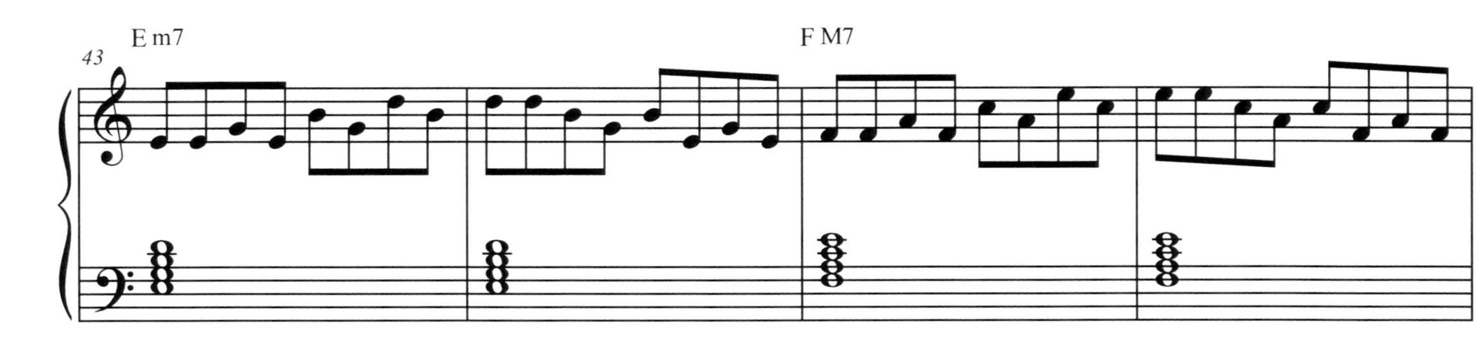
43
E m7
F M7

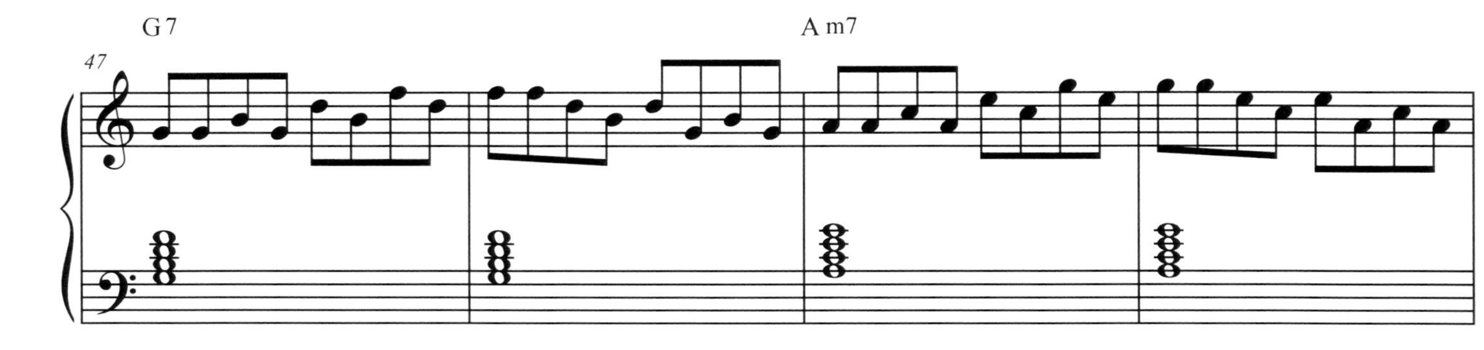
47
G 7
A m7

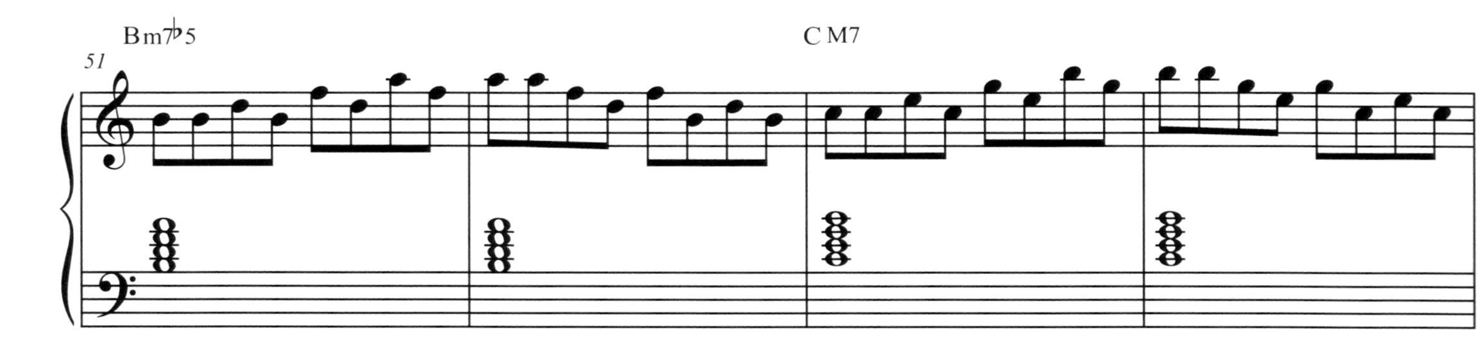
51
Bm7♭5
C M7

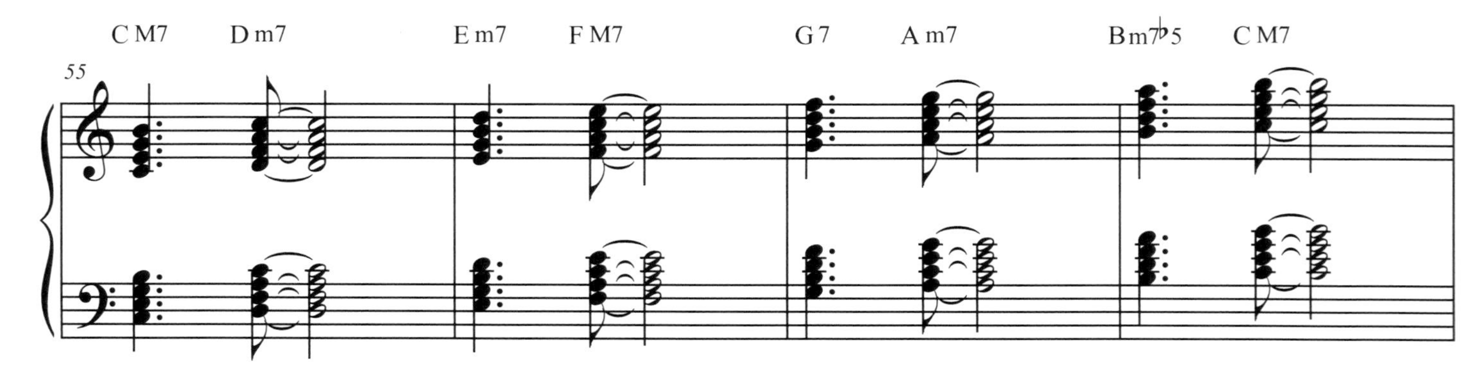
55
C M7
D m7
E m7
F M7
G 7
A m7
Bm7♭5
C M7

After playing this in the key of C Major, try to play this jazz exercise in every key signature on the piano moving up in half steps - C, C♯, D, E♭, E, F, F♯, G, A♭, A, B♭, and B.

Right Hand Licks created from notes from the C Major 7th Chord

After playing all of these C Major 7th chord licks in the key of C Major, try to play them in every key signature on the piano moving up in half steps - C, C♯, D, E♭, E, F, F♯, G, A♭, A, B♭, and B. The left hand plays the C Major 7th chord while the right hand improvises and plays around with the notes from the C Major 7th chord (some of the examples do have a few accidentals placed a half step below the E, G, and B (i.e. E flat, G flat, and B flat).

Swing the 8th notes with these examples below.

MM0000106

Lesson for Summer Skies

"Summer Skies" follows a progression of 7th chords ascending diatonically (according to the major scale). Each chord is built from the notes of the C major scale. The C major scale is C D E F G A B C. Play the C major scale below. Some of what I present on this page is a review of what we have learned so far.

Once you feel comfortable playing this scale one octave, try two, three, and four octaves up and down the keyboard.

Each chord is created using intervals. An "interval" is defined as the distance (comprised of whole and half steps) between two notes. The major scale uses "Perfect" and "Major" intervals. The perfect intervals are the primary notes (from which the primary chords are created) from the major scale (i.e. 1 or C; 4 or F: and 5 or G). The major intervals are the secondary notes (from which the secondary chords are created) from the major scale (i.e. 2 or D; 3 or E; 6 or A; and 7 or B). Look at the intervals of the C major scale below (once you feel comfortable playing this exercise in the key of C - try playing it in every key moving up chromatically in half steps.)

Perfect intervals can become a *diminished interval* by playing the flat (i.e. C and G♭ is a diminished 5th interval) and an *augmented interval* by playing the sharp (i.e. C and G♯ is an augmented 5th interval). Major intervals can become a *diminished interval* by playing the double flat (C and B♭♭ is a diminished 7th interval), can become a *minor interval* by playing the flat (i.e. C and B♭ is a minor 7th interval), and an *augmented interval* by playing the sharp (i.e. C and B♯ is an augmented 7th interval).

Play the seventh chords below. Try figuring out which intervals have been used to create the chords.

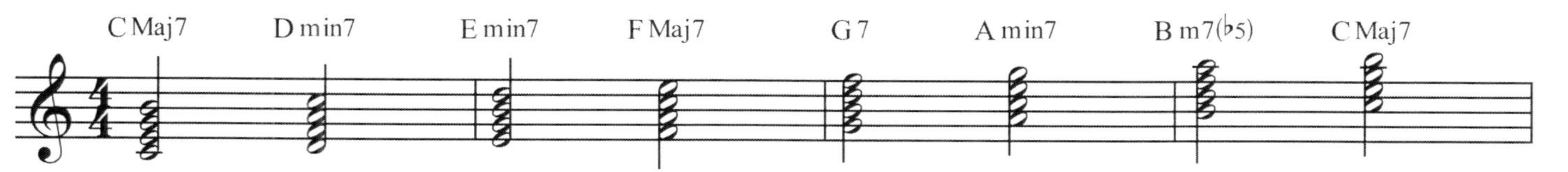

As a review from lesson one, all major 7th chords are created with a perfect 1st interval, a major 3rd interval, a perfect 5th interval, and a major 7th interval. All minor 7th chords are created with a perfect 1st interval, a minor 3rd interval, a perfect 5th interval, and a minor 7th interval. All dominant 7th chords are created with a perfect 1st interval, a major 3rd interval, a perfect 5th interval, and a minor 7th interval. The minor 7th flat the 5th chord is created with a perfect 1st interval, a minor 3rd interval, a diminished 5th interval, and minor 7th interval. Try playing all the seventh chords with both hands (for fun, play this progression of chords in every key signature).

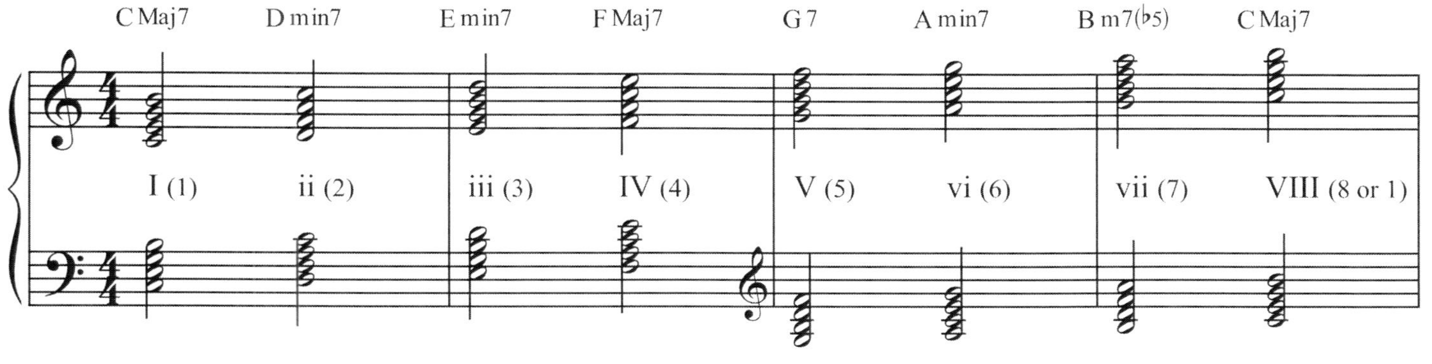

Summer Skies
(Written for and named after my daughter, Summer)

By Jerald Simon

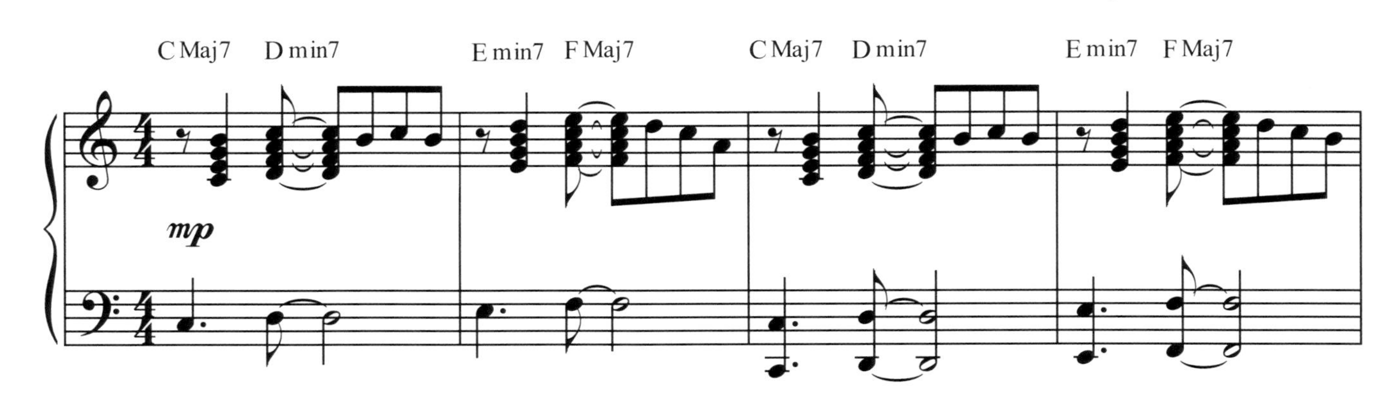

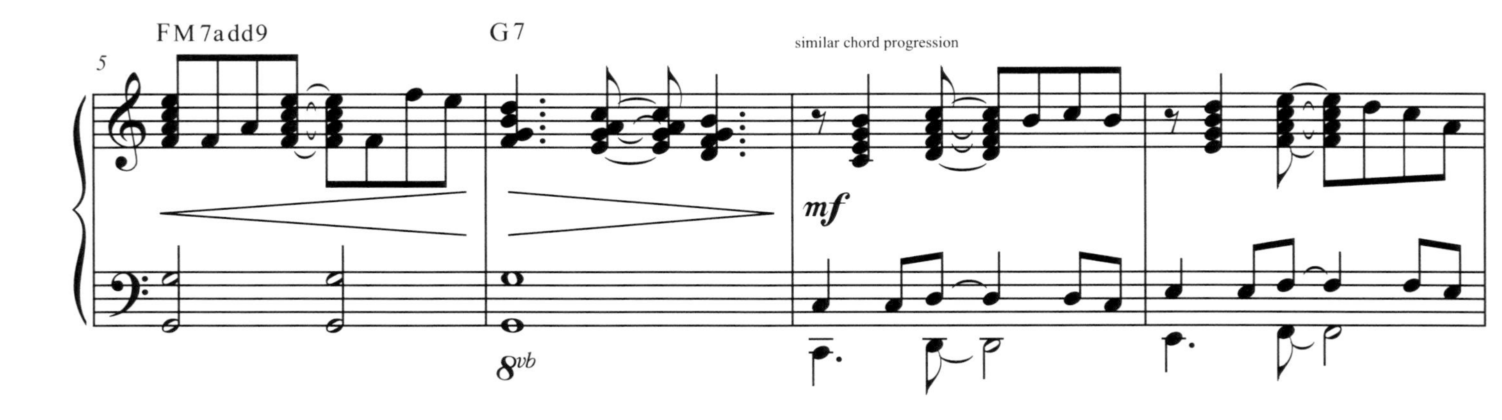

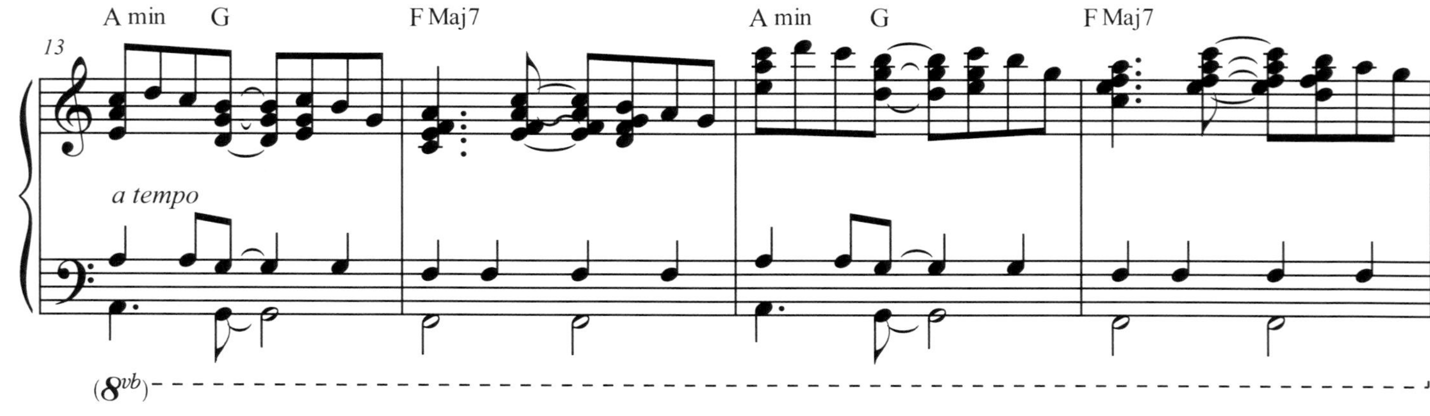

8va
17
C Maj7
D min7
f
8vb
21
E min7
F Maj7
similar chord progression
throughout the song
8vb
25
rit.
f
(8vb)
29
quick
fermata
rit.
a tempo
8vb
33
8va
(8vb)

MM00001064

(8va)
37
8vb
mp
41
45
49
play straight
(don't swing)
rit.
mp
a tempo
53
mf
8vb

MM00001064

6TH AND 7TH CHORD EXERCISE

THIS IS A FUN WAY TO PRACTICE PLAYING THE 6TH AND 7TH CHORDS!

After playing this jazz exercise in the key of C Major, try to play it in every key signature on the piano moving up in half steps - C, C♯, D, E♭, E, F, F♯, G, A♭, A, B♭, and B.

C7
etc.
C m7
etc.
Cm7(♭5)
etc.
etc.
Cm7(♯5)

37
8va
41
C dim7
1
2
3
4
etc.
8va
5
1
2
1
2
1
3
4
44
Play any 6th or 7th chord you want to play!
49
54

MM00001066

59

64

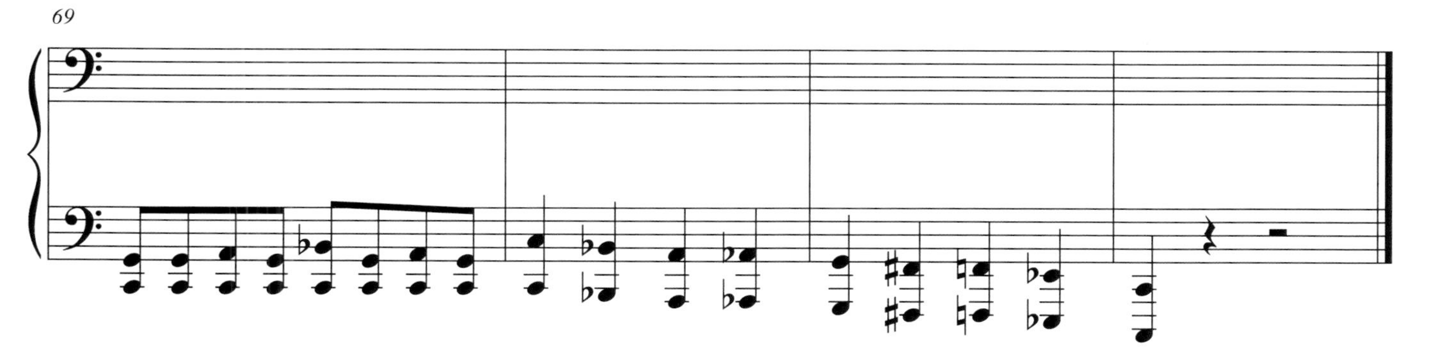
69

Lesson for "Railroad Ruckus" (raucous)

"Railroad Ruckus" uses a combination of the C, F, and G blues scales played in segments or their entirety. As a reminder (from lesson one), play the C blues scale below. First try the one octave scale, then proceed to the two, three, and four octave blues scales (as in lesson one, play each exercise in every key moving up chromatically in half steps).

This is the C blues scale going up one octave (try playing the scale going up and down one octave).

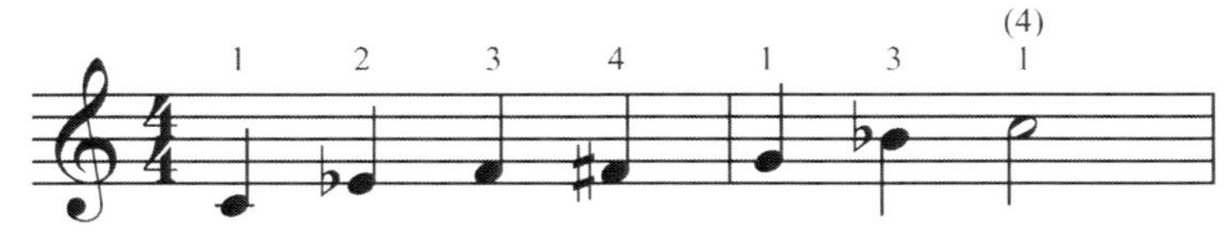

Once you feel comfortable playing this scale one octave try two, three, and four octaves up and down the keyboard - see each example below.

This is the C blues scale going up and down two octaves.

This is the C blues scale going up and down three octaves.

This is the C blues scale going up four octaves (try playing the scale going up and down four octaves).
This example shows the scale played as triplets. Three eighth notes played in a triplet = 1 quarter note.

Railroad Ruckus uses a left hand pattern of a perfect 5th interval (C and G), a major 6th interval (C and A), a minor 7th interval (C and B♭), and returns to the major 6th interval (C and A) (for a reminder on intervals refer to lesson four on page 17). This pattern is repeated on C, F, and G.

Once you feel comfortable playing the examples to the left, try playing the same pattern of intervals in every key signature moving up chromatically in half steps. Begin with your pinkie on C and your thumb (or your second finger - whichever fingering you prefer) on G, and play the patterns. Try playing the progression of intervals as quarter notes and then try playing them as eighth notes. Once you've practiced playing with your left hand, try playing the same exercises with your right hand in every key signature. Then play with both hands at the same time.

Before I have you learn how to play "Railroad Ruckus" (Raucous is the correct spelling, but I intentionally spelled it incorrectly because I liked the "uck" sound in "ruckus"), I would like to have you learn individual sections from the piece. Learn these measures separately before playing the entire piece.

First learn measures 1 - 4. These few measures are repeated throughout the entire piece.

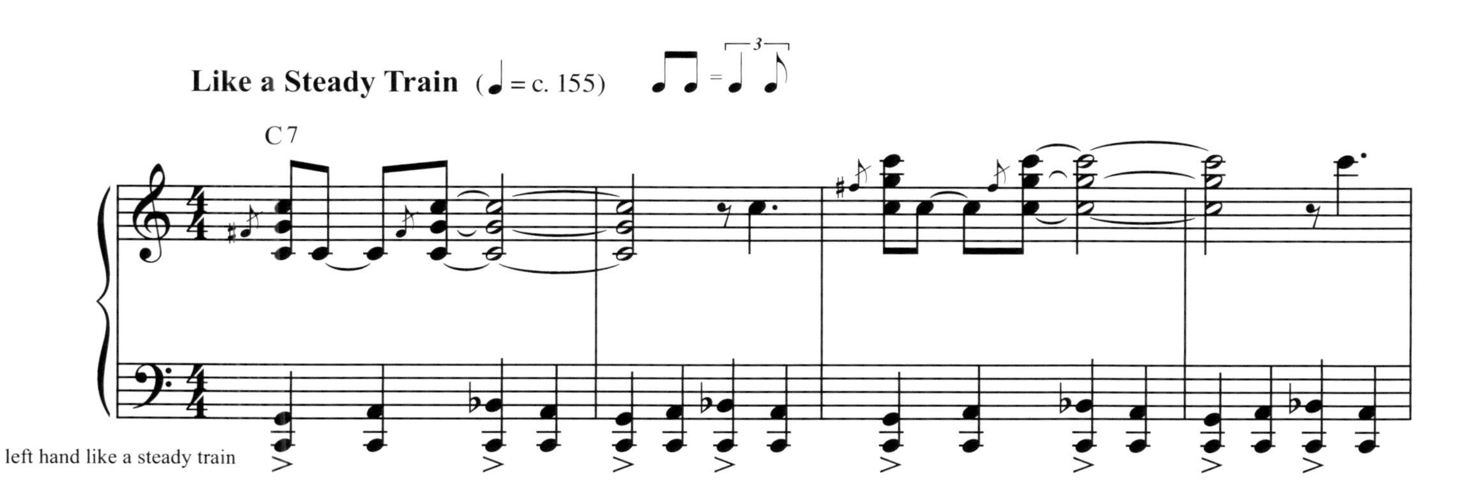

Now, try playing measures 17-20. The left hand plays the same pattern as before but starts on G and F, in addition to C. The right hand is playing a pattern of triplets.

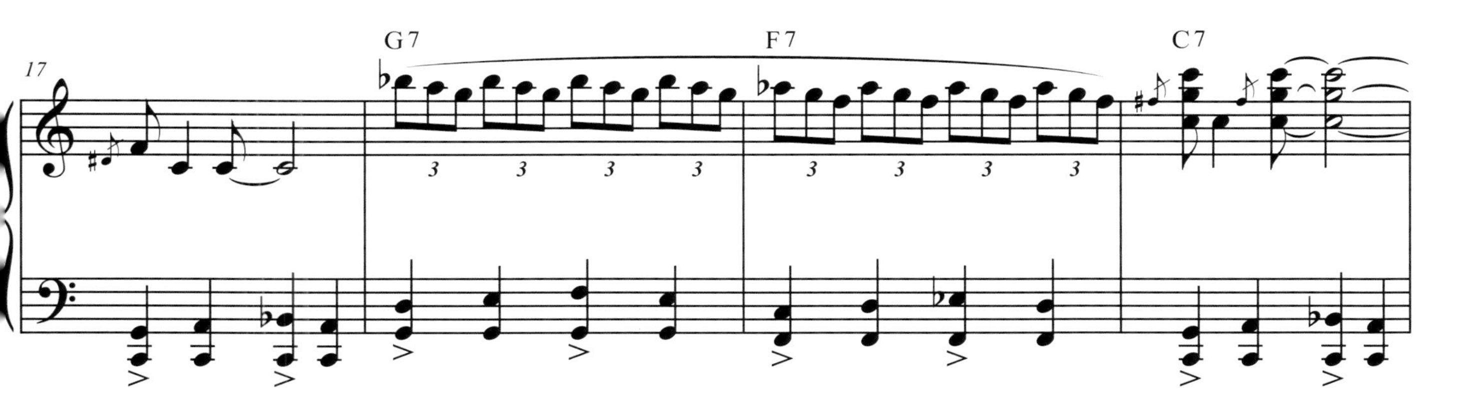

Now, try playing measures 21 - 24. The left hand plays the same pattern as before, but now the right hand is playing the C minor blues scale descending (backwards) down the scale as triplets. Once you can play these three patterns/sections, you can essentially play the entire piece as "Railroad Ruckuss" is a play on these parts.

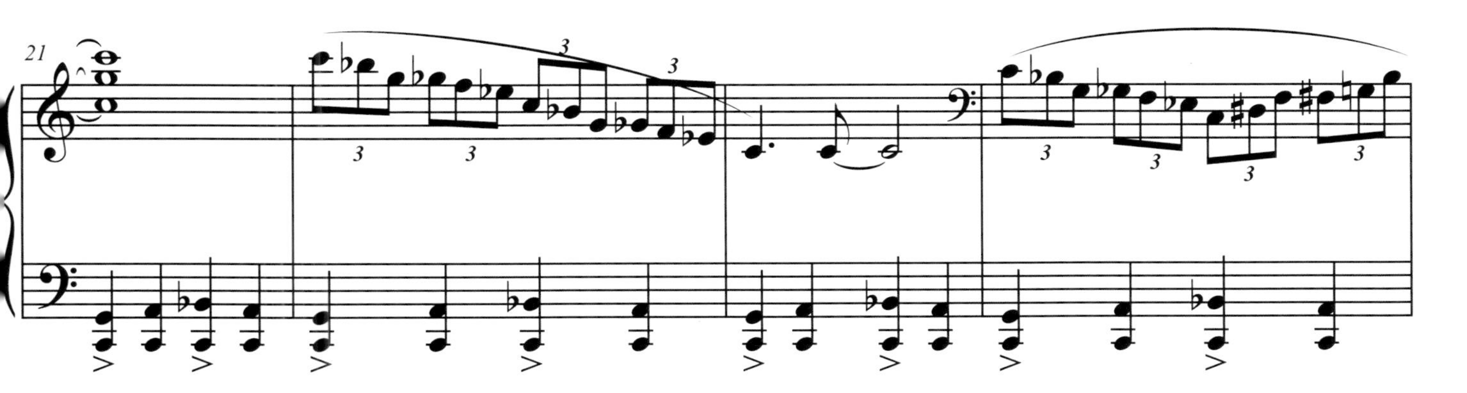

"Railroad Ruckuss" (Raucous)

By Jerald Simon

17
G7
F7
C7
21
25
F7
C7
29
G7
F7
C7
33
8va
C7
8va

C 7
F 7
C 7
G 7
F 7

(8va)
55
3
C 7
58
G 7
61
F 7
rit.
8va
8vb

The Blues Scale (played as Octaves)

First play the Blues Pentascale and then the full Blues scale

I have written this exercise out in every key signature. We are following the cycle of 4ths (i.e. C - F - B flat - E flat - etc.). First you will play the blues pentascale (the first five notes from the blues scale) and then you will play the entire blues scale. Only the thumb and pinky of each hand play the notes moving up and down according to the minor blues scale (sometimes just referred to as the blues scale).

13
16
19
22
25

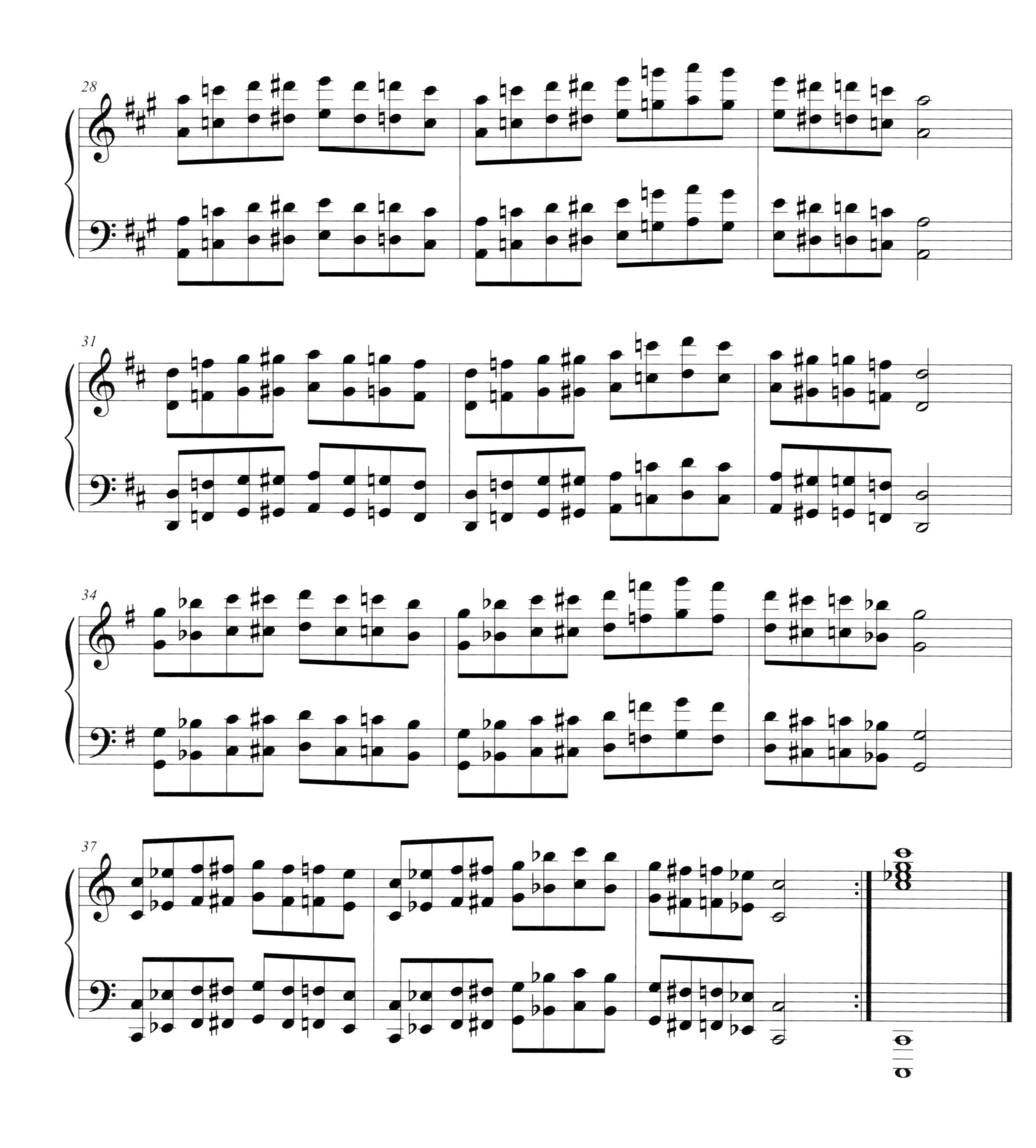
28
31
34
37

Merriam-Webster defines the 'Blues' as "low spirits; melancholy <suffering a case of the blues>; a song often of lamentation characterized by usually 12-bar phrases, 3-line stanzas in which the words of the second line usually repeat those of the first, and continual occurrence of blue notes in melody and harmony; and jazz or popular music using harmonic and phrase structures of blues."

The word "blues" refers to blue devils (downtrodden spirits). When someone sings the blues, it comes from the soul because they feel the blues and want the audience to feel what they have felt.

"The Big Bad Blues" is a little different, in that it varies from "traditional" blues songs. The song begins very slow and sad, like traditional blues songs. After the first 11 measures, however, the feel of the piece changes dramatically. The song transforms into a BIG BAD blues song because the song picks up speed. It almost sounds like something big and bad is coming after you.

The song uses a combination of several of the chords, scales, and progressions presented in this book (much of what is presented in the song has been taught in the previous lessons). "The Big Bad Blues," introduces a left hand blues pattern, crushed notes (notes played simultaneously with the following note and released immediately), and the tremolo (alternating rapidly between two notes or chords).

Below is a left hand blues pattern repeated almost throughout the entire song, "The Big Bad Blues." The pattern begins by playing a perfect 5th interval (C and G) two times followed by a major 6th interval (C and A) one time and playing the dominant note from the major scale (G) one time before repeating the pattern another time.

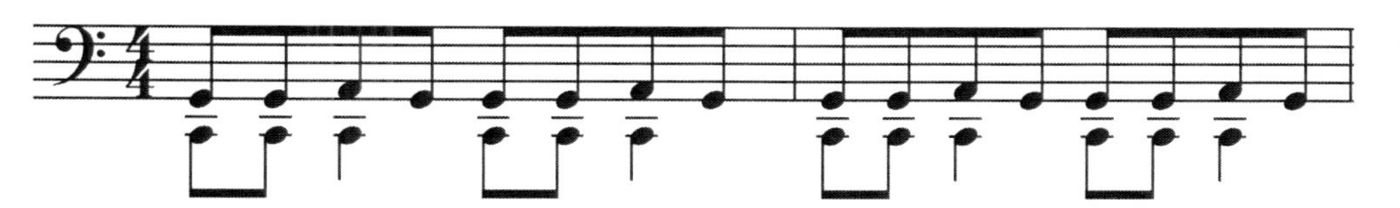

For fun, try this example in every key moving up chromatically in half steps.

The crushed note is created by playing the notes simultaneously with the following note and releasing it immediately. In jazz terminology, the crushed note is similar to a grace note (for classically trained students). Play the crushed note/grace note (D sharp) with the second finger (play C and E with the first and third fingers), or play D sharp with the third finger (that way you're sliding your third finger down from D sharp to E natural).

Although used in previous songs in this book, the 'tremolo' has not yet been described in the previous lessons. Simply put, the tremolo is created by alternating rapidly between two notes or chords. This is what it looks like in music.

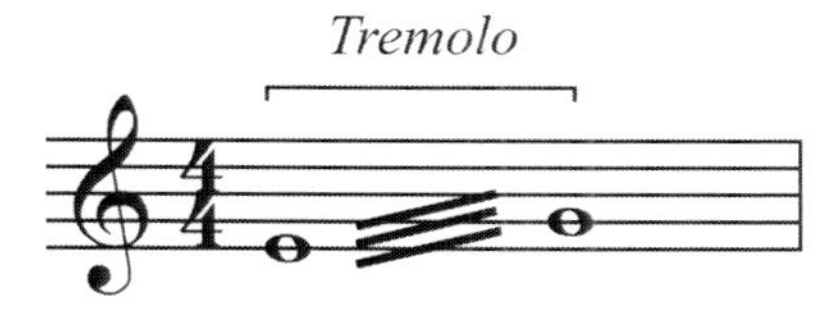

Quickly alternate between E and G as if you were rocking back and forth from one note to the other. This can be thought of as being something like a trill for classically trained students. Instead of thinking of two whole notes imagine playing the same notes as 16th and 32nd notes - quickly playing one and then the other.

The Big Bad Blues

By Jerald Simon

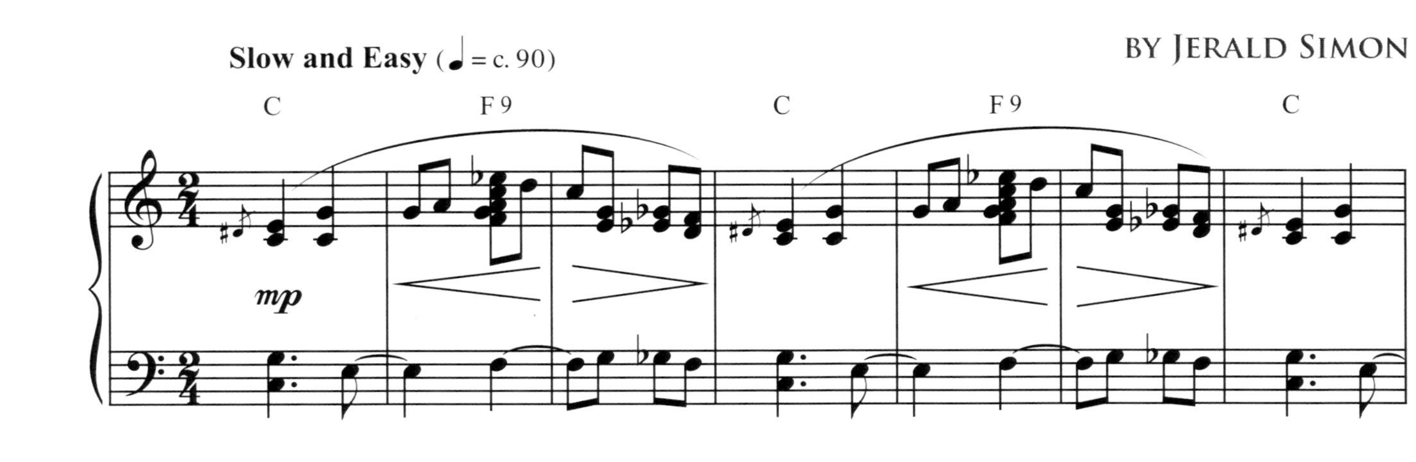

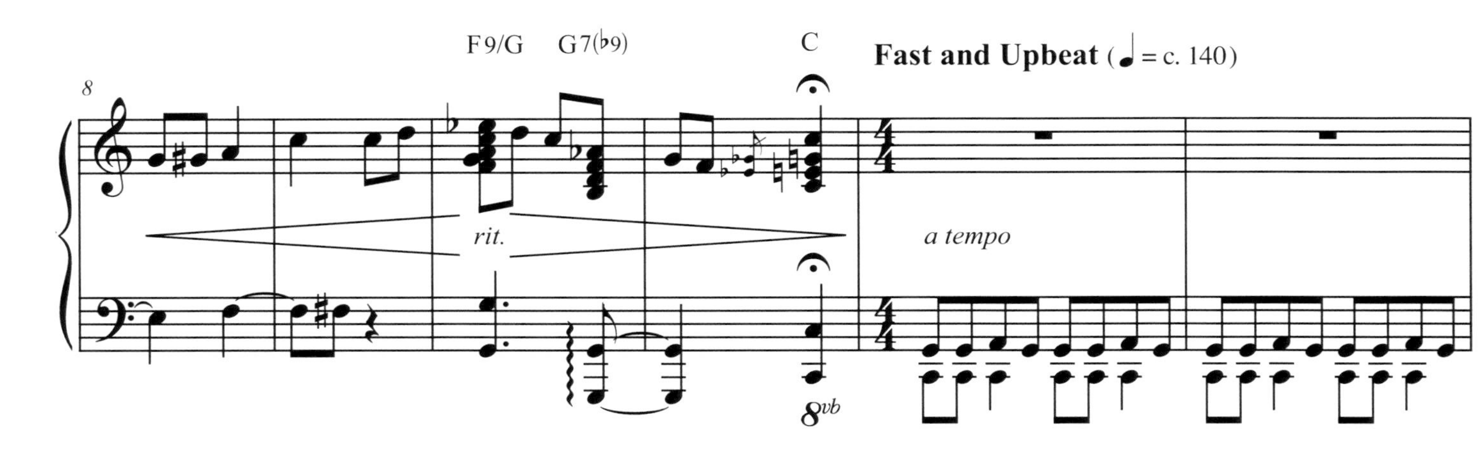

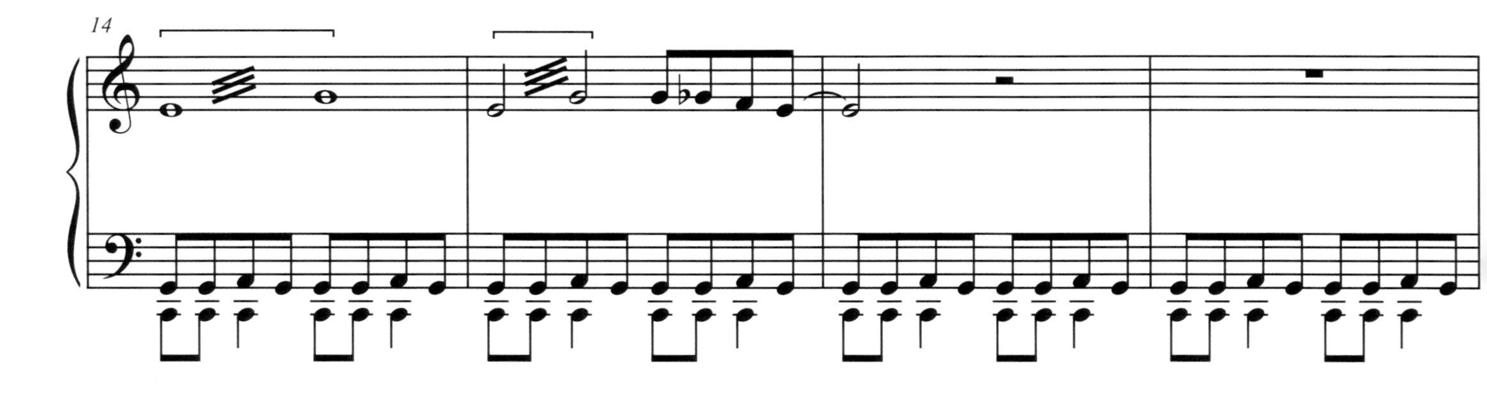

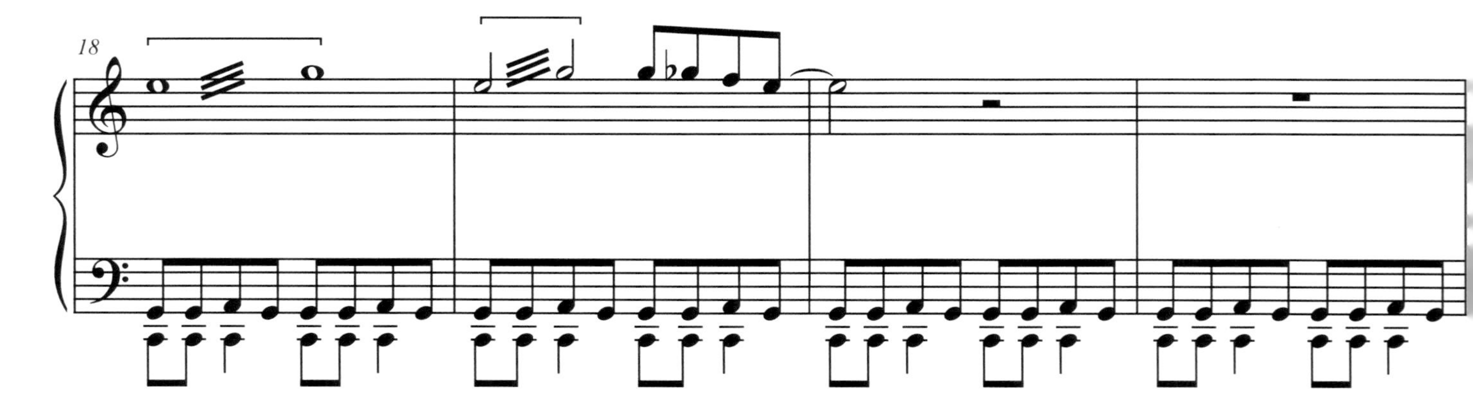

22
F
27
C
32
Em7/G
E♭m7/G♭
Dm7/F
C
37
F9/C
C
41
F9/C

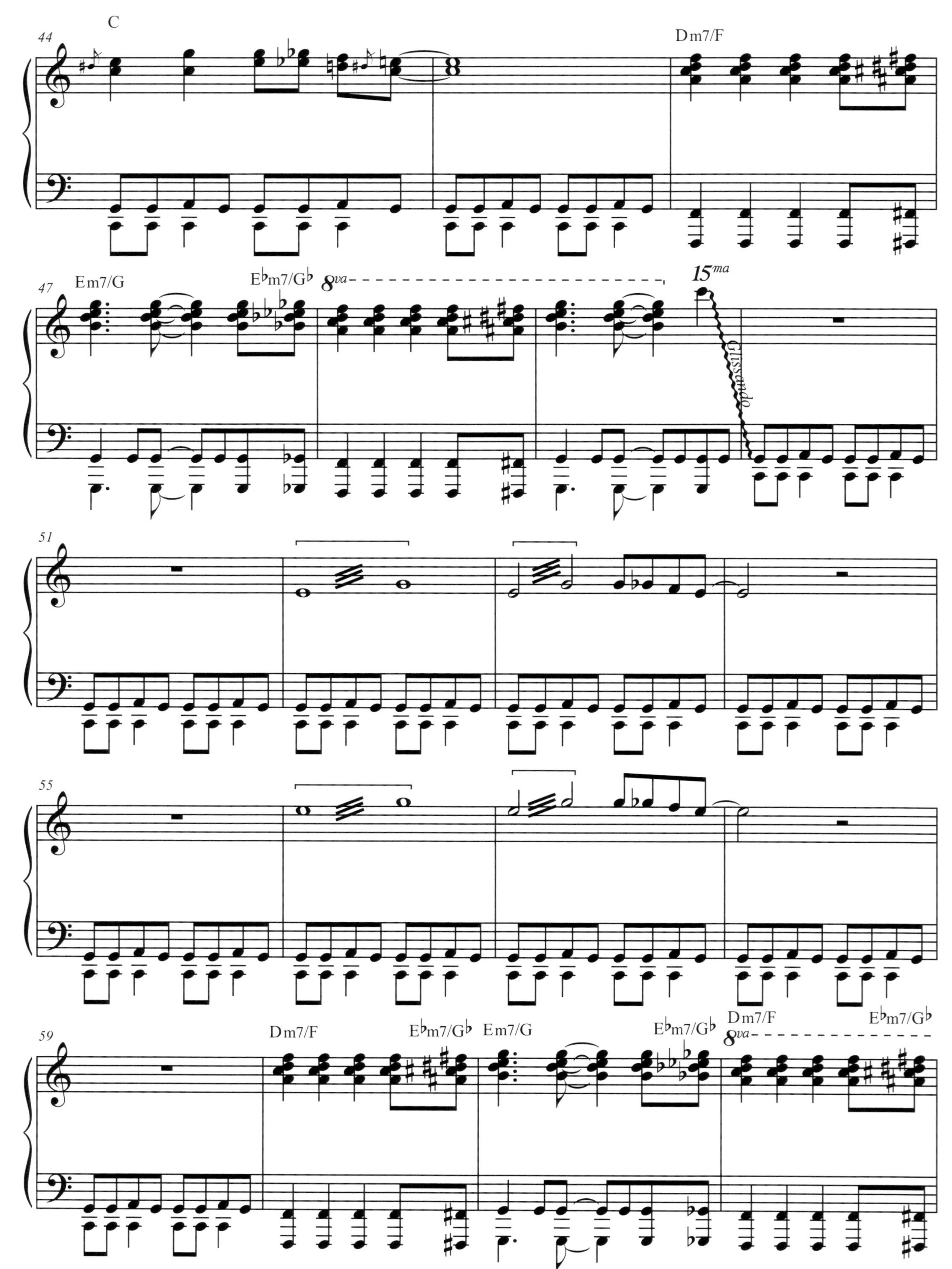
44
C
Dm7/F
47
Em7/G
E♭m7/G♭
8va
15ma
Glissando
51
55
59
Dm7/F
E♭m7/G♭
Em7/G
E♭m7/G♭
Dm7/F
8va
E♭m7/G♭

Em7/G
(8va)
15ma
C
Glissando
F9/C
C
Dm7/F
E♭m7/G♭
Em7/G
E♭m7/G♭
8va
15ma
Glissando
rit.

Slow and Easy (♩ = c. 90)
83
mp
8va
90
(8va)
rit.
8vb

THE C BLUES SCALE PLAYED AS TRIPLETS

2 with the left hand against 3 with the right hand

1M00001064

Ricochet

In this jazz piece, I tried to combine many of the elements we have worked on so far in this book. We follow a ii7 - V7 - I7 chord progression and for much of the piece, the left hand follows a whole half half left hand walking bass pattern. With the right hand, I have tried to incorporate sixth and seventh chords with triplets moving up and down using notes from the chords and various major and minor scales as well. You may also notice several crushed notes that look like grace notes. These little notes are often played together with the notes that follow them and then quickly released.

In this jazz piece, notice how the ascending and descending triplets are moving up and down using the notes from the chords in each measure and sometimes using the C Major Blues Scale as well.

BY JERALD SIMON

11
Dm7
mf
G7
13
Cmaj7
Dm7
16
G7
Cmaj7
19
Dm7
G7
Cmaj7
23
Dm7
G7
Cmaj7
Dm7
G7
Cmaj7(add 9)
mp

A 50s Rock Boogie Woogie

by Jerald Simon

MM000010

C7
C7
C7
8va
F7
C7
11
13
15
17
19

21
G 7
F 7
23
C 7
25
C 7
8vb
27
8va
15ma
8vb
29
8va

Below, I have included a fun variation you can try as well. Once you feel comfortable and confident playing this simple variation in the key of C, try to play it in all key signatures. You can even take this simple example and include it in the jazz piece above. Try to play this example in place of measures 1 and 2, and then play the rest of the piece as normal. You could play this example at the end of the piece in measures 31 and 32 as well. You can even insert this little example anywhere in the piece where you have a C7 chord and would like to vary what the left hand is doing throughout the exercise. Try it and have fun playing this jazz piece.

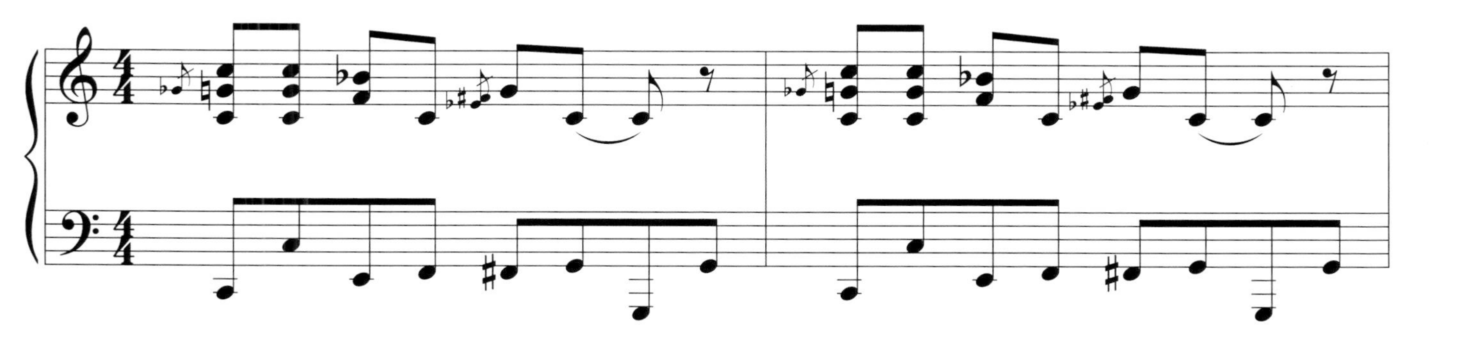

After playing this in the key of C Major, try to play this jazz exercise in every key signature on the piano moving up in half steps - C, C♯, D, E♭, E, F, F♯, G, A♭, A, B♭, and B.

Hill Billy Boogie

Here is a simple 1950s rock piece I composed using the example from above. Some of it will sound similar to the exercise I included on the previous page, and some of it will be different. I start out with a simple walking bass left hand pattern, and then we start playing the octave left hand walking bass pattern. Notice how I use the G Major blues scale in measure 9.

12
15
18
21

1950s Rock Improv Lesson

In this exercise, I demonstrate some patterns we have learned from previous lessons, and also show a series of chords. In measure two, the right hand plays a C6 chord in second inversion, followed by a Cdim 7 chord in second inversion, then an F6 chord in root position, and end with a C6 chord in first inversion. In measure six, we follow the same pattern of chords, but we start with the F6 chord. After playing 12 measures, I allow you to improvise and create your own right hand. Make it up as you go!

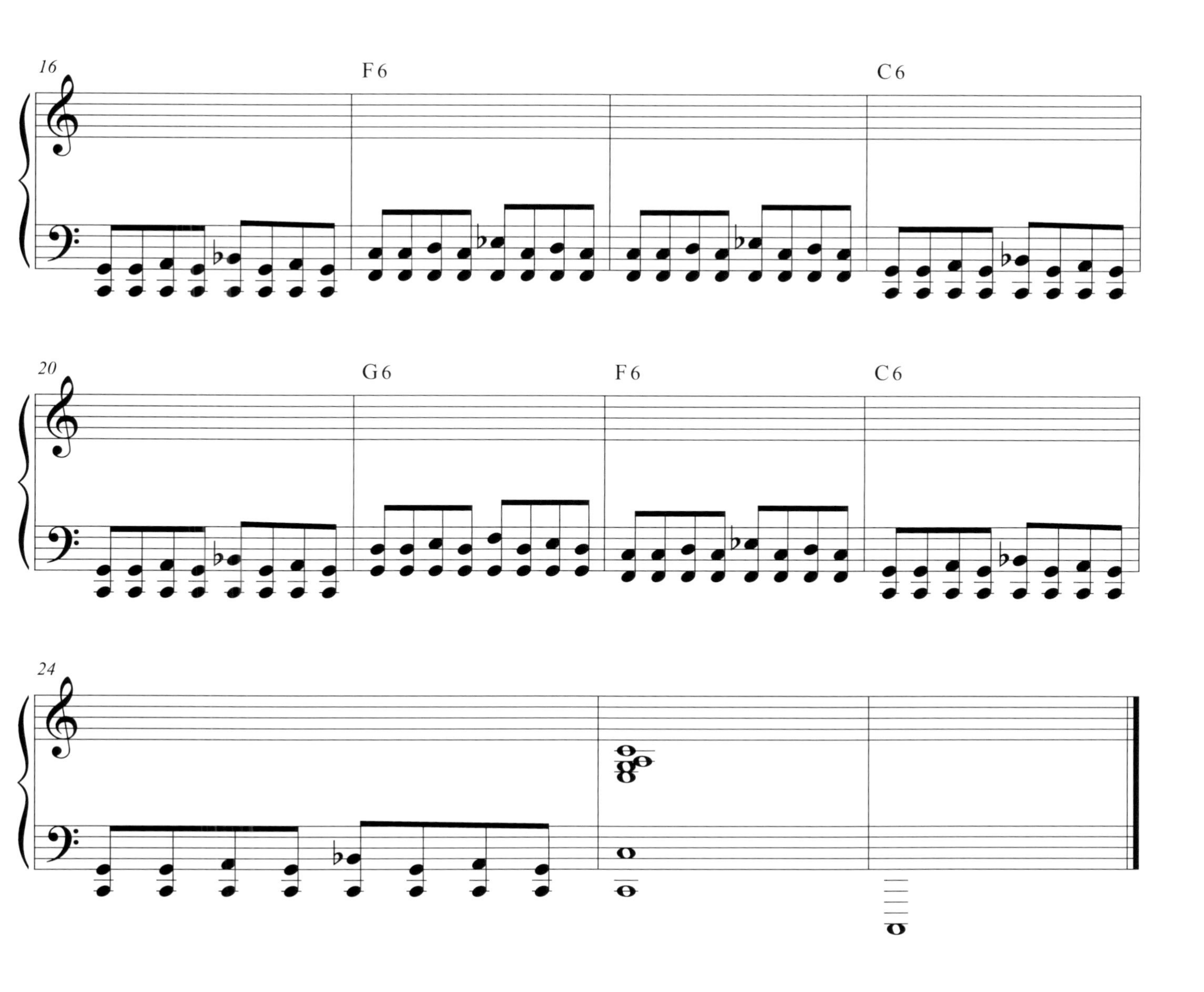

After playing this jazz exercise in the key of C Major, try to play it in every key signature on the piano moving up in half steps - C, C♯, D, E♭, E, F, F♯, G, A♭, A, B♭, and B.

Barrel House Blues Improv Lesson

In this exercise, I have included some of what you learned in the previous exercise and added to it. The left hand is playing a simple pattern created from a perfect 5th interval (i.e. C and G), a major 6th interval (i.e. C and A), a minor 7th interval (i.e. C and B flat), and ending with a major 6th interval (i.e. C and A). We have learned this before earlier in the book. Now we are adding four note chords with the right hand. After playing 12 measures, I allow you to improvise and create your own right hand. Make it up as you go! For fun, try to play this exercise in all key signatures.

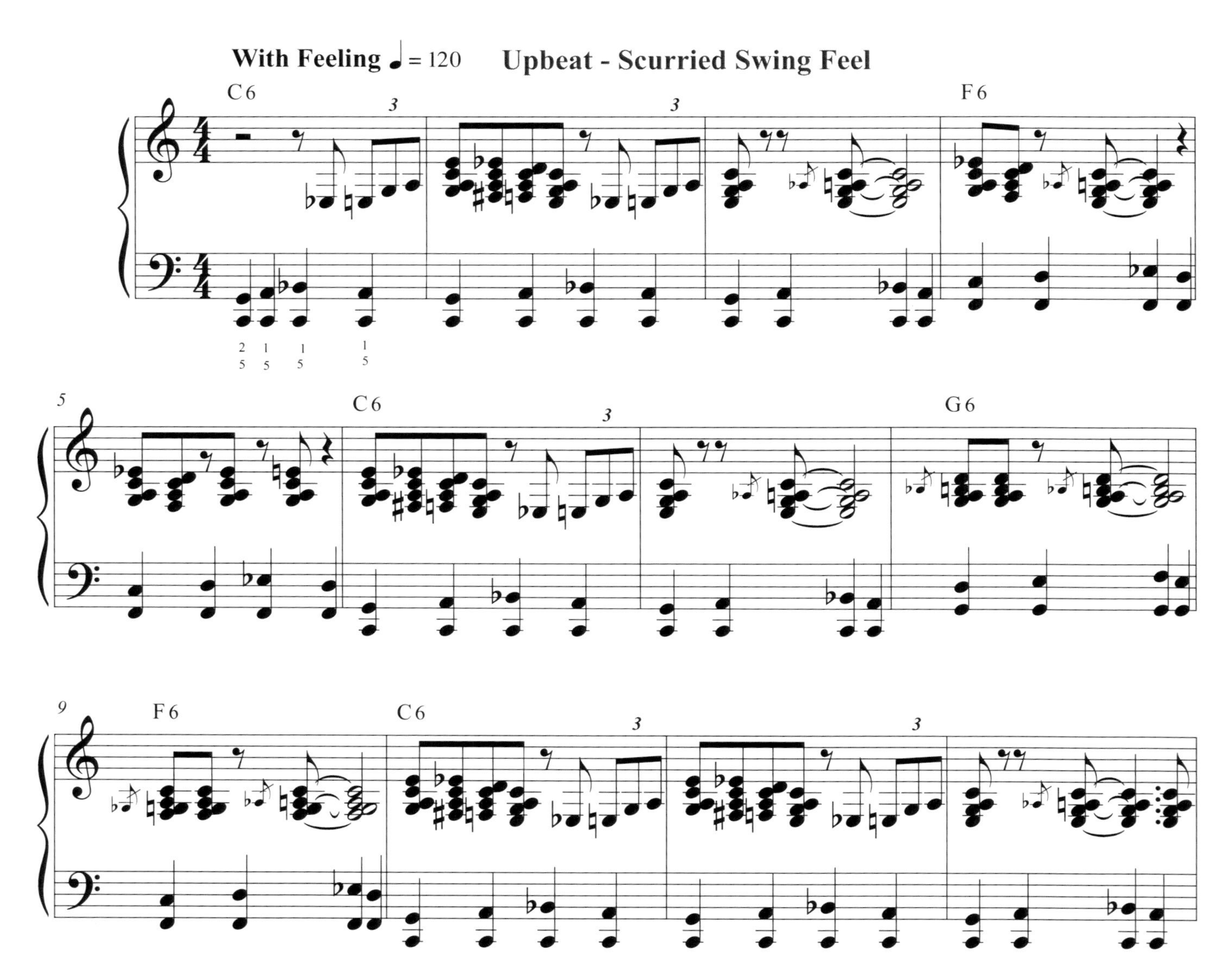

16
F 6
C 6
20
G 6
F 6
C 6
24
28
F 6
C 6
32
G 6
F 6
C 6

Bottom of the Barrel House Blues

By Jerald Simon

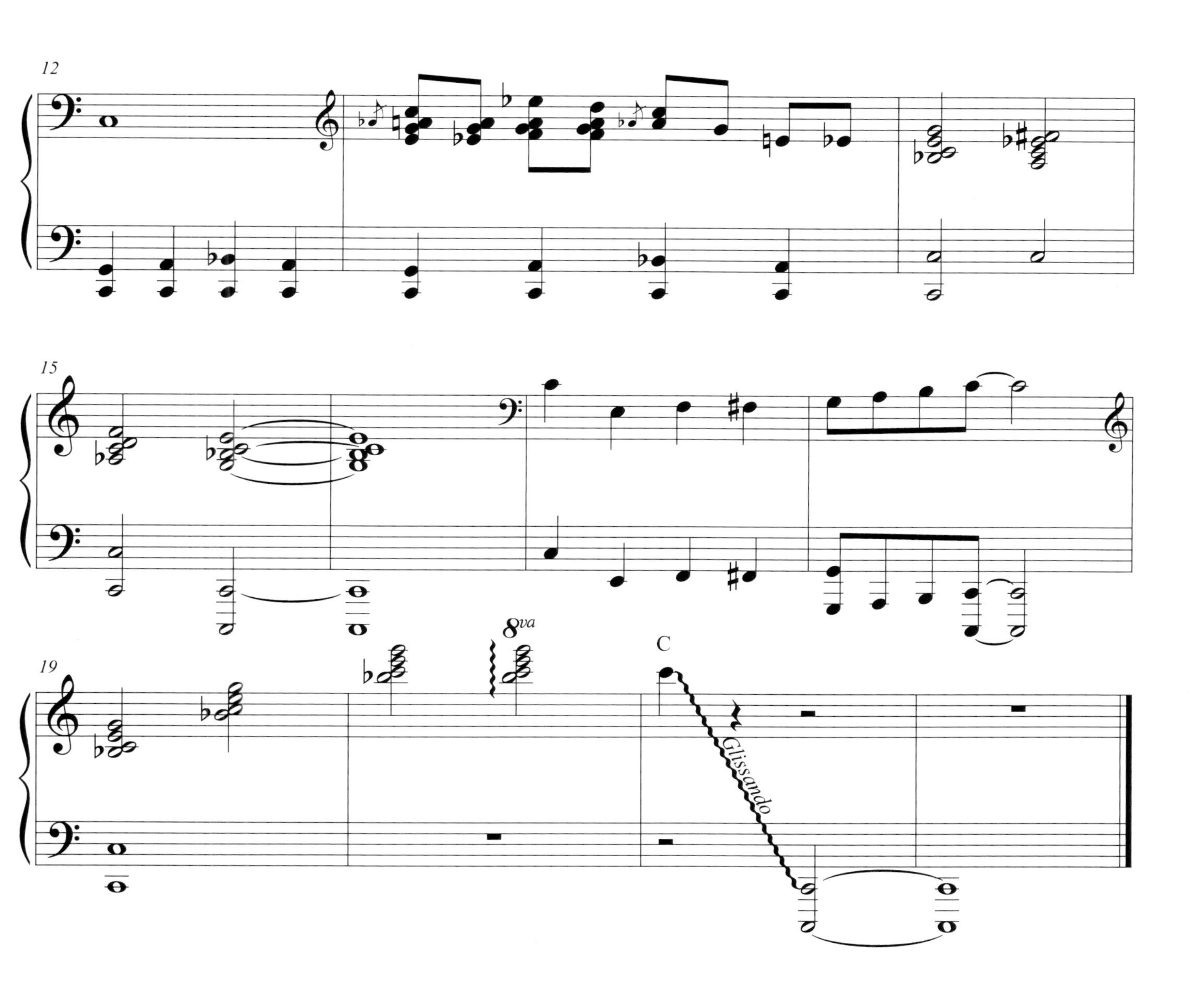
12
15
19
8va
C
Glissando

This is the left hand pattern used in "Playin' Around (Just Having Fun)." When C and G are played together, it is called a perfect 5th interval. When C and A are played together, it is called a major 6th interval.

This left hand pattern is called a *barrelhouse blues* pattern.

Playin' Around primarily uses 6th and 7th chords. Measure 1 shows the C major 6th chord in root position (meaning the C note is on bottom). Measures 2 through four show the C minor 6th chord in root position (shown in measure 2), first inversion (shown in measure 3), and second inversion (shown in measure 4).

This is the C minor 6th chord using the second inversion played as a broken chord (not together). This pattern is used throughout Playin' Around.

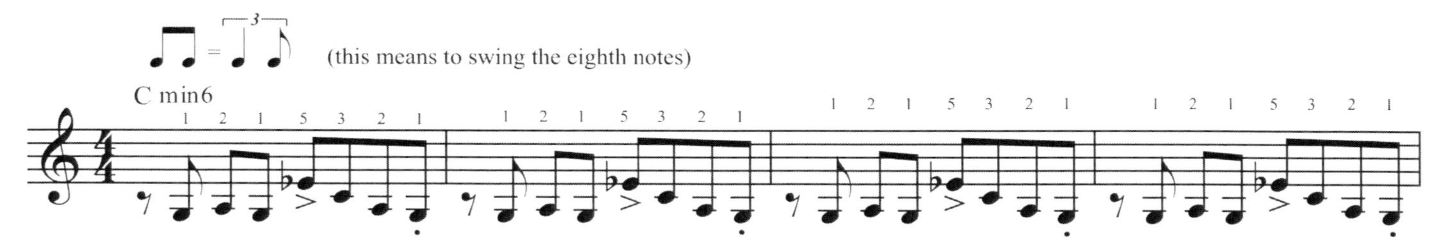

Measure 1 shows the C major 6th chord followed by a C diminished 7th*, F major 6th, and C minor 6th chord (all shown in root position). Once these have been played, try playing each chord with every inversion (root, 1st, 2nd, & 3rd).

* The C diminished 7th chord is actually spelled C E♭ G B♭♭ - each being stacked on top of the other where the 7th interval (in this case B) is a double flat which creates the diminished 7th interval. I notated it with an A instead of B♭♭(which is the same note) because I wanted to simplify it for the student. It actually becomes a different chord when notated like this, but for this example we will keep it simple and refer to it as a C diminished 7th chord.

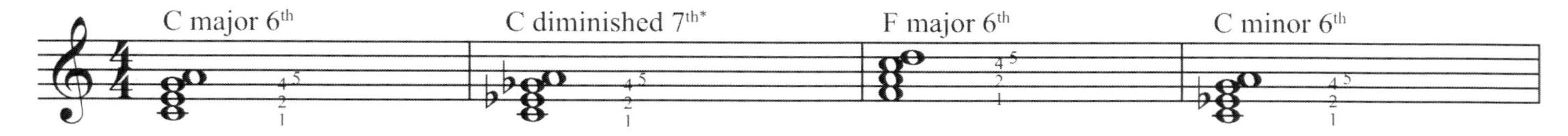

Measure 1 begins with an 8th rest followed by a C major 6th chord (2nd inversion) then a C diminished 7th chord (2nd inversion)*, which is followed by an F major 6th chord (root position) and ends with a C major 6th chord (1st inv.).

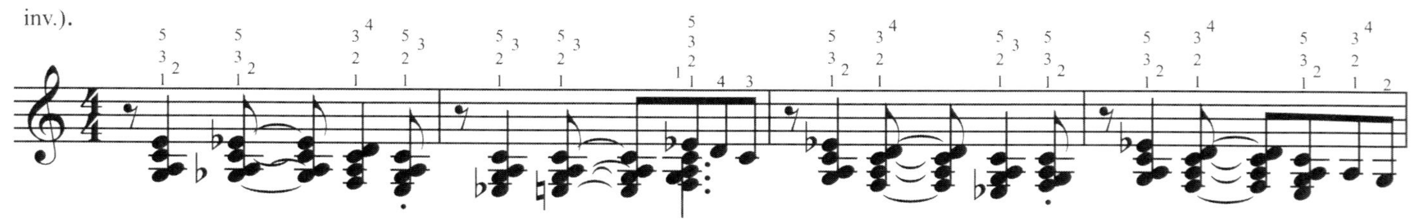

Before I have you learn how to play "Playin' Around" (Just Having Fun), I would like to have you learn individual sections from the piece. Learn these measures separately before playing the entire piece.

First learn measures 1 - 4. These few measures are repeated throughout the entire piece.

Now, try playing measures 9-12. The left hand plays the same pattern as before but starts on F starting in measure 11. The right hand is playing sixth chords in various inversions (I explained this on the bottom of the previous page.

Now, try playing measures 25 - 28. After playing these three lines, you have essentially played the entire piece.

Playin' Around (Just having FUN!)

17
F 9
C 6
21
G
F 6
C 6
C 6
25
C 6
F 9
29
C 6
Gsus2
33
F 9
C 6
C min6

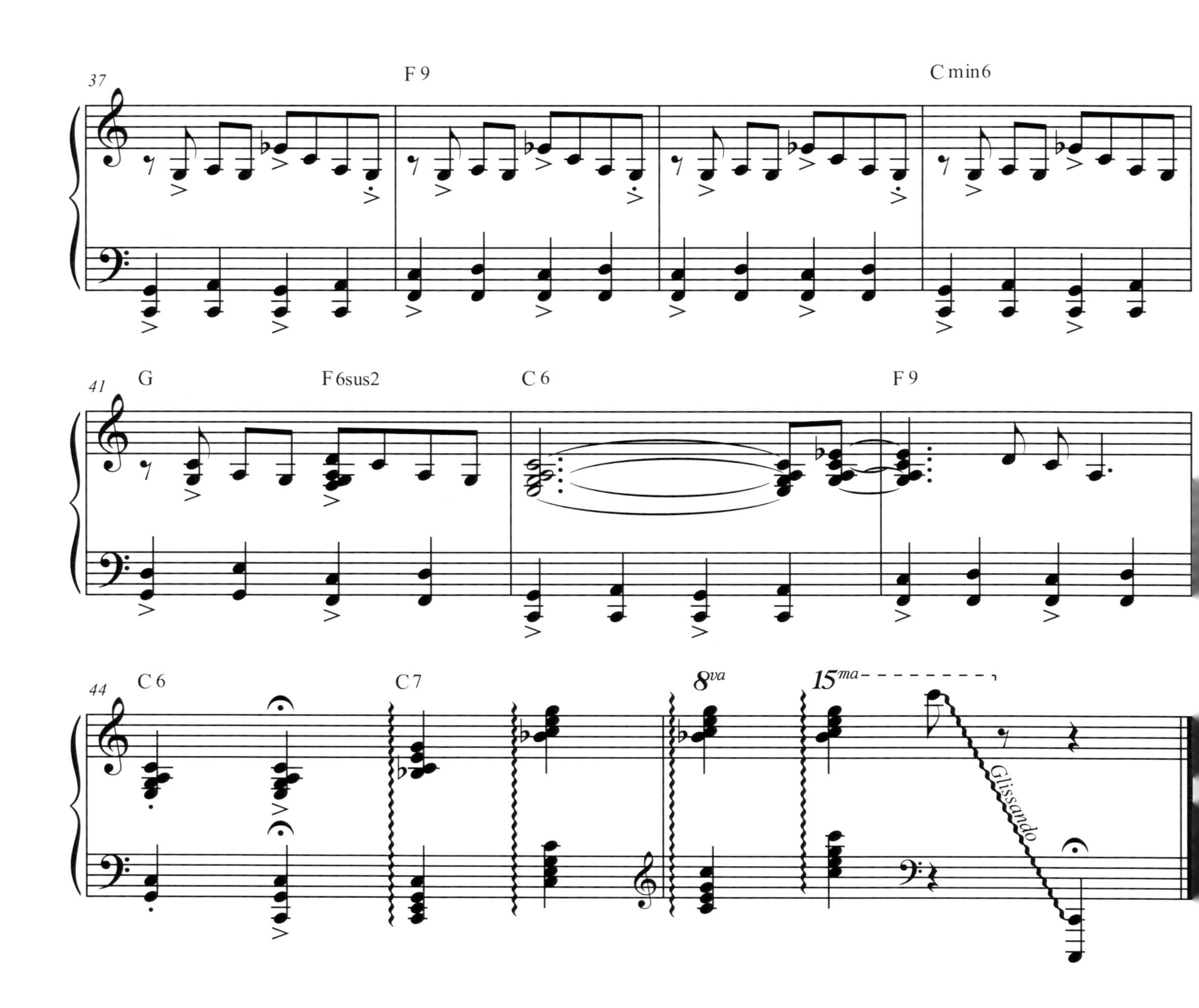
37
F 9
C min6
41
G
F 6sus2
C 6
F 9
44
C 6
C 7
8va
15ma
Glissando

Blues Boogie Woogie Improv Lesson

In this exercise, the left hand is playing a simple pattern created from a perfect 5th interval (i.e. C and G), a major 6th interval (i.e. C and A), a minor 7th interval (i.e. C and B flat), and ending with a major 6th interval (i.e. C and A). We are playing two of each at a slow to medium speed with a bluesy feeling. The right hand is improvising using the notes from the C blues scale (also referred to as the C minor blues scale). After playing 24 measures, I allow you to improvise and create your own right hand. Make it up as you go!

Cm7
Cm7
Now you can improvise and create your own right hand pattern. Follow what I did in the previous measures.

M00001064

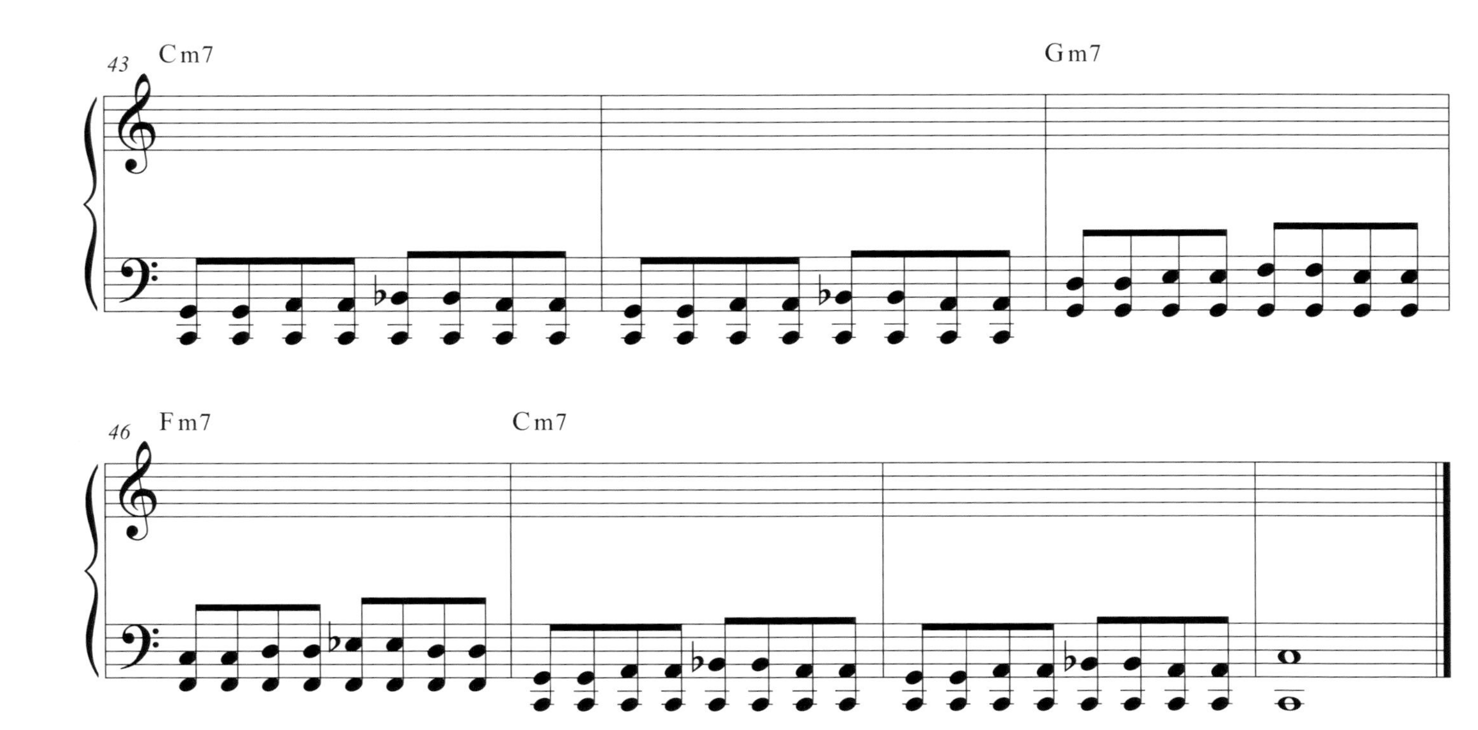

After playing this jazz exercise in the key of C Major, try to play it in every key signature on the piano moving up in half steps - C, C♯, D, E♭, E, F, F♯, G, A♭, A, B♭, and B.

On the next page, we will introduce "The Jazz Song" which is a wild and upbeat fun ride. This jazz piece starts on page 214 and continues until 221. At every concert or piano recital my piano students do, at least one or two piano students want to perform "The Jazz Song" or my piece, "Triumphant." Those two pieces are piano recital favorites every time. It seems a little intimidating, but it is ALL about patterns. Once you know the theory behind the patterns, the song is very easy. First, look at the C major blues scale at the top of the next page. "The Jazz Song" has several variations of this scale played with the right hand.

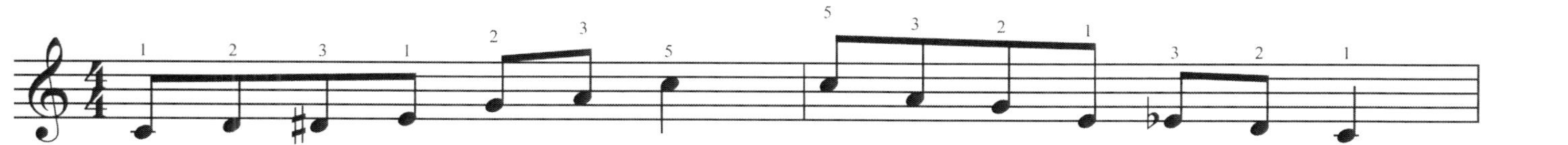

An easy way to think of this scale (and to remember it) is to break it down into clumps (notes played together at the same time that will create your pattern for you). Play the following notes:

This is the pattern: play any three notes (a whole step between the first two notes and a half step between the second and third notes) followed by the Major 6th chord (of the first note you played from your three notes) in first inversion. That's it! Now for fun, try it in all keys. Below is the variation I created from the major blues scale for the right hand of "The Jazz Song." After you play it, try creating your own variation.

Now let's look at the left hand of "The Jazz Song." The left hand is a simple walking bass pattern. It begins on the tonic (or 1st interval) then plays a major 3rd, a perfect 5th, a major 6th, a minor 7th interval and comes back down. Play the walking bass pattern below:

To commit this pattern to memory, simply play a sixth chord (major sixth) with your left hand (in this case it's a C 6th) and then play the note that is half a step above the sixth interval (or in other words, the note that is half a step above the top note of the chord you just played).

Now try playing the same walking bass as octaves (you'll play the same note twice - one after the other).

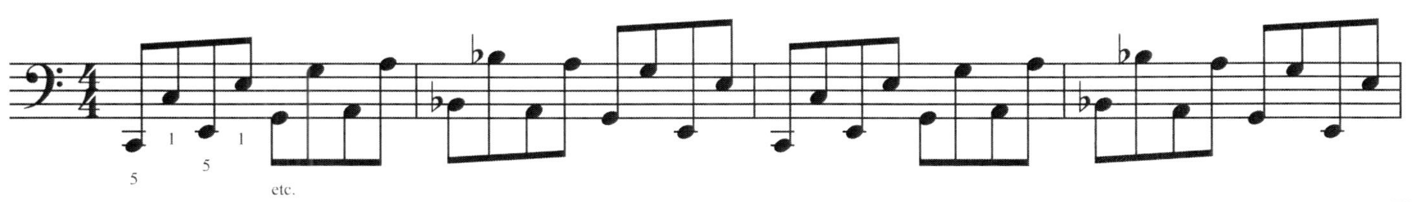

THE JAZZ SONG

BY JERALD SIMON

Wild and Upbeat (♩ = c. 120 - 160) I play it 'Wild and Upbeat', but you may swing it if you prefer

I don't swing this when I play it!

Pedal ad-lib throughout the song

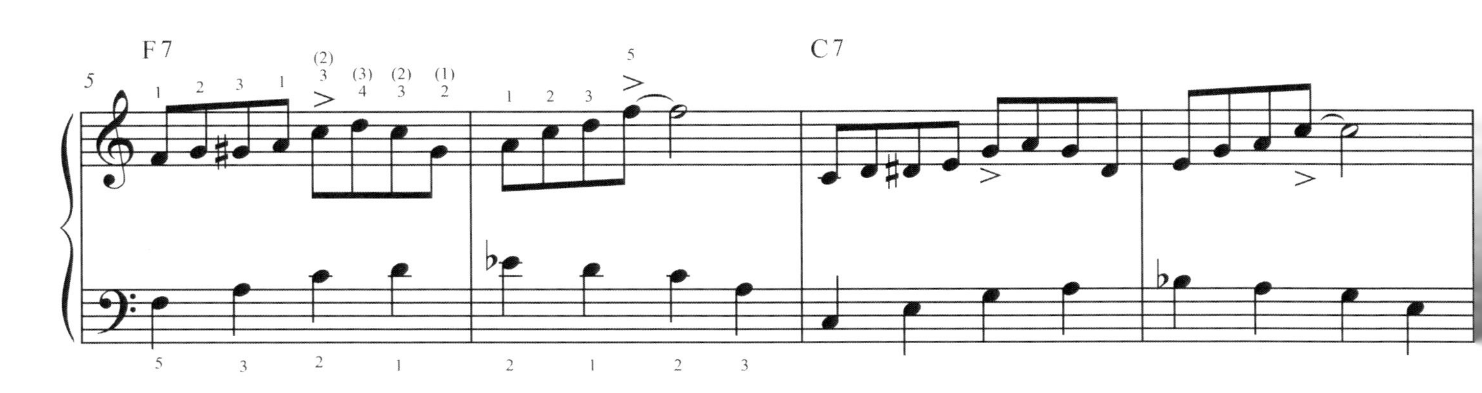

F
A min7/C
E min7/G
D min7/F
Section B
A min7/C
C 7
F 7

C 7
G 7
F 7
C 7
Section C
C 7
F 9
A m7(♭5)/C

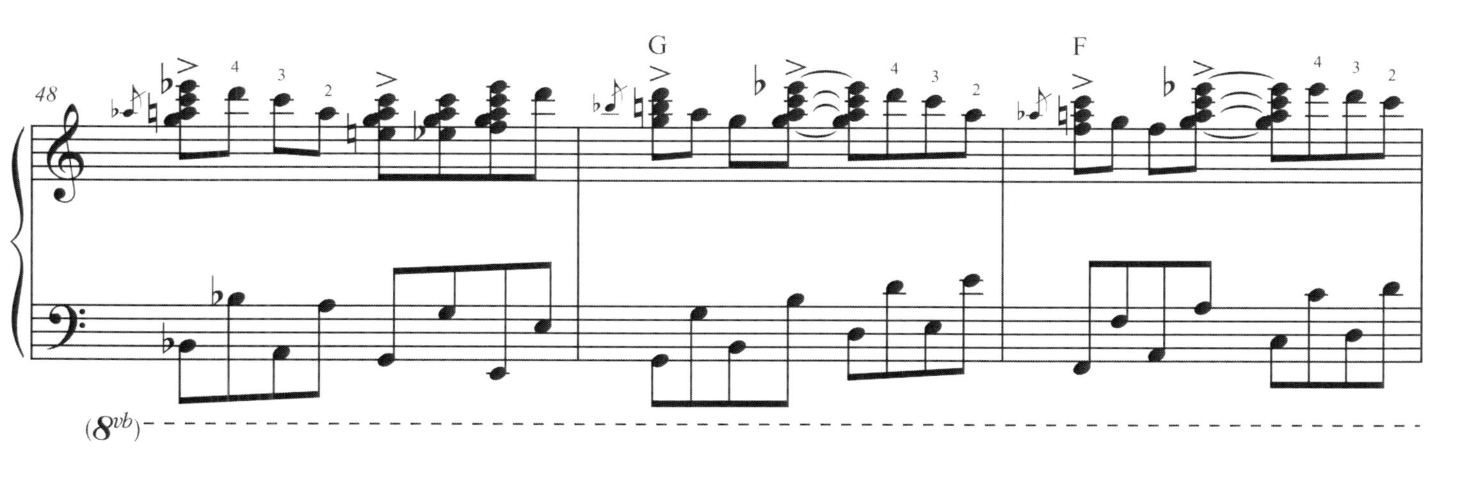
48
G
F
(8vb)

Section D

51
Am7/C
15ma
Glissando
(8vb)

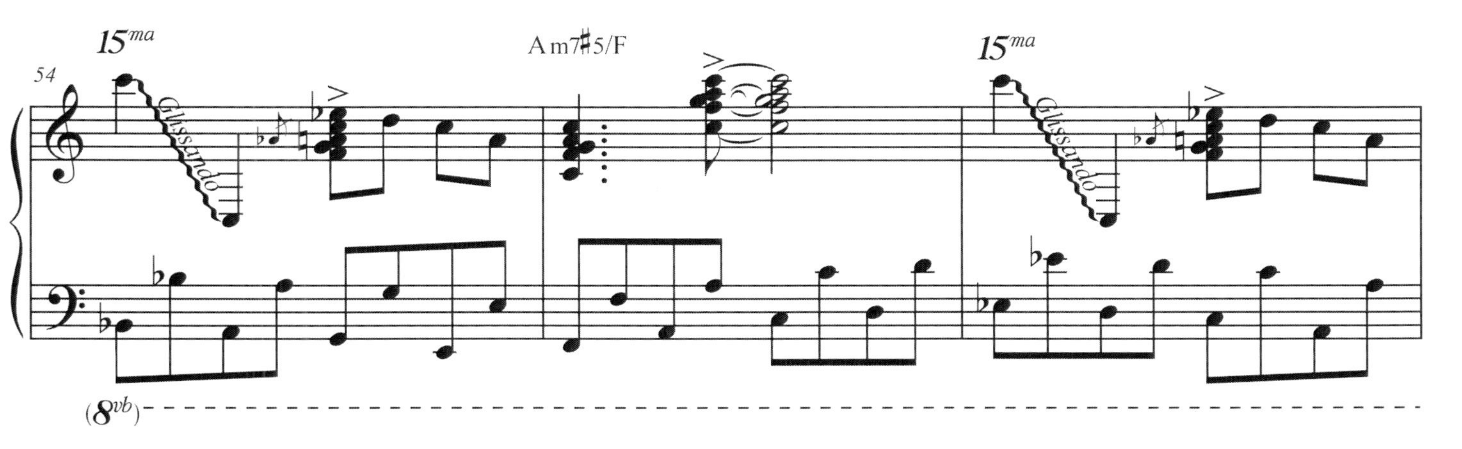
54
15ma
Glissando
Am7♯5/F
15ma
Glissando
(8vb)

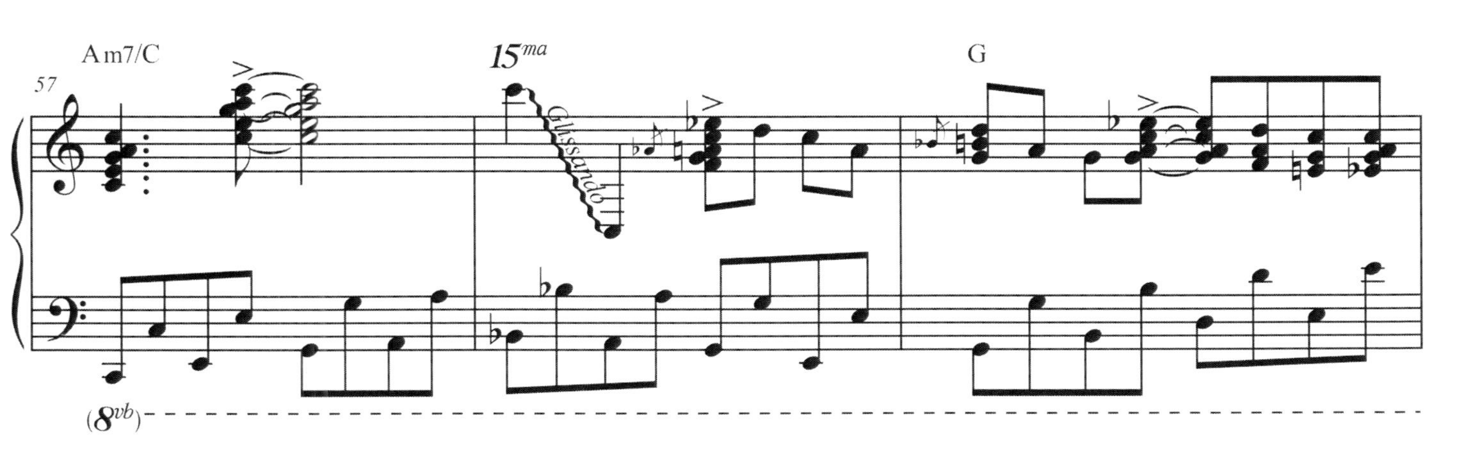
57
Am7/C
15ma
Glissando
G
(8vb)

60
F
C
8va
(8vb)
63
C
F
8vb
66
C
(8vb)
69
G
F
Am7/C
Section E
8vb

15ma
Glissando
Am7/C
15ma
Glissando
(8vb)
Am7♯5/F
ff
15ma
Glissando
Am7/C
(8vb)

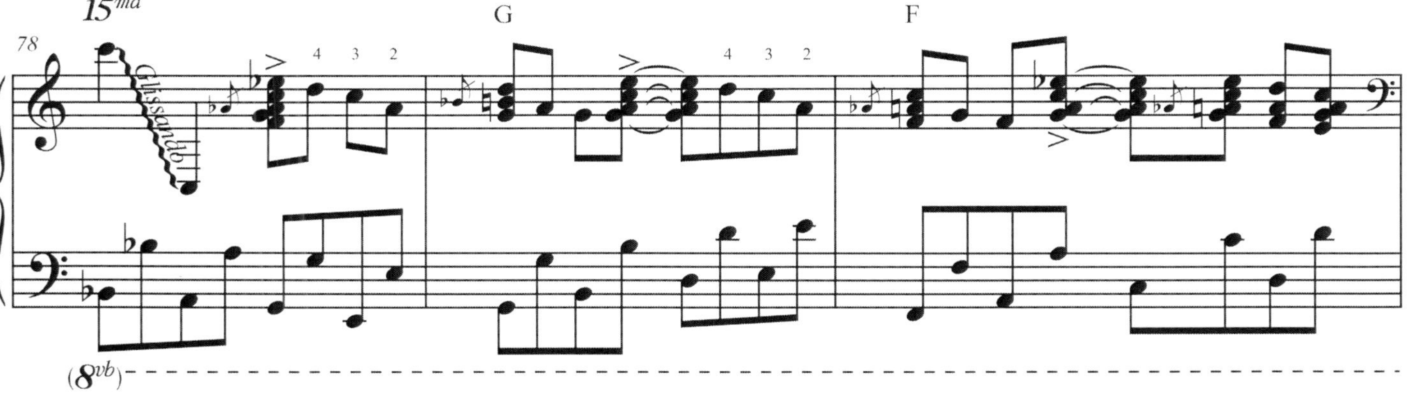
15ma
Glissando
G
F
(8vb)

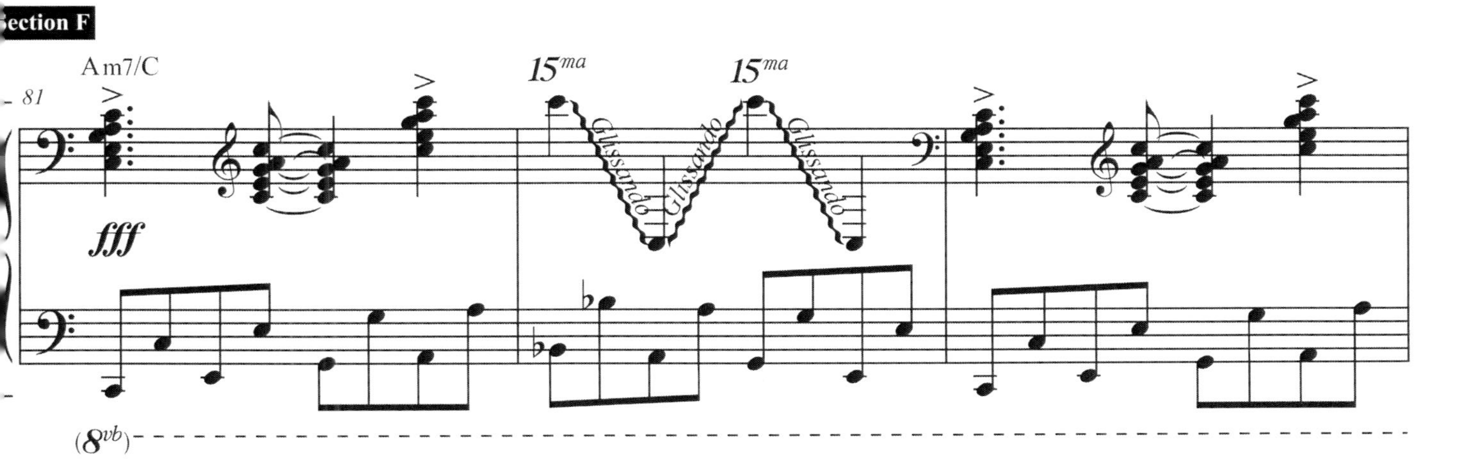
Section F
Am7/C
fff
15ma
Glissando
15ma
Glissando
Glissando
(8vb)

15ma
Glissando
Am7♯5/F
Am7/C
G
F
C
rit.
8vb

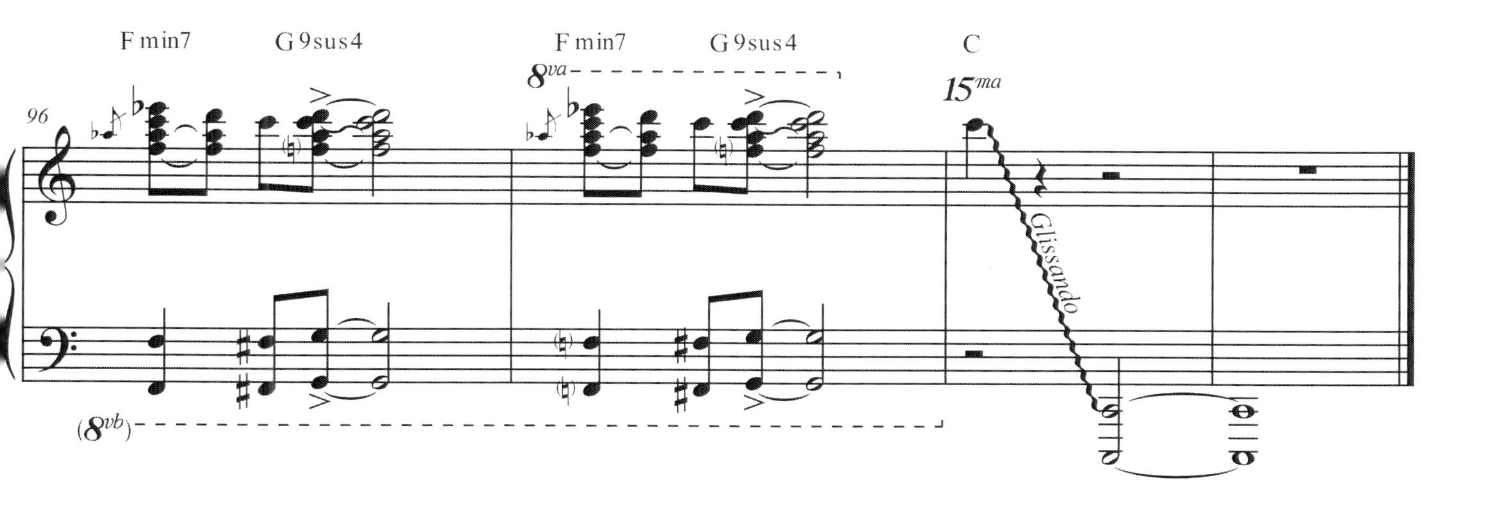

As a review, brush up on the explanations that were presented on learning the modes back on pages 100 - 106. On the next few pages, we are going to practice improvising with the modes. We will start by improvising with the Dorian mode in the right hand while the left hand plays the minor 7th chord.

In the next exercise, you will note that I am playing random minor 7th chords with the left hand while the right hand improvises over the Dorian mode that corresponds with that minor 7th chords. As an example, if I am playing a D minor 7th chord with my left hand, then I would improvise with the notes from the D Dorian mode (D - D using the notes from the C major scale). To get you started, we will only use the notes from the minor pentascale (i.e. D E F G A), which happens to be the first five notes of the D Dorian mode.

On the next page, I will only use the first three notes from each Dorian mode as a way to ease you into using the Dorian mode.

Modal Jazz Improvisation for the Right Hand

The right hand is only improvising on the minor pentascale (the first five notes of the Dorian mode).

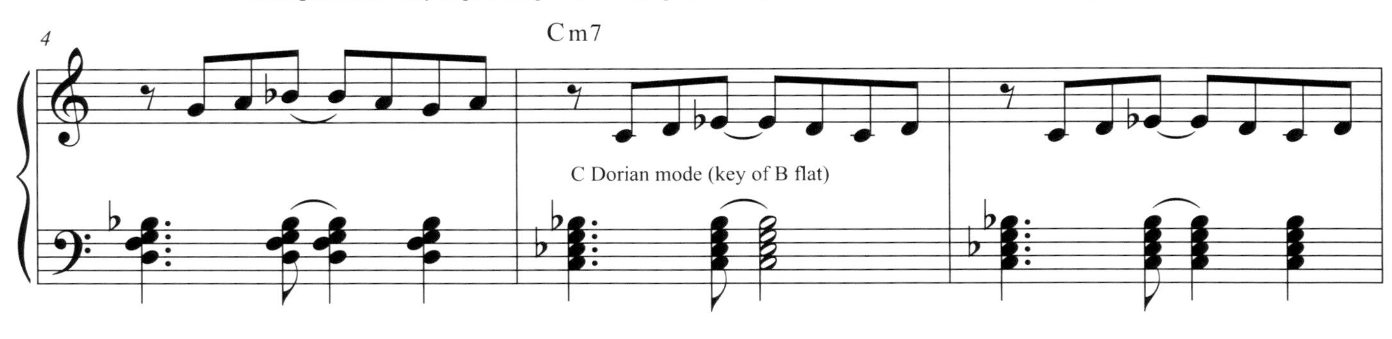

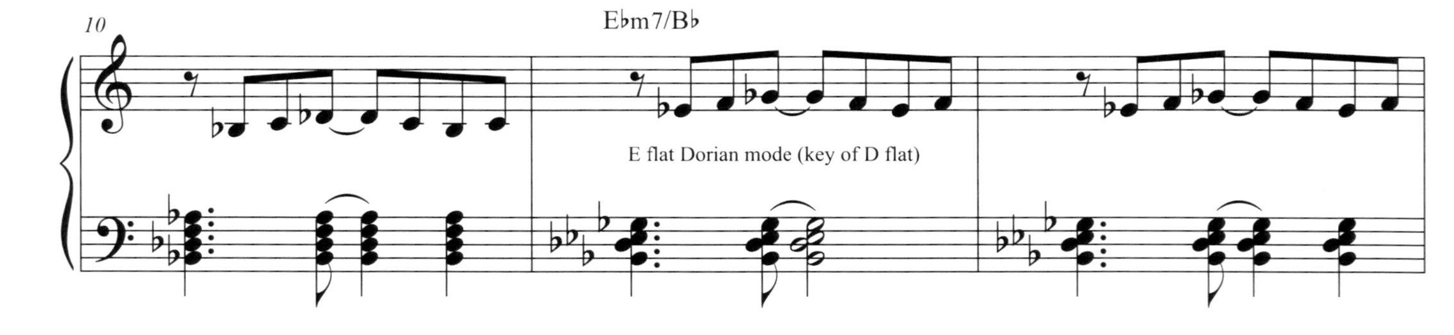

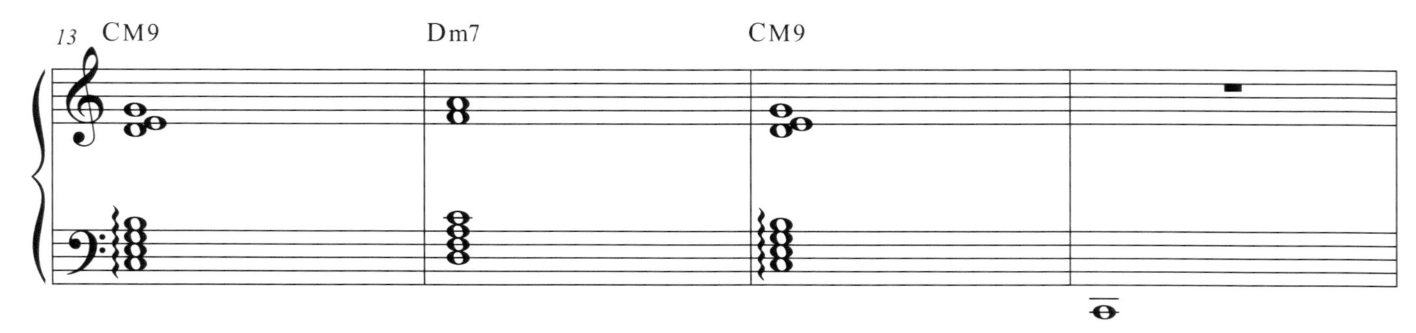

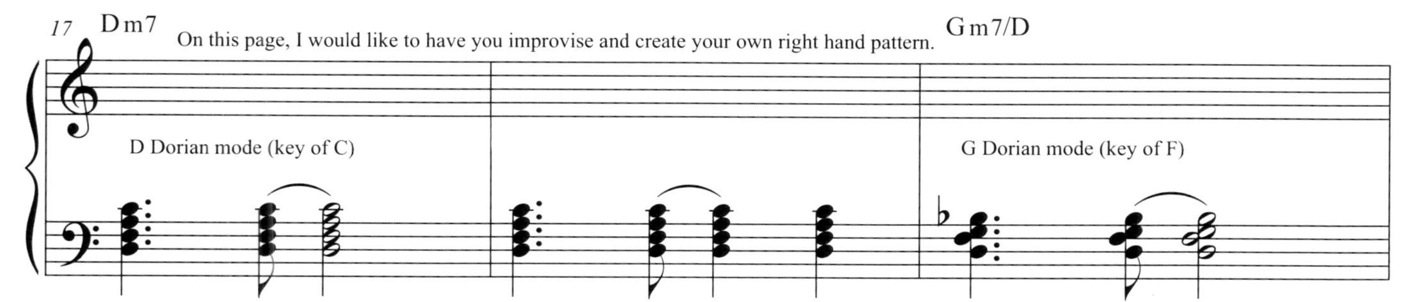

As I did on the previous page, you can use the notes from the minor pentascale (the first five notes of the Dorian mode), to start improvising.
If you feel more confident, try to improvise using all of the notes from the associated Dorian mode that corresponds with the minor 7th chord.

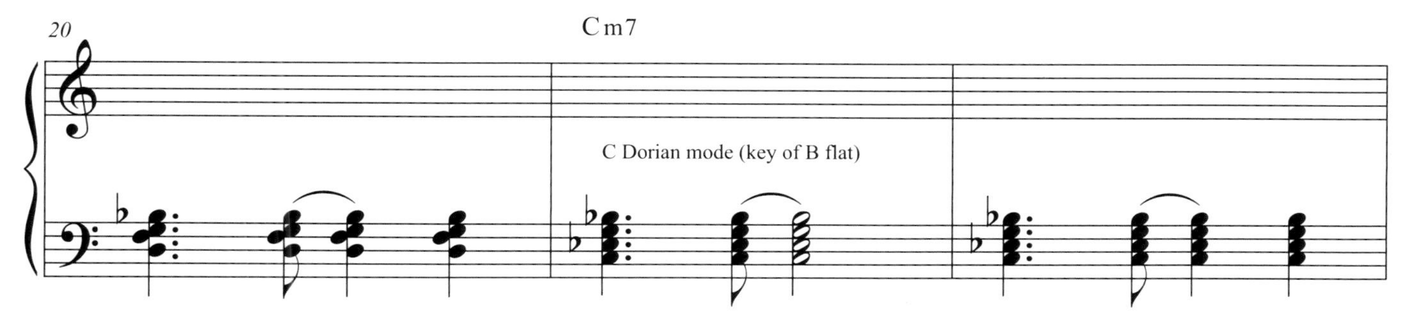

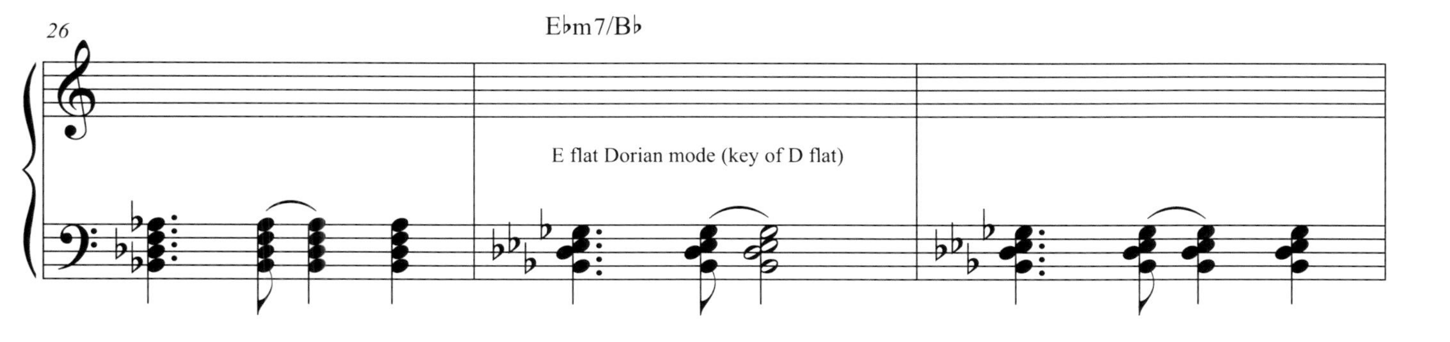

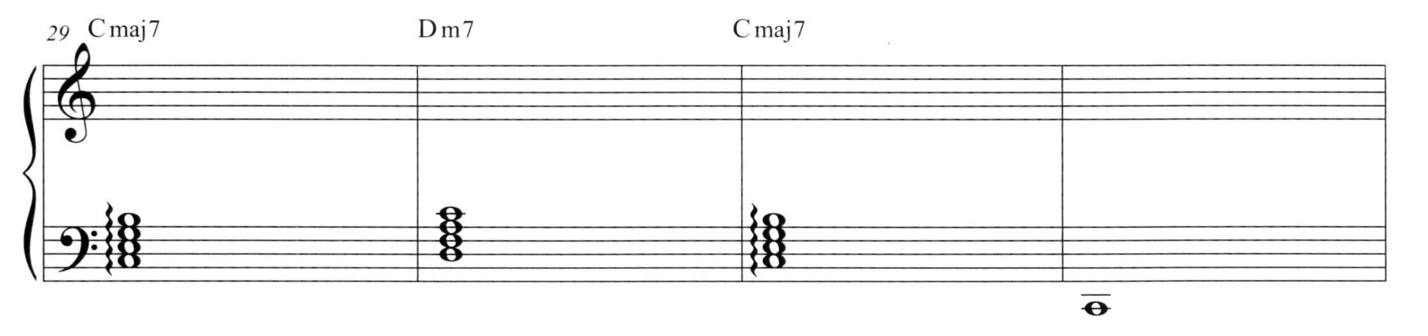

Dorian: ii - ii Modal Jazz Improvisation

The Dorian ii - ii (ii7 - ii7) modal jazz improvisation refers to the ii7 or minor 7th chord being played with the Dorian mode. The best way to get started with the ii7 - ii7 chord progression is to practice playing all minor 7th chords with the left hand while playing the minor pentascale with the right hand. The minor pentascale contains the first five notes from the Dorian mode.

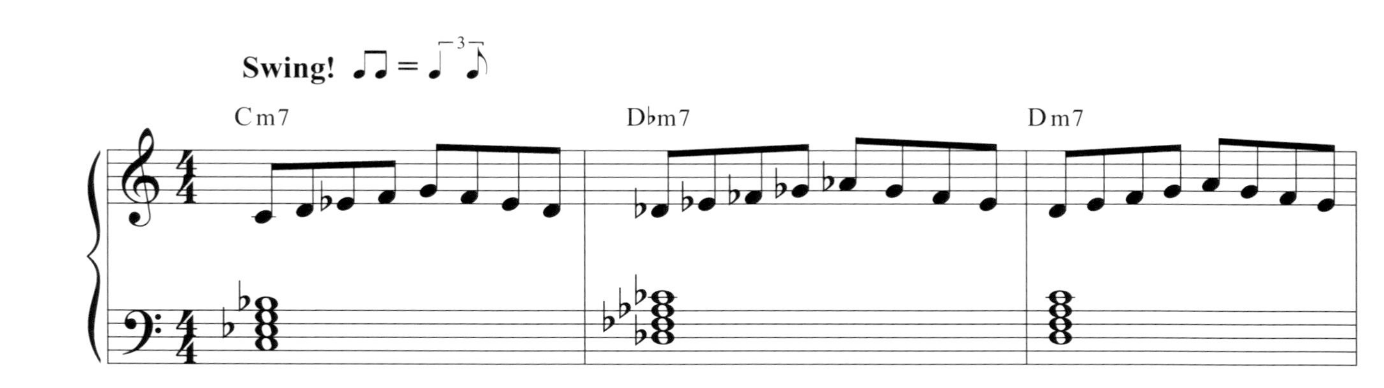

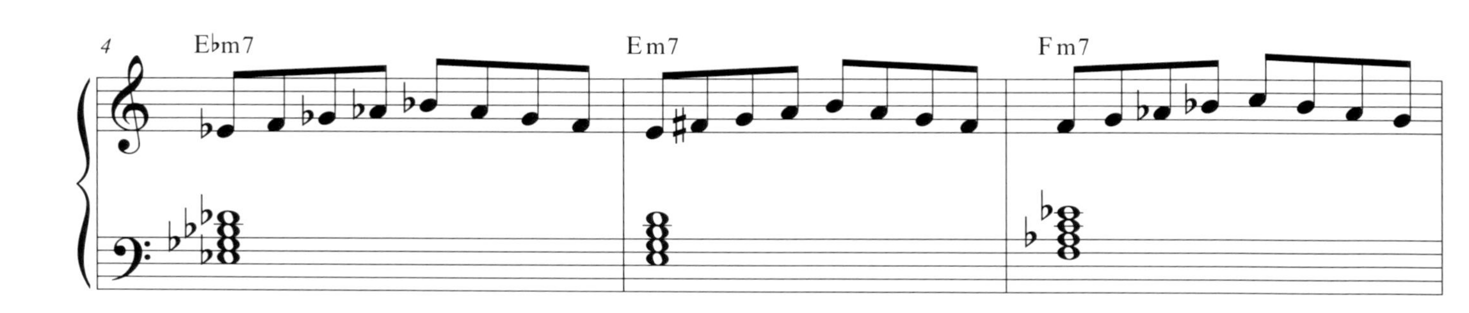

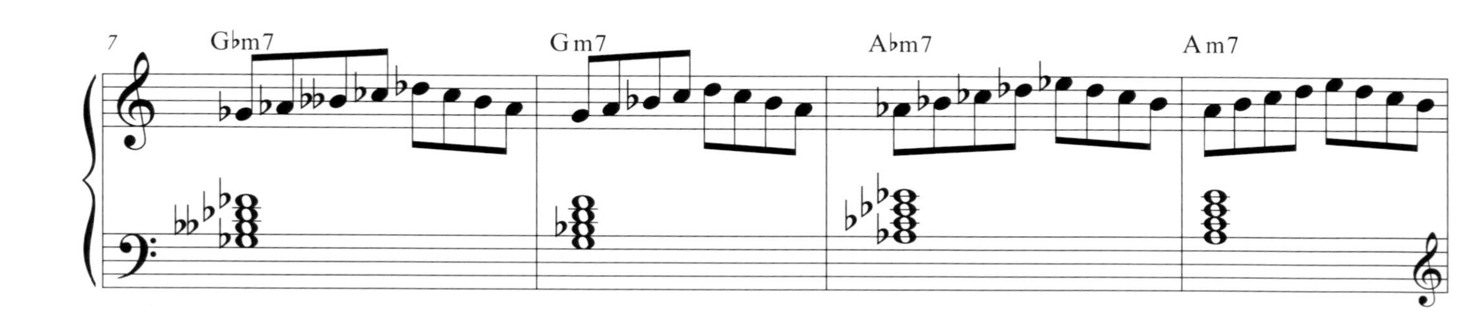

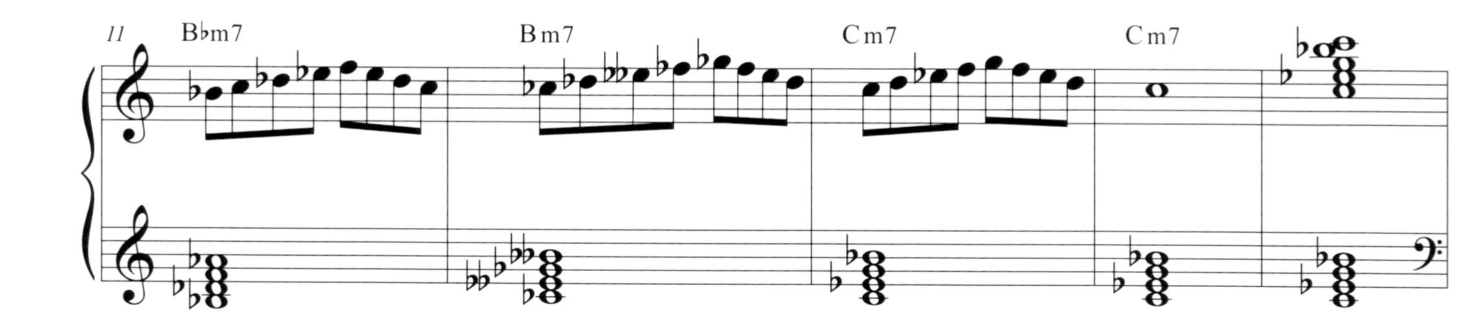

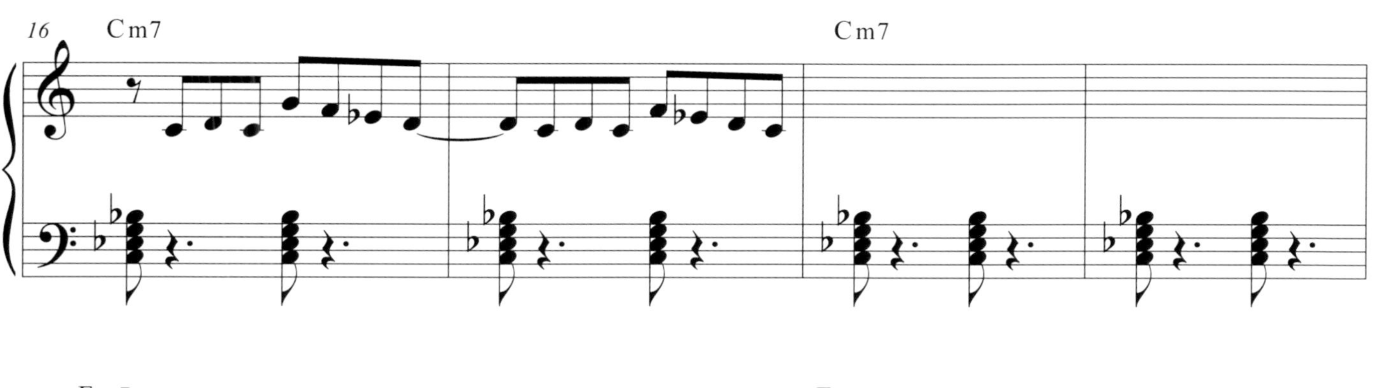

Create any right hand melody or lick using any minor pentascale (don't forget to swing the 8th notes)
Repeat as often as you want in any key you want (minor 7th chord with the left hand - minor pentascale with the right hand)

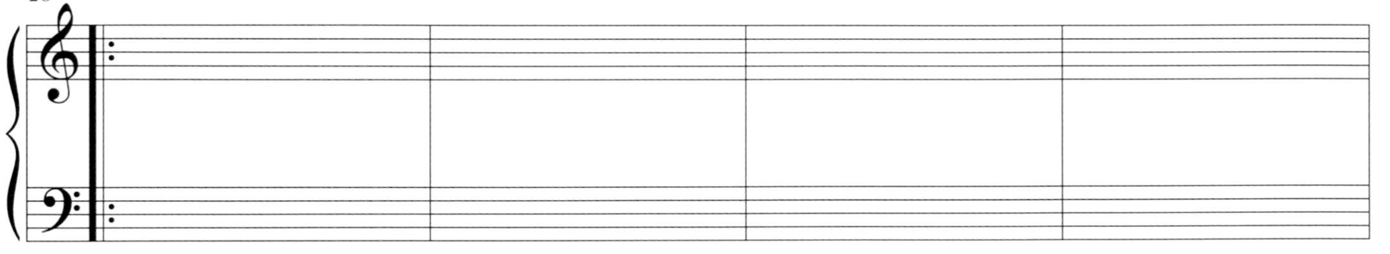

Add any minor 7th chord in the left hand and play it any rhythm you want - this is where you can improvise and play around!

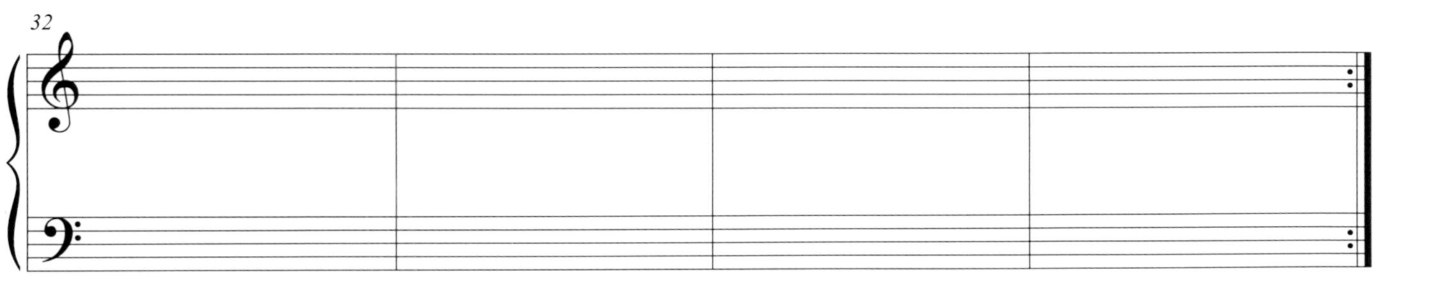

Dorian to Dorian (Modal Jazz Improv)

In this exercise, we are practicing playing any minor 7th chord with the left hand while the right hand plays notes from the accompanying mode (Dorian). To start off, we will only include a few of the first five notes from the associated Dorian mode. An easy way to think of this is to play any minor pentascale with the right hand (i.e. D E F G A) while the left hand plays the accompanying minor 7th chord (i.e. D minor 7 is the accompanying chord that goes with the D minor pentascale and the D Dorian mode).

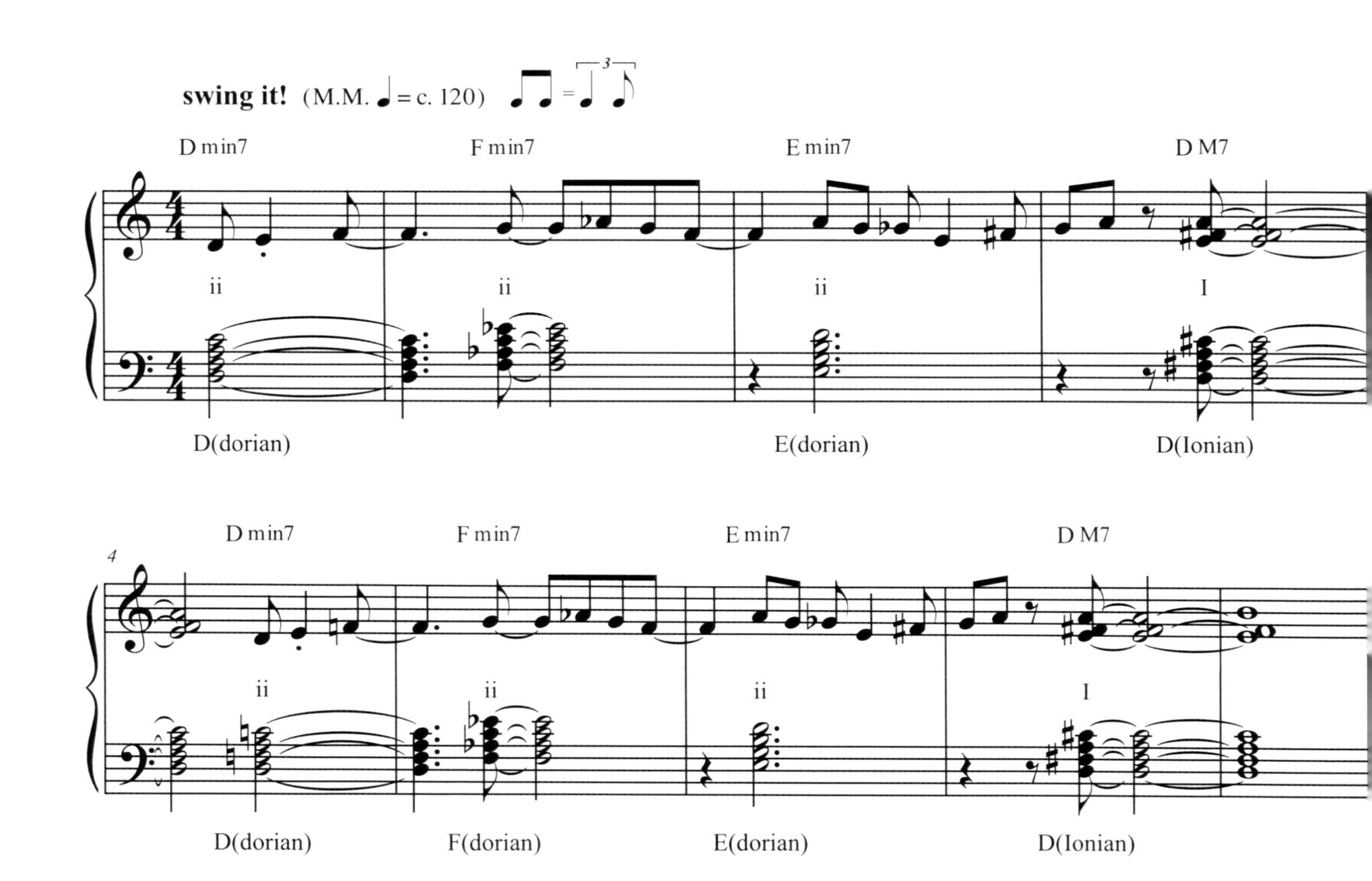

Dorian to Dorian (Pentascale Improv)

Here is another example. In this example, I did not choose a specific chord progression at all. I simply selected random minor 7th chords with the left hand and improvised with the accompanying Dorian mode with the right hand. I start off with an Fm7 chord with the left hand while the right hand plays the F minor pentascale (the first five notes from the F Dorian mode). Then we move to an Em7 chord with the left hand while the right hand plays the notes from the E minor pentascale (the first five notes from the E Dorian mode). Then I play an E flat minor 7th chord with the left hand while the right hand plays around with the E flat minor pentascale (the first five notes from the E flat Dorian mode). After playing the E flat minor 7th chord I move onto the Dm7 chord with the left hand while the right hand improvise with the notes from the D minor pentascale (the first five notes from the D Dorian mode). I finally end with the C major7 (add 9) chord (which is also called the CM9 chord). I simply voice the notes from the chord and move up the piano. Starting in measure 7, we begin the same chord progression over again, but this time I modify or change what the right hand does slightly. After playing this jazz exercise in the key of C Major, try to play it in every key signature on the piano moving up in half steps - C, C♯, D, E♭, E, F, F♯, G, A♭, A, B♭, and B.

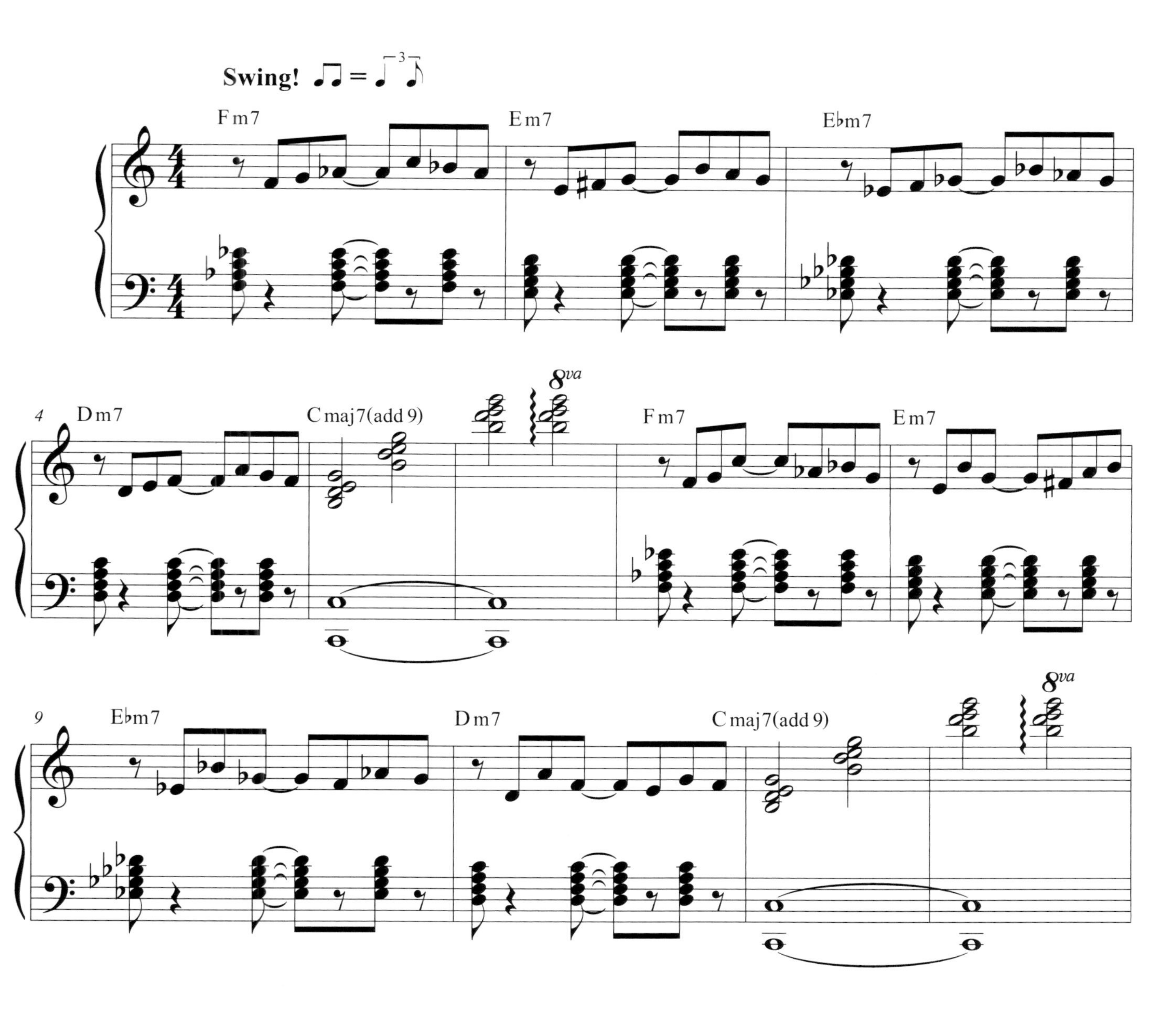

Ionian - Locrian (Modal Improv)

In this exercise, we are practicing playing any minor 7th chord with the left hand while the right hand plays notes from the accompanying mode.

We are moving up according to the C major scale (i.e. Cmaj7 - Dm7 - Em7 - Fmaj7 - G7 - Am7 - and Bm7(flat5) chords.

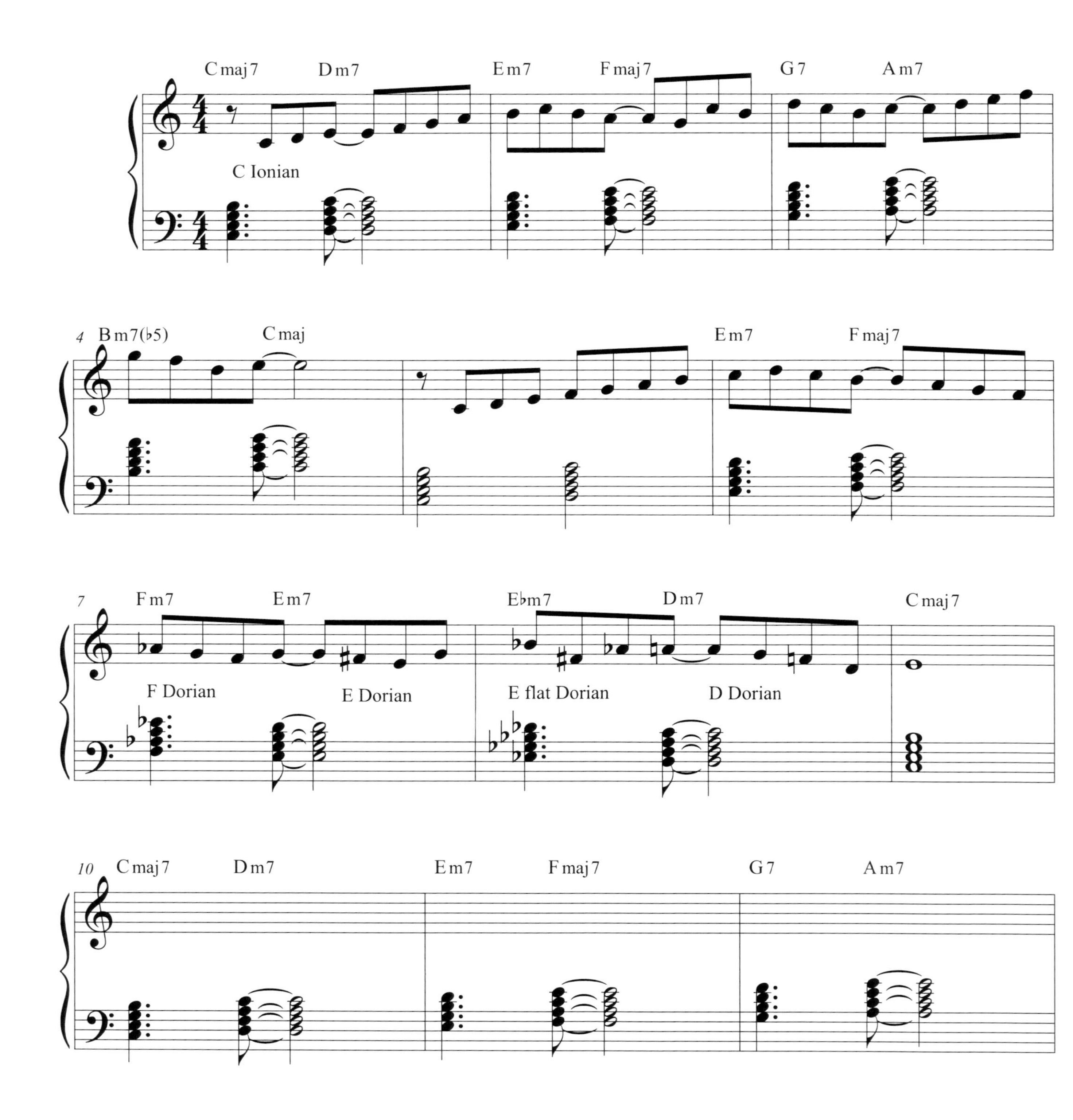

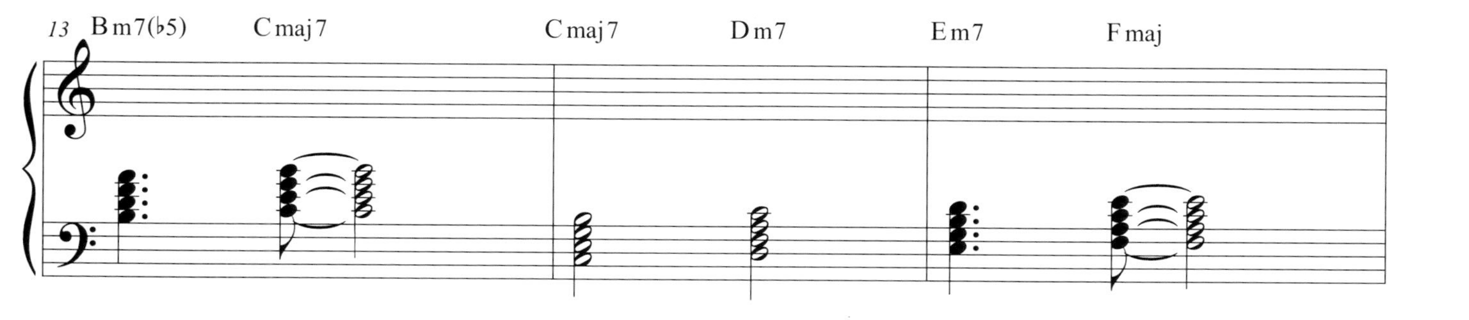

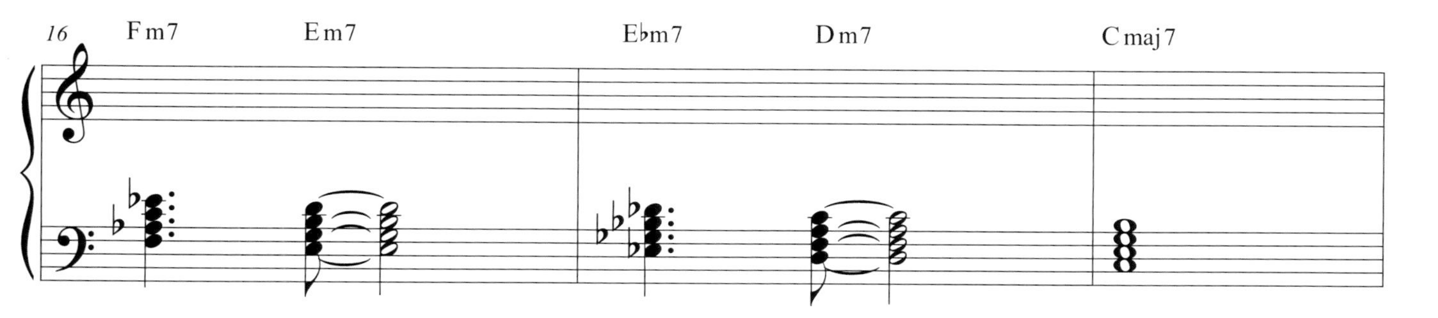

For the remaining three measures, come up with your own chord progression and modal jazz improvisation using either the major scale (Ionian mode), or the Dorian mode.

2 Be or not 2 Be

This is an example of modal jazz - primarily using the ii7 - ii7 jazz chord progression (minor seventh to minor seventh while the right hand improvises with the Dorian to Dorian mode that corresponds with the accompanying minor seventh chord). Play this as it is written and then play around with this jazz piece. Try to create your own modal jazz piece using minor seventh chords and improvise with the Dorian mode. See what you can create on your own!

By Jerald Simon

MM0000106

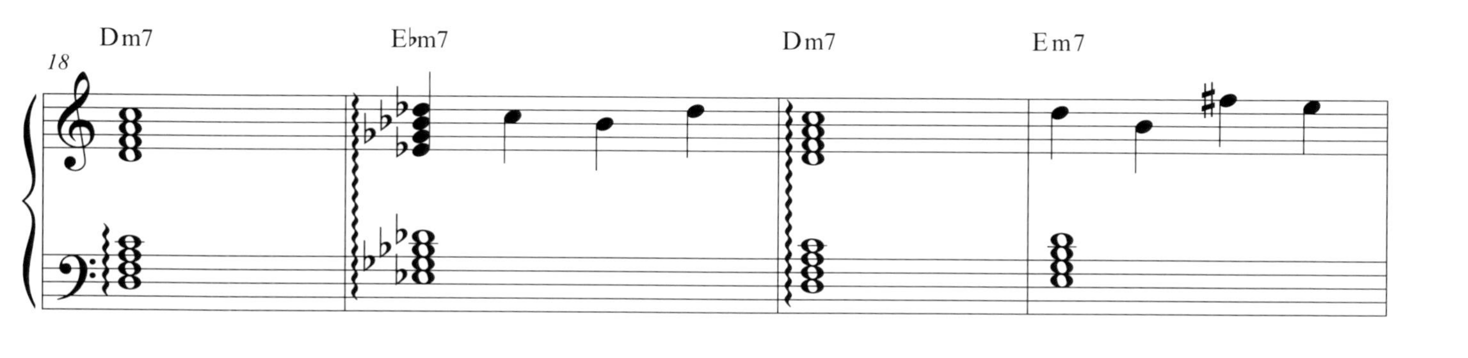
18
Dm7
E♭m7
Dm7
Em7

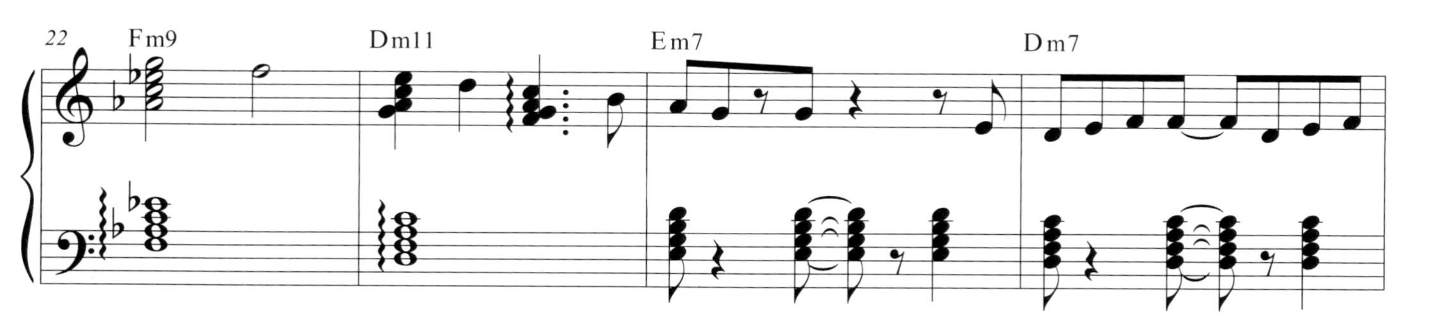
22
Fm9
Dm11
Em7
Dm7

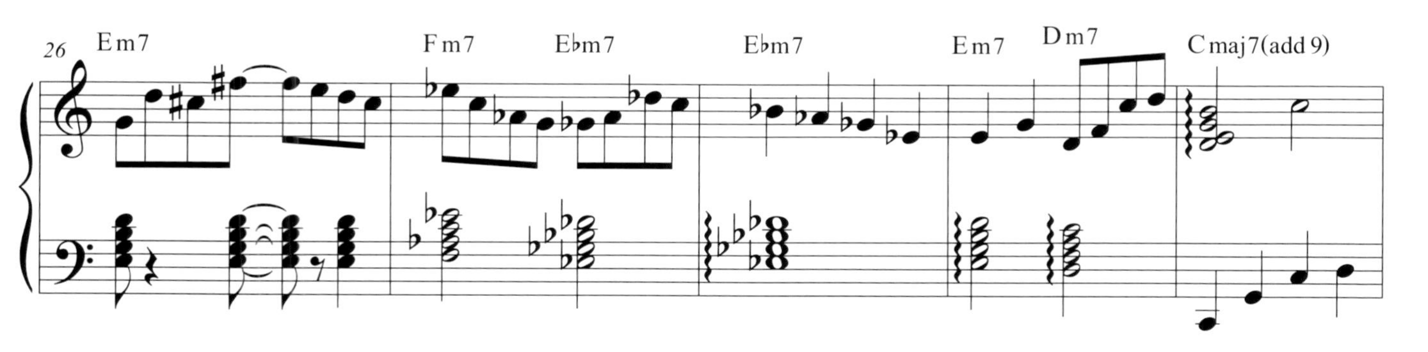
26
Em7
Fm7
E♭m7
E♭m7
Em7
Dm7
Cmaj7(add 9)

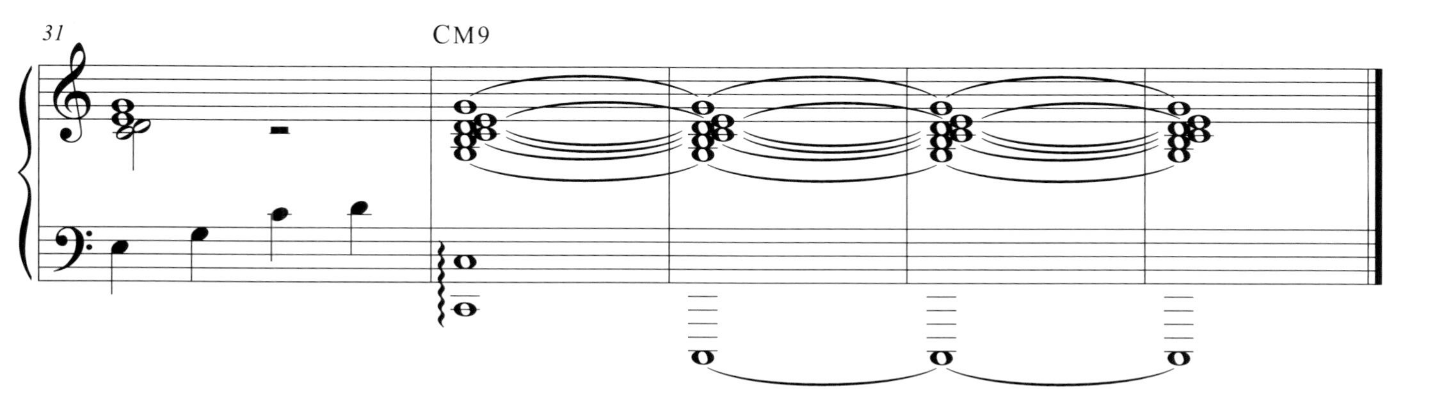
31
CM9

Momentum (Modal Moments)

This is a fun modal jazz piece I composed using a simple 7th chord progression: Cm7 - F7 - Dm7 - Gm7 - E flat major 7 - F7 - Dm7 - Gm7 and then repeat throughout the entire piece. The right hand is improvising using notes from modes that correspond with the accompanying 7th chord.

By Jerald Simon

16
Gm7/D
Cm7
F7/C
Dm7
20
Gm7/D
E♭maj7
F7/E♭
Dm7
24
Gm7/D
Cm7
F7/C
Dm7
28
Gm7/D
E♭maj7
F7/E♭
Dm7
32
Gm7/D
E♭maj7
F7/C
Dm7

Gm7/D
E♭maj7
F7/E♭
Dm7
Gm7/D
E♭maj7
F7/C
Dm7
Gm7/D
E♭maj7
F7/E♭
Dm7
Gm7/D
E♭maj7
F7/C
Dm7
Gm7/D
E♭maj7
F7/E♭
Dm7

56
Gm7/D
E♭maj7
3
F7/C
59
Dm7
Gm7/D
E♭maj7
F7/E♭
63
Dm7
Gm7/D
E♭maj7
66
F7/C
Dm7
Gm7/D
69
E♭maj7
F7/E♭
Dm7
Gm7/D

73
Cm7
F7/C
Dm7
76
Gm7/D
Cm7
F7/C
79
Dm7
Gm7/D
Cm7
83
C7
E♭/F
E♭
B♭/F
87
Cm/F
F
B♭
8va
8vb

INTRODUCING 9TH CHORDS (MAJOR AND MINOR)

On this page, I have included the most common 9th chords. There are more, and we could go more in depth than this, but I think I will leave that for a more advanced Essential Jazz Piano Exercises book where we only focus on 9th, 11, and 13th chords and voicings, upper structures, and more. For now, let's just look at 9th chords and explain what they are.

First, refer to the chord chart I included back on page 19.

We have discussed how a major triad is created using the root, major third interval, and the perfect 5th interval (i.e. C E G). A major 7th chord is created by adding a major 7th interval on top of a major triad (i.e. C E G B - where B is the major 7th interval from C).

An easy way to think about 9th chords is as follows:

Let's think about building blocks and building towers. Stay with me here. I like to paint a picture visually to help you understand concepts musically. Chords are all created from intervals - blocked or broken - since we can have blocked and broken chords (arpeggiated chords).

Major, minor, perfect, augmented, and diminished intervals can all be stacked on top of each in different ways to produce different chords, variations, and sounds (inversions, etc.).

All 9th chords are built on top of 7th chords. You could have major or minor 7th chords with all of their different variations, but 9th chords are built on top of 7th chords. 11th chords are built on top of 9th chords, which are built on top of 7th chords, which are built on top of triads. 13th chords are built on top of 11th chords, which are built on top of 9th chords, which are built on top of 7th chords, which are built on top of triads.

It's a very simplistic explanation, but, I want you to think of towers and building blocks stacking on top of each other because it does paint a picture.

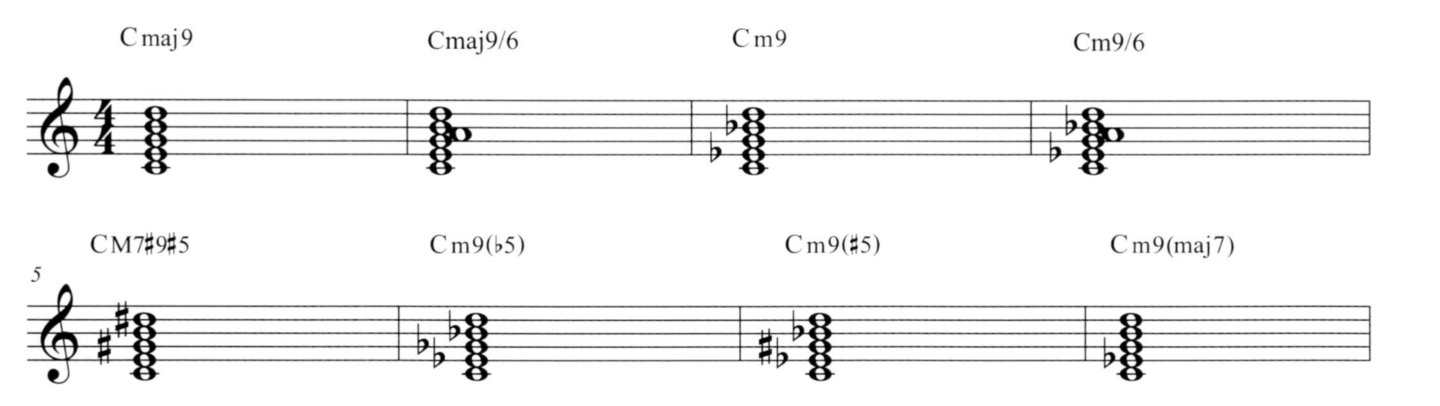

Now, obviously, we cannot play most 9th, 11th, and 13th chords with one hand because more notes are added and the spread is larger than the average hand size. With triads and 7th chords, we can do inversions where the notes are played in different positions. With anything bigger than a 7th chord, we do chord voicings where the notes of the chord are split between two hands.

All Major 9th Chords in all Keys

In this exercise, we are playing voicings of all major 7 (add9) chords moving up in half steps through every key signature. The left hand is playing an octave interval while the right hand completes the major 9th chord.

C maj9
9
D♭maj9
D maj9
E♭maj9
12
E maj9
F maj9
G♭maj9
15
G maj9
A♭maj9
A maj9
18
B♭maj9
B maj9
C maj9
21

Major 9th Chords Voicings)

In this exercise, we are playing additional voicings of all major 9ths chords. I have only presented them in the key of C major, but you can use the previous two pages as an example when moving up in half steps through every key signature. The left hand is playing an octave interval while the right hand completes the major 9th chord.

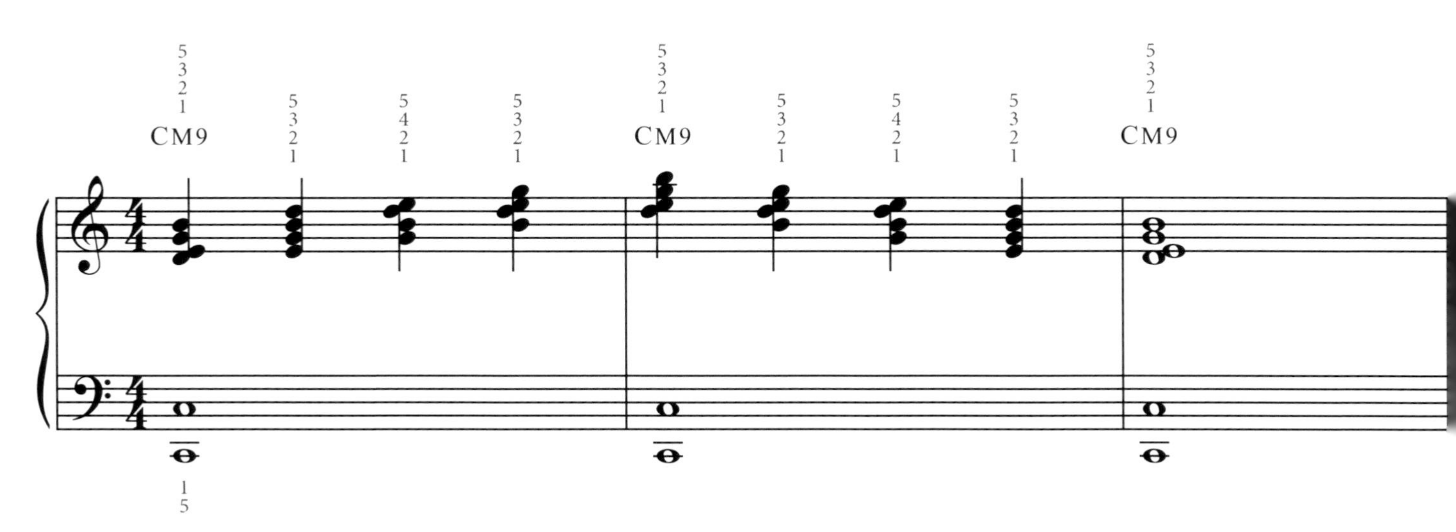

In this exercise, we are playing additional voicings of all minor 9ths chords. I have only presented them in the key of C minor, but you can use the previous two pages as an example when moving up in half steps through every key signature. The left hand is playing an octave interval while the right hand completes the minor 9th chord.

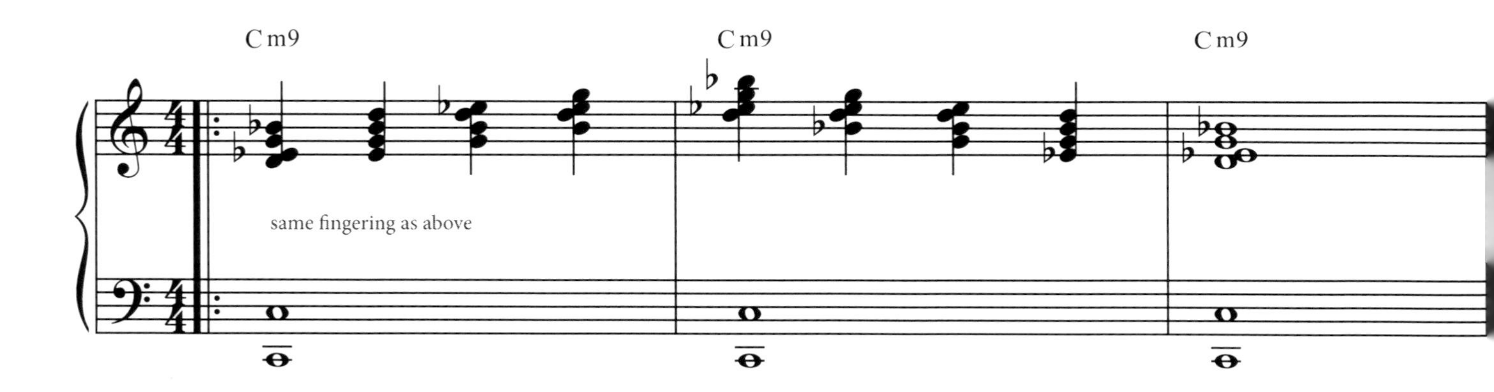

Once you can play the above exercises as written, try to play them both blocked and broken where you break the notes up from the chords and play them one note after another. You can practice playing these exercises up and down the piano 1, 2, and 3 octaves blocked and broken. For fun, try to play the left hand as half notes (i.e. two Cs - each played as half notes). Then try to play the left hand as quarter notes, 8th notes, and even 16rh notes. You can swing the 8th notes or play them straight.

After playing this jazz exercise in the key of C Major, try to play it in every key signature on the piano moving up in half steps - C, C♯, D, E♭, E, F, F♯, G, A♭, A, B♭, and B.

IM9 - IVM9

In this exercise, where are playing one voicing of Cmaj9 to another voicing of the same chord within the measure. Then we follow a similar pattern but start on the Fmaj9 chord. We rotate back and forth from Cmaj9 (CM9), to Fmaj9 (FM9).

This almost creates a song-like sound and quality that is very jazzy and also very pleasing to listen to (and fun to play, I might add).

Smooth and Laid Back - no swing (♩ = c. 110)

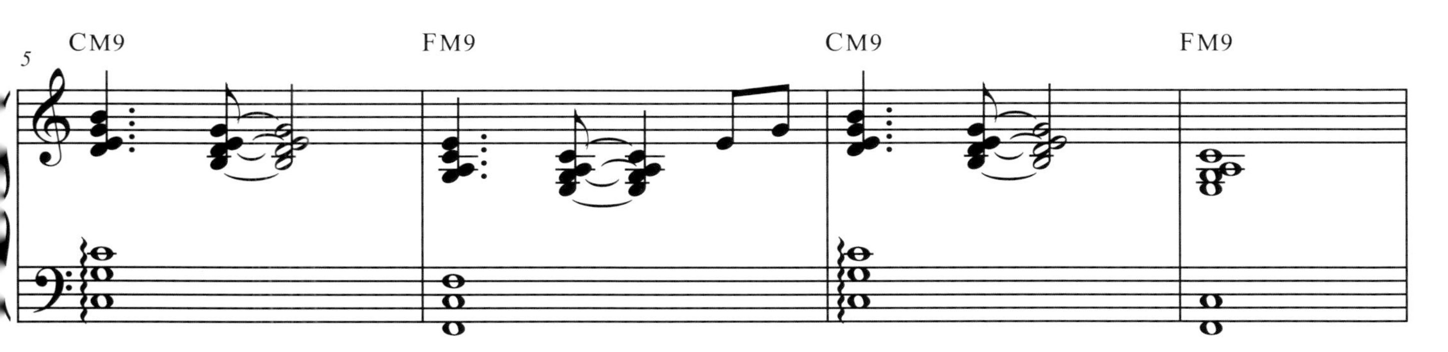

Once you can play the above exercises as written, try to play them both blocked and broken where you break the notes up from the chords and play them one note after another. You can practice playing these exercises up and down the piano 1, 2, and 3 octaves blocked and broken. For fun, try to play the left hand as half notes (i.e. two Cs - each played as half notes). Then try to play the left hand as quarter notes, 8th notes, and even 16rh notes. You can swing the 8th notes or play them straight.

After playing this jazz exercise in the key of C Major, try to play it in every key signature on the piano moving up in half steps - C, C♯, D, E♭, E, F, F♯, G, A♭, A, B♭, and B.

IIMINOR7 - V7 - IM9

In the example below, we will now play a Dmin7, followed by a G7, and ending with a CM9 chord. This is a ii-V-Imaj9 chord progression.

This is modal jazz, in that we are using 7th chords and we also happen to be following the ii-V-I jazz chord progression. We are, technically, playing a Dorian, Mixolydian, and Ionian mode with the left hand. Anyone who has purchased my book, "100 Left Hand Patterns Every Piano Player Should Know," will immediately recognize the left hand patterns as one of the new age patterns we present in the new age left hand patterns section (1 - 5- 8 - 9 - 10 - 11 - 12 - 14 left hand pattern).

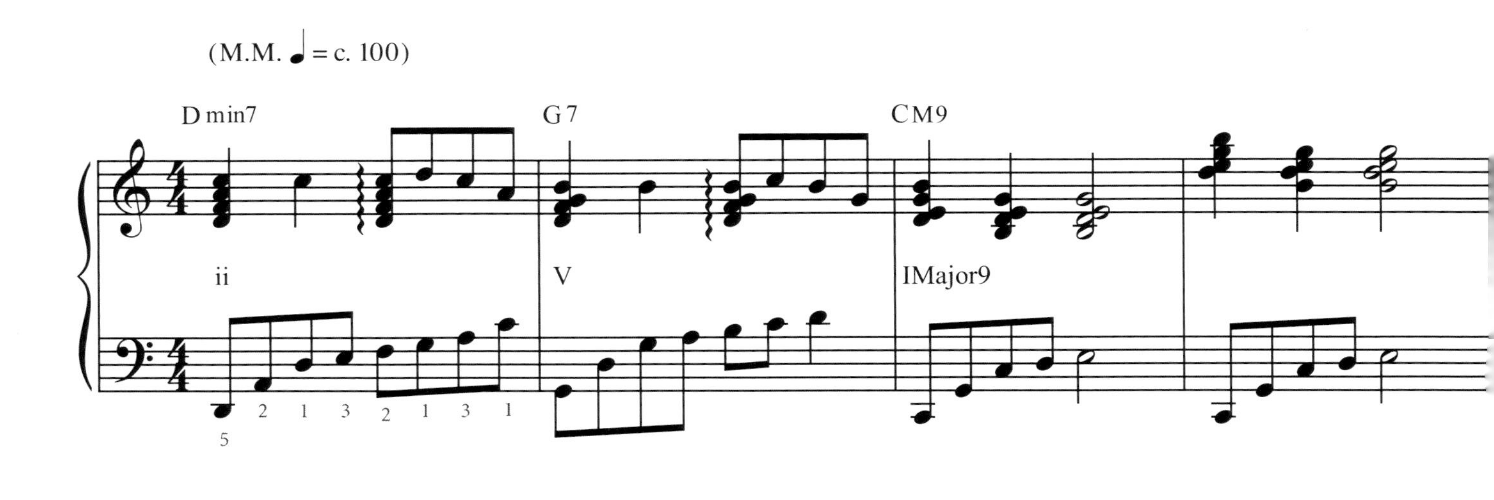

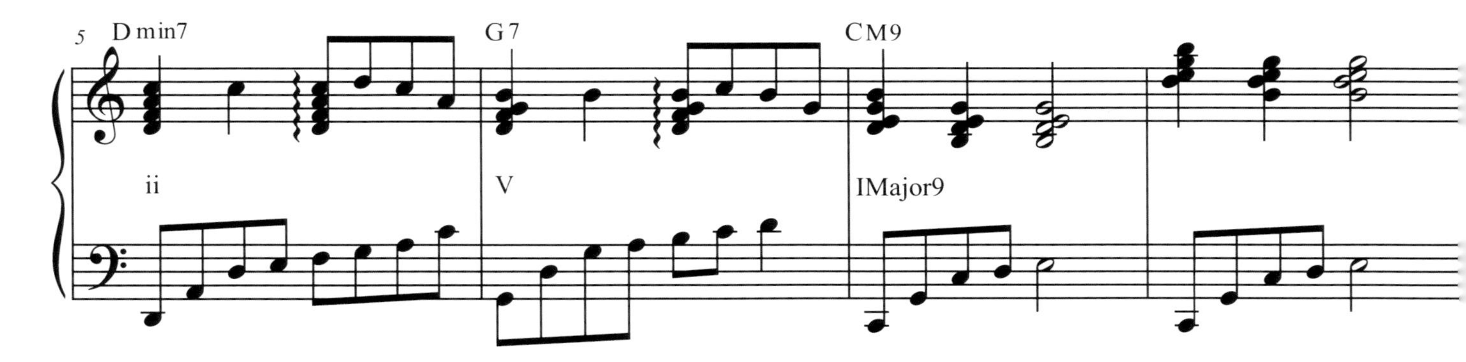

Once you can play the above exercise as written, try to go up and down one, two, or three octaves on the piano. Can you play the example above in a different way or style? Could you use the example above to compose a jazz piece of your own? What if you took measure one and tried to play that measure starting on each of the notes from the C major scale (i.e. C, D, E, F, G, A, B, and C)? What would happen? We have already discussed modal jazz and playing the same song in different keys and in different modes. How would it sound to play the above example in a major form (i.e. D maj7 - Gmaj7 - C#M9)? Play around with this and see what you can create on your own.

After playing this jazz exercise in the key of C Major, try to play it in every key signature on the piano moving up in half steps - C, C♯, D, E♭, E, F, F♯, G, A♭, A, B♭, and B.

IIMINOR9 - V9 - IM9

Now that you have had a chance to practice playing the previous pattern of Dmin7 - G7 - CM9, we are going to add a few notes and embellish this pattern. Now we will play Dm9 - G9 - CM9 and repeat the pattern. The 9th interval creates a wonderful jazz quality in music and it's not as difficult to do. You can add the 9th interval to any music. If you add th 9th to a triad, it becomes an add9 chord (i.e. Cadd9), and if you add the 9th interval to a 7th chord then it becomes either a major or minor 9th chord.

VMINOR 9 - VMINOR9 - VMINOR 9

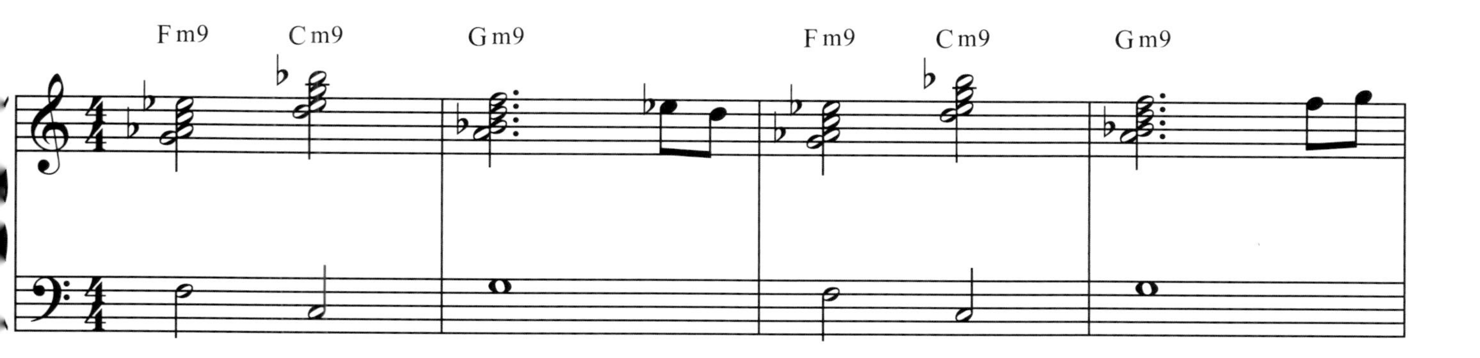

After playing this jazz exercise in the key of C Major, try to play it in every key signature on the piano moving up in half steps - C, C♯, D, E♭, E, F, F♯, G, A♭, A, B♭, and B.

Modulating from one Key to Another

In this example, You will move according to the circle of 5ths

First, we start with the major 7th chord, then move to diminished 7th chord, and finally end with the minor7(sharp5) chord of the new key signature to which we are transposing or modulating key signatures. After playing this as written, try to swing it or embellish it any way you like. Be creative!

13
E maj7
E°7
D♯m7(♯5)/B
16
B maj7
B°7
A♯m7(♯5)/F♯
19
F♯maj7
F♯°7
F m7(♯5)/C♯
22
C♯maj7
C♯°7
C m7(♯5)/G♯
25
A♭maj7
A♭°7
G m7(♯5)/E♭

28
E♭maj7
E♭°7
D m7(♯5)/B♭
31
B♭maj7
B♭°7
A m7(♯5)/F
34
F maj7
F°7
E m7(♯5)/C
37
C maj7
C°7
B m7(♯5)/G

Modulating Keys (Variation)

In this example, You will move in thirds according to the aug. chord

After playing this jazz exercise below following the C augmented chord (C E G sharp or A flat), try to play it in every key signature on the piano moving up in half steps - C, C♯, D, E♭, E, F, F♯, G, A♭, A, B♭, and B.

Over 100 Measures of RH Minor Blues scale
Riffs & Patterns Created from the C blues Scale

After playing this jazz exercise in the key of C Major, try to play it in every key signature on the piano moving up in half steps - C, C♯, D, E♭, E, F, F♯, G, A♭, A, B♭, and B.

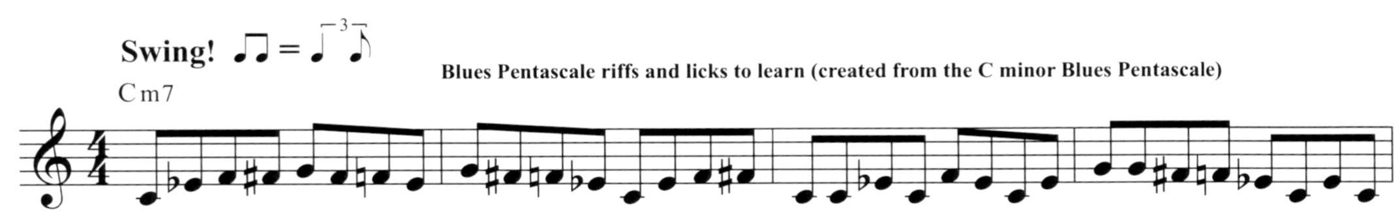

The left hand can play a Cm7 chord for any of these or you can play any left hand pattern you want from this book.

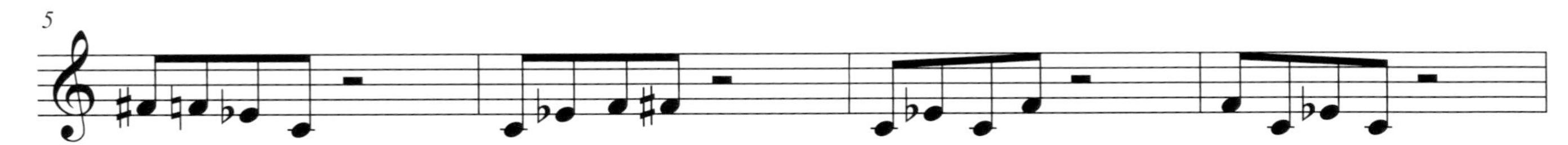

You can use any of these right hand licks or patterns with any left hand chord combination you'd like to play!

Each measure is it's own individual lick or riff and can be combined with any left hand pattern in any order. Mix and match and see what you can come up with on your own.

Complete Blues Scale riffs and licks to learn (created from the C minor blues scale)

69
73
77
81
85
89
93
97
101

Complete Blues Scale riffs and licks to learn (created from the C minor blues scale and C minor 7th Chord in all inversions)

M00001064

Over 100 Measures of RH Major Blues scale
Riffs & Patterns Created from the C Major Blues Scale

After playing this jazz exercise in the key of C Major, try to play it in every key signature on the piano moving up in half steps - C, C♯, D, E♭, E, F, F♯, G, A♭, A, B♭, and B.

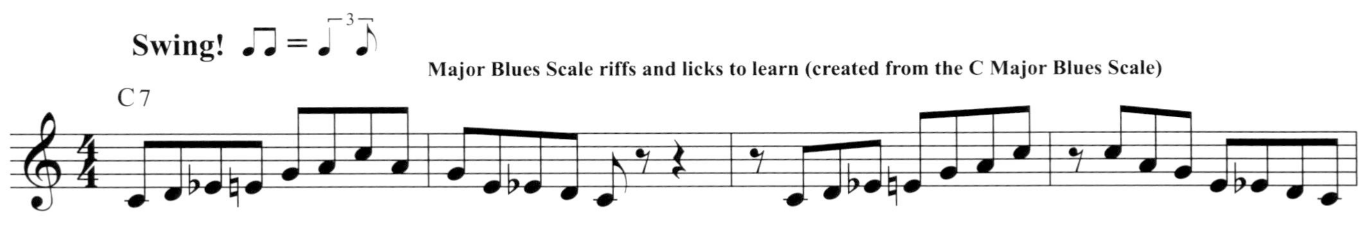

The left hand can play a C7 (or F7) chord for any of these or you can play any left hand pattern you want from this book.

You can use any of these right hand licks or patterns with any left hand chord combination you'd like to play!

Each measure is it's own individual lick or riff and can be combined with any left hand pattern in any order. Mix and match and see what you can come up with on your own.

M00001064

69
71
75
79
83
87
91
95
99
3

Descending 7th Chords
Created from the C Major Scale

This is the same chord progression found on pages 148 - 149. The chord progression is descending in 5ths (i.e. F - B - E - A - D - G - C). We change the rhythms and invert the chords into other inversions instead of keeping everything in root position. After playing this jazz exercise in the key of C Major, try to play it in every key signature on the piano moving up in half steps - C, C♯, D, E♭, E, F, F♯, G, A♭, A, B♭, and B.

Create your own right hand improvisational pattern. You can use the notes from the chord broken apart, or play around with the modes starting on the root note from the chord (Fmaj 7 means you can play an F lydian mode with the right hand).

Here is what I suggest all jazz piano players (and all piano players in general) should be able to do in all key signatures and in all inversions:

Play the following (these are all written out in every key signature in my book, **"Essential Piano Exercises Every Piano Player Should Know"**):

- **All Intervals** (Harmonic and Melodic)
- **All Major Pentascales** in every key signature
- **All Minor Pentascales** in every key signature
- **All Diminished Pentascales** in every key signature
- **All Tetra Chords** for all keys
- **All Major and Minor Scales** (natural, harmonic, and melodic) 1, 2, and 3 octaves in every key signature
- **All Major and Minor Scales** contrary and parallel motion - 1, 2, and 3 octaves in every key signature
- **All Major Triads** (root, first, and second inversions) in every key signature
- **All Minor Triads** (root, first, and second inversions) in every key signature
- **All Diminished Triads** (root, first, and second inversions) in every key signature
- **All Augmented Triads** (root, first, and second inversions) in every key signature
- **All Sus4 Triads** (root, first, and second inversions) in every key signature
- **All Sus2 Triads** (root, first, and second inversions) in every key signature
- **All 6th Chords** (root, first, second, and third inversions) in every key signature
- **All Minor 6th Chords** (root, first, second, and third inversions) in every key signature
- **All Major 7th Chords** (root, first, second, and third inversions) in every key signature
- **All Minor Major 7th Chords** (root, first, second, and third inversions) in every key signature
- **All 7th Chords** (root, first, second, and third inversions) in every key signature
- **All Minor 7th Chords** (root, first, second, and third inversions) in every key signature
- **All Minor 7 Flat 5 Chords** (root, first, second, and third inversions) in every key signature
- **All Minor 7 Sharp 5 Chords** (root, first, second, and third inversions) in every key signature
- **All Diminished 7th Chords** (root, first, second, and third inversions) in every key signature
- **I - IV - V - V7 - I Chord Progression** (in every inversion and in every key signature)
- **i - iv - V - V7 - i Chord Progression** (in every inversion and in every key signature)
- **All Triads Built from the Major Scales** (in every inversion and in every key signature)
- **All 7th Chords** (moving up diatonically) in every key signature
- **All Major Octave** Chords in every key signature

In addition to the above, you should also be able to play the following:

- **All Major Blues Scales** in every key signature
- **All Minor Blues Scales** in every key signature
- **All Major Pentatonic Scales** in every key signature
- **All Modes** (i.e. Ionian, Dorian, Phrygian, Lydian, Mixolydian, Aeolian, Locrian) in every key signature
- **All 9th Chords, 11th Chords, and 13th Chords** in every voicing and in every key signature

This is just a simple outline to get you going. There is actually so much more we can learn that we could include in our list, but the list would turn into an entire book or many more books (which they may). In this book I have taught basic and fundamental jazz piano exercises in a fun way through original jazz pieces I have composed. Both the jazz pieces and jazz exercises are essentially just jazz patterns and I hope you have had fun playing these essential jazz piano exercises!

A Few Additional Ideas for Piano Teachers and Parents of Piano Students

You can visit this link to read the original blog post from which this presentation was created: (https://musicmotivation.com/dont-teach-music-theory-unless-you-teach-the-practical-application/).

In the blog post I talked specifically about 10 steps to begin teaching the practical application of music theory so students know their theory inside and out. I thought I would share the 10 steps here from the blog post:

Before any piano student plays their piece, I believe they should be able to do the following (this is what I try to have my students do with their music):

1. Tell their music teacher the key signature and time signature

2. Identify all of the sharps or flats in the key signature and name them

3. Play all of the intervals created from the major key signature of the piece they are playing - this is more for piano students and possibly guitar students as many instruments only allow one note at a time. If the student is younger or new to their instrument, they can play the intervals created from the pentascales, or five note scales created from the first five notes of the major or minor scales.

4. Play through the major scale of the key signature of the piece at least 1-2 octaves up and down the piano (parallel and or contrary motion). If the student is younger or new to their instrument, as stated before, they can play the pentascales, or five note scales created from the first five notes of the major or minor scales.

5. Play or be able to play what I refer to as the "Essential Piano Exercises" from each key signature. (In the blog post I show an example from the key of C major from my book "Essential Piano Exercises" - Intervals, Scales, and Chords in all Keys and in all Inversions - a 288 page book with all intervals, scales, and simple triads and 6th and 7th chords in all keys and inversions).

These are the other 5 steps:

Once a student can do the above five essential "getting started steps" in any given key signature (and many times I will do the following steps even if they can't do the above steps in every key signature), I then challenge them to do the following five essential "music theory application steps":

1. Once the student has learned and perfected the piece, ask them to take the song up half a step and down half a step. In the beginning, this is a good start. Later on, when they are better able to do so, have them play the piece in any key signature. Start with simple pieces like "Mary Had a Little Lamb" and "Twinkle, Twinkle, Little Star." Have the students try playing these in all key signatures.

2. Ask the student to come up with at least 5-10 variations or arrangements of their piece.

3. Ask the student to compose 3-4 motifs (or single melodic line or phrase), and then put them together. This can be the beginning of creating a simple piece. I have students begin using scales and skipping notes here and there. We then have them take a simple pattern created from the notes of the major scale (1 2 3 4 5 6 7 8).

4. Ask the student to "Play a Rainbow." When I say this to students, I then begin to ask them to "play" anything. I may say: "Play me a shadow," "Play me a swing set," "Play me a thunderstorm," "Play me a puddle, a rock, a tree, a meadow, a light, etc.". The sky is the limit. I first begin with tangible objects and eventually move on to intangible ideas and concepts: "Play me loneliness," "Play me disturbed, agitated, angered, humbled, pensive, schizophrenic, etc.". Again, the sky is the limit. It is wonderful to see what students can create, even if they don't know all the rules of composition or terminology. Everyone has music within them.

5. I have students begin notating their music. I enjoy and prefer Finale, but that is because I have used it for so long and am familiar with it. There are many great programs available. After we have their music put down on paper, I then export the music from Finale as a midi file and open the midi file in Logic Pro. We then begin having them add additional instruments so they can create background tracks (this is how I create all of my weekly "**Cool Songs**" from my **COOL SONGS Series** - you can watch all of the videos of the weekly "**Cool Songs**" with the minus tracks to get an idea of what I mean at this link: https://www.youtube.com/playlist?list=PL9eocDI3QWNhiErbkK29DtnFZ24vvR8yx). The students then have a PDF copy of their composition and an MP3 "minus track" to accompany them as they play. Talk about music motivation!

In addition, here is a link to a handout I created that I give to my own students and other piano teachers to help them learn what I call the 7 Markers of Musical Success: https://musicmotivation.com/learning-to-read-music-notation-on-the-piano/

Join the **Essential Piano Exercises Course** by Jerald Simon

https://www.essentialpianoexercises.com/

Gain lifetime access to the PDF books listed below (which also includes video piano lesson tutorials where Jerald Simon demonstrates examples from the books and gives piano pointers, tips to try, and the practical application of music theory where). Jerald demonstrates how to use the music theory to arrange and compose music of your own!

This course features pre-recorded video lessons so you can watch and learn how to play the piano at your convenience. You choose when and where you learn to play the piano.

Join the Essential Piano Exercises Course and receive the following PDF books along with access to weekly video lessons taught by Jerald Simon for a one time payment of $199.95.

This includes lifetime access to this course created for anyone who plays the piano!
Current books (weekly video lessons are being uploaded on these right now):
You will be able to download all of these books in PDF format...

Essential Piano Exercises Every Piano Player Should Know by Jerald Simon
100 Left Hand Patterns Every Piano Player Should Know by Jerald Simon
Wintertide by Jerald Simon
Sweet Melancholy by Jerald Simon
The Dawn of a New Age by Jerald Simon
Sea Fever by Jerald Simon
Triumphant by Jerald Simon
Hymns of Exaltation by Jerald Simon
Sea Fever by Jerald Simon
Jingle Those Bells by Jerald Simon
Ghosts and Goblins and Freaks and Ghouls by Jerald Simon
Sand Castles by Jerald Simon
Platinum by Jerald Simon
I Want to Do What Jesus Taught (40 original children's primary hymns) by Jerald Simon
Jazzed about Christmas (PDF book is already available - videos coming soon)
Jazzed about 4th of July (PDF book is already available - videos coming soon)

These PDF books will be added within the course soon:

Essential Jazz Piano Exercises Every Piano Player Should Know by Jerald Simon **(coming in the late summer/ fall of 2020)**
Essential New Age Piano Exercises Every Piano Player Should Know (coming in the late winter of 2021)
Essential Pop Piano Exercises Every Piano Player Should Know (coming in the spring of 2021)
Essential Rock Piano Exercises Every Piano Player Should Know (coming in the summer of 2021)
100 Chord Progressions Every Piano Player Should Know (coming in the late spring of 2021)

Join the COOL SONGS Club and start using my COOL SONGS Series...

If you would like to learn more about the COOL SONGS Series I created to help motivate and inspire piano students - especially during their teenage years, you can visit my website: **https://musicmotivation.com/coolsongs**.

I compose COOL SONGS to help motivate and inspire piano students!

Parents praise COOL SONGS, piano teachers rave about them, and piano students can't wait to play them! Every piano recital instantly turns into a COOL concert when students perform COOL SONGS.

There are three ways to start using the COOL SONGS I have composed and continually compose each week.

1. If you haven't already, visit this link to download my FREE COOL SONGS Starter package (12 FREE COOL SONGS with accompaniment minus tracks: **http://coolsongsclub.com/freebook**. There are 4 beginning level, 4 early intermediate level, and 4 intermediate - advanced level COOL SONGS) so you can start using my COOL SONGS (these are actually the same ones I have included in this book, but you will be able to download the accompaniment MP3 minus tracks and watch the video lessons as well). You will also receive my FREE 130 page PDF Book: "20 Ways to Motivate Teen Piano Students to Want to Play the Piano - the FUN WAY!"

2. If you'd like to purchase the COOL SONGS Series, you can visit this link to Purchase the entire COOL SONGS Series Course single use license (Over 4 years worth of piano lessons - 163 COOL SONGS complete with video lessons and accompaniment MP3 minus tracks) for a one time payment of $49.95: https://www.coolsongsclub.com/order. You'll have lifetime access to all of the COOL SONGS in the series (piano teachers will also be able to upgrade their single use license to a lifetime piano teacher studio license if they'd like to when checking out).

3. Once you have purchased the COOL SONGS Series for $49.95 and/or upgraded to a studio license if you are a piano teacher, you will then be able to join the Essential Piano Exercises Course as an added upgrade. Learn more about my Essential Piano Exercises Course at **https://www.essentialpianoexercises.com/**

Download this **FREE PDF book** -
"20 Ways to Motivate Teen Piano Students to Want to Play the Piano" at:
https://www.coolsongsclub.com/freebook.

Subscribe to my YouTube Channel:

youtube.com/jeraldsimon

I upload new videos on Mondays, Wednesdays, and Fridays on my YouTube channel, **youtube.com/jeraldsimon**. I have a few different playlists filled with great content for beginning - advanced piano students. The videos are geared for everyone from brand new piano students to music majors, professional pianists, and piano teachers of all skill levels.

There are three main playlists for my **free online piano lessons.** I offer in person piano lessons, Zoom/FaceTime piano lessons, and step by step piano lesson packages you can purchase and watch at home, but the ones listed below are FREE to everyone who subscribes to my YouTube channel:

1. **PIANO FUNdamentals** (emphasis on the word FUN!)
2. **5 Minute Piano Lessons with Jerald Simon** (sponsored by Music Motivation®)
3. **Theory Tip Tuesday Piano Lessons**

I frequently release new videos. Some are piano lessons, and others are filmings of workshops, masterclasses, or concerts. I also have these additional types of videos on my YouTube channel:

a. Meditation/Relaxation Music Composed by Jerald Simon
b. Hymn Arrangements by Jerald Simon
c. Motivational Messages by Jerald Simon
d. Motivational Poetry by Jerald Simon
e. Theory Tip Tuesday (FREE Weekly Piano Lesson Videos) by Jerald Simon
f. Cool Songs by Jerald Simon (musicmotivation.com/coolsongs)
g. Assemblies, Workshops, Firesides, and more...

Let me know if you have a tutorial you'd like me to come out with to better help you learn the piano. I'm happy to help in any way I can and love hearing feedback from others about what they personally are looking for in piano lesson videos to help them learn to play the piano better. I primarily focus on music theory, improvisation/arranging, and composition. I refer to these as THEORY THERAPY, INNOVATIVE IMPROVISATION, and CREATIVE COMPOSITION.

I have also produced hundreds of COOL SONGS that teach students music theory the fun way. If you'd like to learn more about the COOL SONGS, that I composed to motivate my own piano students, or if you would like to purchase the COOL SONGS series featuring the music/books, simply visit musicmotivation.com/coolsongs to be taken to the page on my website that explains a little more about the COOL SONGS. You can also watch piano video tutorial lessons featuring 85 of the 200 + COOL SONGS (youtube.com/jeraldsimon). Let me know what you think. I'd love your feedback about the music. It helps me as I compose more COOL SONGS to motivate more piano students. I'm excited to have you watch my free video piano lessons on YouTube.com/jeraldsimon.

Perceptions, Parables, and Pointers by JERALD SIMON (read more at this link): http://musicmotivation.com/shop/motivationalself-help-books/perceptions-parables-and-pointers-by-jerald-simon/

What do you really want to do with your time? What is your mission in life? Where have you been, and where would you like to go? What are your dreams, your hopes, and your wishes? If you could do anything in the world, what would it be?

The main goal in writing down these perceptions, parables, and pointers, and in creating this book in general, is to present ideas that will help get people thinking, imagining, planning, creating, and actively participating in life.

The "As If" Principle (motivational poetry) by JERALD SIMON features 222 original motivational poems written by Simon to inspire and motivate men, women, businesses, organizations, leaders, mentors, advisers, teachers, and students. The poems were written to teach values and encourage everyone everywhere to do and be their best. (read more at this link): http://musicmotivation.com/shop/motivationalself-help-books/the-as-if-principle-by-jerald-simon/

CHECK OUT JERALD'S MOTIVATIONAL BOOKS

PERCEPTIONS, PARABLES, AND POINTERS
$19.95

216 PAGES

A SELF-HELP MOTIVATION MANUAL

MOTIVATION IN A MINUTE
$18.95

FULL COLOR PICTURES AND MOTIVATIONAL MESSAGES

THE "AS IF" PRINCIPLE (MOTIVATIONAL POETRY)
$16.95

154 PAGES

222 INSPIRATIONAL AND MOTIVATIONAL POEMS WRITTEN BY JERALD

ALL BOOKS ARE AVAILABLE ON AMAZON, BARNES AND NOBLE, AND ALL ONLINE AND TRADITIONAL BOOK STORES

Jerald's Albums & Singles

are available from all online music stores

Stream Jerald's music on

Pandora, Spotify, iTunes, Amazon, and all streaming sites.

Music Books, Albums, MP3s, Self Help and Motivational Books, Poetry Books and YouTube Videos
Check out my books and music on iTunes, Amazon, Spotify, Pandora, & YouTube.com/jeraldsimon
Motivate Piano Students! Music Motivation® - P.O. Box 1000 - Kaysville, UT 84037-1000

Check out Jerald's Cool Song Piano Packages

Jerald continually produces and releases new "Cool Songs" available for all piano students and piano teachers on his website (***musicmotivation.com***). Each new "*Cool Song*" is emailed to Music Motivation® mentees (piano teachers and piano students) who have enrolled in the "COOL SONGS" monthly subscription program. See which subscription is the best fit for you and for your piano students (if you are a piano teacher) by visiting:

http://musicmotivation.com/coolsongs

At **Music Motivation**®, I strive to produce the best quality products I can to help musicians of all ages better understand music theory (Theory Therapy), improvisation (Innovative Improvisation), and composition (Creative Composition). I try to tailor my products around the needs of piano teachers and piano students of all ages - from beginning through advanced and would love to receive your feedback about what I can do to better help you teach and learn. Let me know if there is a type of piano music, music book, fun audio or video tutorial, or any other educational product you would like to see in the field of music (principally the piano), but have not yet found, that would help you teach and learn the piano better. Please contact me. I look forward to your comments and suggestions. Thank you.

Check out these best sellers by Jerald Simon

visit ***musicmotivation.com*** to purchase, or visit your local music store - Chesbro music is the national distributor for all Music Motivation® books. Contact Chesbro Music Co. if you are a store (1.800.243.7276)

Learn more about

JERALD SIMON

Visit **http://musicmotivation.com/jeraldsimon**

"My purpose and mission in life is to motivate myself and others through my music and writing, to help others find their purpose and mission in life, and to teach values and encourage everyone everywhere to do and be their best." - Jerald Simon

First and foremost, Jerald is a husband to his beautiful wife, Zanny, and a father to his wonderful children. Jerald Simon is the founder of Music Motivation® (musicmotivation.com), a company he formed to provide music instruction through workshops, giving speeches and seminars, and concerts and performances in the field of music and motivation. He is a composer, author, poet, and Music Mentor/piano teacher (primarily focusing his piano teaching on music theory, improvisation, composition, and arranging). Jerald loves spending time with his wife, Zanny, and their children. In addition, he loves music, teaching, speaking, performing, playing sports, exercising, reading, writing poetry and self help books, and gardening.

Jerald created musicmotivation.com as a resource for piano teachers, piano students, and parents of piano students. In 2008 he began creating his Cool Songs to help teach music theory – the FUN way by putting FUN back into theory FUNdamentals. Jerald has also filmed hundreds of piano lesson video tutorials on his YouTube page (youtube.com/jeraldsimon). He is the author/poet of "The As If Principle" (motivational poetry), and the books "Perceptions, Parables, and Pointers", "Motivation in a Minute", and "Who Are You?". Jerald is also the author of 21 music books from the Music Motivation® Series and has also recorded and produced several albums and singles of original music.

Jerald also presents to various music schools, groups, and associations throughout the country doing various workshops, music camps, master classes, concerts and firesides to inspire and motivate teens, adults, music students and teachers. He enjoys teaching piano students about music theory, improvisation, and composition. He refers to himself as a Music Mentor and encourages music students to get motivated by music and to motivate others through music of their own.

SPECIALTIES:

Composer, Author, Poet, Music Mentor, Piano Teacher (jazz, music theory, improvisation, composition, arranging, etc.), Motivational Speaker, and life coach. Visit **http://musicmotivation.com**, to book Jerald as a speaker/performer. Visit **http://musicmotivation.com** to print off FREE piano resources for piano teachers and piano students.

Book me to speak/perform for your group or for a concert or performance:

jeraldsimon@musicmotivation.com - (801)644-0540 - musicmotivation.com